The Small U

SMARTbook

Leader's Reference Guide to Conducting Tactical Operations

Christopher Larsen
Norman M. Wade

The Lightning Press

2227 Arrowhead Blvd.
Lakeland, FL 33813
24-hour Voicemail/Fax/Order: 1-800-997-8827
E-mail: SMARTbooks@TheLightningPress.com

www.TheLightningPress.com

The Small Unit Tactics SMARTbook

Leader's Reference Guide to Conducting Tactical Operations

ISBN: 978-0-9742486-6-0

About our cover photo: Soldiers with the 1st Squadron, 32nd Cavalry Regiment, 1st Brigade Combat Team, 101st Airborne Division (AA), prepare to enter and clear a building near the Bichigan peninsula of the Salah ad Din province, Iraq. Dept. of Army photo by Richard Rzepka, 101st Airborne.

Credits: Photos courtesy of HJ Images; photos by Jeong, Hae-jung. All other photos courtesy Dept. of the Army (Army.mil) and credited individually.

Printed and bound in the United States of America.

The Small Unit Tactics SMARTbook

Editor's Notes

Leader's Reference Guide to Conducting Tactical Operations

Tactics is the employment and ordered arrangement of forces in relation to each other. Through tactics, commanders use combat power to accomplish missions. The tactical-level commander uses combat power in battles, engagements, and small-unit actions.

Establishing a common frame of reference, **doctrine** provides a menu of practical options based on experience. It provides an authoritative guide for leaders and Soldiers but requires original applications that adapt it to circumstances.

The Small Unit Tactics SMARTbook **translates and bridges** operational-level doctrine into tactical application -- in the form of tactics, techniques and procedures -- and provides the **"how to"** at the small-unit level, providing a ready reference at the battalion, company, platoon, squad and fire team level.

Tactics, Techniques and Procedures

Principles alone are not enough to guide operations. Tactics, techniques, and procedures provide additional levels of detail and more specific guidance, based on evolving knowledge and experience. Tactics, techniques, and procedures support and implement fundamental principles, linking them with associated applications. The "how to" of tactics, techniques, and procedures includes descriptive and prescriptive methods and processes. Tactics, techniques, and procedures apply at the operational and tactical levels.

- **Tactics**. Tactics is the employment and ordered arrangement of forces in relation to each other. Effective tactics translate combat power into decisive results. Primarily descriptive, tactics vary with terrain and other circumstances; they change frequently as the enemy reacts and friendly forces explore new approaches.
- **Techniques**. Employing a tactic usually requires using and integrating several techniques and procedures. Techniques are non prescriptive ways or methods used to perform missions, functions, or tasks. They are the primary means of conveying the lessons learned that units gain in operations.
- **Procedures**. Procedures are standard, detailed steps that prescribe how to perform specific tasks. They normally consist of a series of steps in a set order. Procedures are prescriptive; regardless of circumstances, they are executed in the same manner. Techniques and procedures are the lowest level of doctrine. They are often based on equipment and are specific to particular types of units.

SMARTbooks - The Essentials of Warfighting

SMARTbooks can be used as quick reference guides during actual tactical combat operations, as lesson plans in support of training exercises and as study guides at military education and professional development courses. Serving a generation of warfighters, military reference SMARTbooks have become "mission-essential" around the world.

SMARTregister for Updates

Keep your SMARTbooks up-to-date! The Lightning Press will provide e-mail notification of updates, revisions and changes to our SMARTbooks. Users can register their SMARTbooks online at **www.TheLightningPress.com**. Updates and their prices will be announced by e-mail as significant changes or revised editions are published.

The Small Unit Tactics SMARTbook

References

The following references were used in part to compile The Small Unit Tactics SMARTbook. Additionally listed are related resources useful to the reader. All references are available to the general public and designated as "approved for public release; distribution is unlimited." The Small Unit Tactics SMARTbook does not contain classified or sensitive information restricted from public release.

Field Manuals

FM 1-102	Sep 2004	Operational Terms and Graphics
FM 3-0	Feb 2008	Operations
FM 3-07	TBP	Stability Operations
FM 3-19.4 (change 1)	Mar 2002	Military Police Leader's Handbook
FM 3-21.8 (FM 7-8)	Mar 2007	The Infantry Rifle Platoon and Squad
FM 3-21.10 (FM 7-10)	Jul 2006	The Infantry Rifle Company
FM 3-24	Dec 2006	Counterinsurgency
FM 3-90	Jul 2001	Tactics
FM 5-0	Jan 2005	Army Planning and Orders Production
FM 6-0	Aug 2003	Mission Command: Command and Control of Army Forces
FM 7-0	Oct 2002	Training the Force
FM 7-1	Sep 2003	Battle Focused Training
FM 7-85	Jun 1987	Ranger Operations
FM 7-92 (change 1)	Dec 01	The Infantry Reconnaissance Platoon and Squad (Airborne, Air Assault, Light Infantry)
FM 7-93	Oct 1995	Long-Range Surveillance Unit Operations
FM 5-19	Aug 2006	Composite Risk Management

Additional Resources and Publications

ARTEP 7-8-Drill	Jun 2002	Battle Drills for the Infantry Rifle Platoon and Squad
ARTEP 7-10-MTP	Jun 2002	Mission Training Plan for the Infantry Rifle Company
Sean Edwards	2003	Swarming on the Battlefield: Past, Present and Future (RAND; copyrighted)
SH 21-76	Jul 2006	The Ranger Handbook

The Small Unit Tactics SMARTbook

Table of Contents

Chap 1

Tactical Mission Fundamentals

Chap 2 Offensive Operations

Chap 3 Defensive Operations

Chap 4

Stability and Counter-insurgency Operations

Chap 5

Tactical Enabling Operations

Chap 6

Special Purpose Attacks

Chap 7 Urban Operations & Attacking Fortified Areas

Chap 8 Patrols & Patrolling

Index

Chap 1

Tactical Mission Fundamentals

I. The Art of Tactics

Ref: FM 3-90 Tactics, chap. 1 and FM 3-0 Operations (2008), chap. 6.

Tactics is the employment of units in combat. It includes the ordered arrangement and maneuver of units in relation to each other, the terrain and the enemy to translate potential combat power into victorious battles and engagements. (Dept. of Army photo by Staff Sgt. Russell Bassett).

I. The Tactical Level of War

The levels of war are doctrinal perspectives that clarify the links between strategic objectives and tactical actions. Although there are no finite limits or boundaries between them, the three levels are strategic, operational, and tactical. They apply to all types of military operations.

The tactical level of war is the level of war at which battles and engagements are planned and executed to accomplish military objectives assigned to tactical units or task forces. Activities at this level focus on the ordered arrangement and maneuver of combat elements in relation to each other and to the enemy to achieve combat objectives. It is important to understand tactics within the context of the levels of war. The strategic and operational levels provide the context for tactical operations. Without this context, tactical operations are reduced to a series of disconnected and unfocused actions.

Individuals, crews, and small units

Individuals, crews, and small units act at the tactical level. At times, their actions may produce strategic or operational effects. However, this does not mean these elements are acting at the strategic or operational level. Actions are not strategic unless they contribute directly to achieving the strategic end state. Similarly, actions are considered operational only if they are directly related to operational movement or the sequencing of battles and engagements. The level at which an action occurs is determined by the perspective of the echelon in terms of planning, preparation, and execution.

Battles, Engagements and Small-Unit Actions

Tactics is the employment and ordered arrangement of forces in relation to each other. Through tactics, commanders use combat power to accomplish missions. The tactical-level commander uses combat power in battles, engagements, and small-unit actions. A battle consists of a set of related engagements that lasts longer and involves larger forces than an engagement. Battles can affect the course of a campaign or major operation. An engagement is a tactical conflict, usually between opposing, lower echelons maneuver forces (JP 1-02). Engagements are typically conducted at brigade level and below. They are usually short, executed in terms of minutes, hours, or days.

II. The Science and Art of Tactics

The tactician must understand and master the science and the art of tactics, two distinctly different yet inseparable concepts. Commanders and leaders at all echelons and supporting commissioned, warrant, and noncommissioned staff officers must be tacticians to lead their soldiers in the conduct of full spectrum operations.

A. The Science

The science of tactics encompasses the understanding of those military aspects of tactics—capabilities, techniques, and procedures—that can be measured and codified. The science of tactics includes the physical capabilities of friendly and enemy organizations and systems, such as determining how long it takes a division to move a certain distance. It also includes techniques and procedures used to accomplish specific tasks, such as the tactical terms and control graphics that comprise the language of tactics. While not easy, the science of tactics is fairly straightforward. Much of what is contained in this manual is the science of tactics—techniques and procedures for employing the various elements of the combined arms team to achieve greater effects.

Mastery of the science of tactics is necessary for the tactician to understand the physical and procedural constraints under which he must work. These constraints include the effects of terrain, time, space, and weather on friendly and enemy forces. However—because combat is an intensely human activity—the solution to tactical problems cannot be reduced to a formula. This realization necessitates the study of the art of tactics.

B. The Art

The art of tactics consists of three interrelated aspects: the creative and flexible array of means to accomplish assigned missions, decision making under conditions of uncertainty when faced with an intelligent enemy, and understanding the human dimension—the effects of combat on soldiers. An art, as opposed to a science, requires exercising intuitive faculties that cannot be learned solely by study. The tactician must temper his study and evolve his skill through a variety of relevant, practical experiences. The more experience the tactician gains from practice under a variety of circumstances, the greater his mastery of the art of tactics.

The tactician invokes the art of tactics to solve tactical problems within his commander's intent by choosing from interrelated options, including—

- Types and forms of operations, forms of maneuver, and tactical mission tasks
- Task organization of available forces, to include allocating scarce resources
- Arrangement and choice of control measures
- Tempo of the operation
- Risks the commander is willing to take

Aspects of the Art of Tactics

Ref: FM 3-90 Tactics, pp. 1-4 to 1-6. (Note: These aspects are not labeled in FM 3-90).

There are three aspects to the art of tactics that define a competent tactician:

1. Domain Knowledge

Note: For more complete discussion of domain knowledge, see The Leader's SMARTbook or FM 6-22 Army Leadership, pp. 6-5 to 6-9.

The first is the creative and flexible application of the tools available to the commander, such as doctrine, tactics, techniques, procedures, training, organizations, materiel, and soldiers in an attempt to render the enemy's situational tactics ineffective. The tactician must understand how to train and employ his forces in full spectrum operations. The factors of mission, enemy, terrain and weather, troops, time available, and civil considerations (METT-TC) are variables whose infinite mutations always combine to form a new tactical pattern.

They never produce exactly the same situation; thus there can be no checklists that adequately address each unique situation. Because the enemy changes and adapts to friendly moves during the planning, preparation, and execution of an operation, there is no guarantee that a technique which worked in one situation will work again. Each tactical problem is unique and must be solved on its own merits.

2. Battle Command

The second aspect of the art of tactics is decision making under conditions of uncertainty in a time-constrained environment and demonstrated by the clash of opposing wills—a violent struggle between two hostile, thinking, and independent opposing commanders with irreconcilable goals. Each commander wants to impose his will on his opponent, defeat his opponent's plans, and destroy his opponent's forces. Combat consists of the interplay between these two opposing commanders, with each commander seeking to accomplish his mission while preventing the other from doing the same. Every commander needs a high degree of creativity and clarity of thought to outwit a willing and able opponent. He must quickly apply his judgment to a less than omniscient common operational picture provided by his command and control (C2) system to understand the implications and opportunities afforded him by the situation. The commander always uses the most current intelligence in order to facilitate his visualization of the enemy and environment. That same C2 system transmits the decisions resulting from his situational understanding to those individuals and units required to engage and destroy the enemy force.

3. The Human Dimension

The third and final aspect of the art of tactics is understanding the human dimension—what differentiates actual combat from the problems encountered during training and in a classroom. Combat is one of the most complex human activities, characterized by violent death, friction, uncertainty, and chance. Success depends at least as much on this human aspect as it does on any numerical and technological superiority.

The tactician cannot ignore the human aspect. He seeks to recognize and exploit indicators of fear and weakness in his enemy, and to defeat the enemy's will, since soldiers remain key to generating combat power. More than any other human activity, continuous combat operations against an intelligent enemy takes a toll on soldiers, severely straining their physical and mental stamina. This creates in soldiers the tangible and intangible effects of courage, fear, combat experience, exhaustion, isolation, confidence, thirst, and anger.

Leaders must be alert to indicators of fatigue, fear, lapses in discipline standards, and reduced morale in friendly and enemy soldiers. These conditions can have a cumulative effect on units that can lead to collapse. The tactician must understand how they affect human endurance and factor them into his plans. He must understand the limits of human endurance in combat.

III. Hasty vs. Deliberate Operations

A hasty operation is an operation in which a commander directs his immediately available forces, using fragmentary orders (FRAGOs), to perform activities with minimal preparation, trading planning and preparation time for speed of execution. A deliberate operation is an operation in which a commander's detailed intelligence concerning the situation allows him to develop and coordinate detailed plans, including multiple branches and sequels. He task organizes his forces specifically for the operation to provide a fully synchronized combined arms team. He conducts extensive rehearsals while conducting shaping operations to set the conditions for the conduct of his decisive operation.

Most operations lie somewhere along a continuum between these two extremes. The 9th Armored Division's seizure of the bridge at Remagen in March 1945 illustrates one end, a hasty operation conducted with the forces immediately available. At the other end of the continuum is a deliberate operation, such as the 1st Infantry Division's breach operation during the opening hours of Operation Desert Storm.

Choices and Trade-offs

The leader must choose the right point along the continuum to operate. His choice involves balancing several competing factors. He bases his decision to conduct a hasty or deliberate operation on his current knowledge of the enemy situation, and his assessment of whether the assets available (to include time), and the means to coordinate and synchronize those assets, are adequate to accomplish the mission. If they are not he takes additional time to plan and prepare for the operation or bring additional forces to bear on the problem. The commander makes that choice in an environment of uncertainty, which always entails some risk.

Uncertainty and Risk

Uncertainty and risk are inherent in tactical operations and cannot be eliminated. A commander cannot be successful without the capability of acting under conditions of uncertainty while balancing various risks and taking advantage of opportunities. Although the commander strives to maximize his knowledge about his forces, the terrain and weather, civil considerations, and the enemy, he cannot let a lack of information paralyze him. The more intelligence on the enemy, the better able the commander is to make his assessment. Less information means that the commander has a greater risk of making a poor decision for the specific situation. A commander never has perfect intelligence, but knowing when he has enough information to make a decision within the higher commander's intent and constraints is part of the art of tactics and is a critical skill for a commander.

It is better to err on the side of speed, audacity, and momentum than on the side of caution when conducting military operations, all else being equal. Bold decisions give the best promise of success; however, one must differentiate between calculated risks and a military gamble. A calculated risk is an operation in which success is not a certainty but which, in case of failure, leaves sufficient forces to cope with whatever situations arise. The willingness to take calculated risks requires military judgment to reduce risk by foresight and careful planning and to determine whether the risk is worth taking to grasp fleeting opportunities.

The commander should take the minimum time necessary in planning and preparing to ensure a reasonable chance of success. Reduced coordination at the start of the operation results in less than optimum combat power brought to bear on the enemy, but often allows for increased speed and momentum while possibly achieving surprise.

The commander can be less deliberate in planning and preparing for an operation when facing a clearly less-capable and less-prepared enemy force. In these circumstances, the commander can forego detailed planning, extensive rehearsals, and significant changes in task organization.

II. Full Spectrum Operations (FM 3-0)

Ref: FM 3-0 Operations (2008), chap. 3. For complete discussion of full spectrum operations, see The Operations SMARTbook (4th Revised Edition), chap. 1.

The Army's operational concept is full spectrum operations: Army forces combine offensive, defensive, and stability or civil support operations simultaneously as part of an interdependent joint force to seize, retain, and exploit the initiative, accepting prudent risk to create opportunities to achieve decisive results. They employ synchronized action—lethal and nonlethal—proportional to the mission and informed by a thorough understanding of all variables of the operational environment. Mission command that conveys intent and an appreciation of all aspects of the situation guides the adaptive use of Army forces.

Full Spectrum Operations

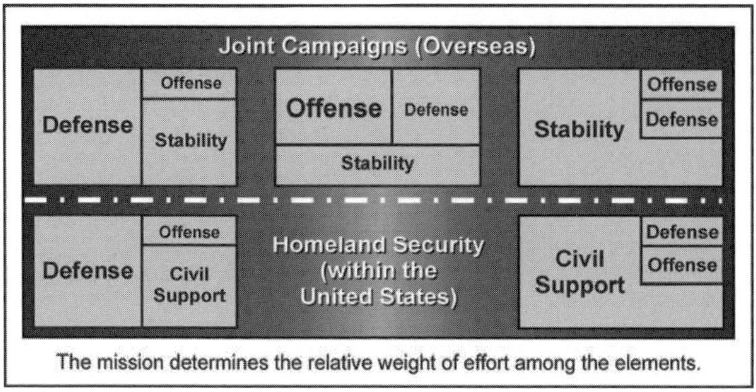

Full spectrum operations require continuous, simultaneous combinations of offensive, defensive, and stability or civil support tasks. In all operations, commanders seek to seize, retain, and exploit the initiative while synchronizing their actions to achieve the best effects possible. (Ref: FM 3-0 Operations, fig. 3-1).

Operations conducted outside the United States and its territories simultaneously combine three elements—offense, defense, and stability. Within the United States and its territories, operations combine the elements of civil support, defense, and offense in support of civil authority. Army forces operate using mutually supporting lethal and nonlethal capabilities.

Army forces use offensive and defensive operations to defeat the enemy on land. They simultaneously execute stability or civil support operations to interact with the populace and civil authorities. Three elements of full spectrum operations—offense, defense, and stability—are necessary in most campaigns and major operations conducted outside the United States and its territories. In most domestic operations, Army forces conduct only civil support tasks. However, an extreme emergency, such as an attack by a hostile foreign power, may require simultaneous combinations of offensive, defensive, and civil support tasks. Stability tasks typically characterize peace operations, peacetime military engagement, and some limited interventions.

Operations today require versatile, well-trained units and tough, adaptive commanders. There is no set formula for applying landpower. Each campaign and major operation requires an original design and flexible execution. Army forces must be able to operate as part of a joint or multinational force anywhere on the spectrum of conflict. Varying combinations of the elements of full spectrum operations appropriate to the situation are necessary as well. The concept of operations combines and weights these elements as the situation requires.

Full spectrum operations involve continuous interaction between friendly forces and multiple groups in the area of operations. In addition to enemy forces and the local populace, Soldiers deal with multinational partners, adversaries, civil authorities, business leaders, and other civilian agencies. This interaction is simple in concept but complex in application. For example, enemies and adversaries may consist of multiple competing elements. Civil authorities range from strategic-level leaders to local government officials to religious leaders. Populations may include people of differing tribes, ethnic groups, and nationalities. Within the United States and its territories, the roles and responsibilities of Army forces and civil authorities are substantially different from overseas. For that reason, Army forces conduct civil support operations domestically and stability operations overseas, even though stability and civil support have many similarities.

The operational concept addresses more than combat between armed opponents. Army forces conduct operations in the midst of populations. This requires Army forces to defeat the enemy and simultaneously shape civil conditions. Offensive and defensive tasks defeat enemy forces; stability tasks shape civil conditions. Winning battles and engagements is important but alone may not be decisive. Shaping civil conditions (in concert with civilian organizations, civil authorities, and multinational forces) is just as important to campaign success. In many joint operations, stability or civil support are often more important than the offense and defense.

The emphasis on different elements of full spectrum operations changes with echelon, time, and location. In an operation dominated by stability, part of the force might be conducting simultaneous offensive and defensive tasks. Within the United States, civil support operations may be the only activity actually conducted. In short, no single element is always more important than the others. Rather, simultaneous combinations of the elements, which commanders constantly adapt to conditions, are the key to successful land operations.

I. Initiative

All Army operations aim to seize, retain, and exploit the initiative and achieve decisive results. Operational initiative is setting or dictating the terms of action throughout an operation. Initiative gives all operations the spirit, if not the form, of the offense. It originates in the principle of the offensive. The principle of the offensive is not just about attacking. It is about seizing, retaining, and exploiting the initiative as the surest way to achieve decisive results. It requires positive action to change the situation on the ground and in the information environment. Risk and opportunity are intrinsic in seizing the initiative. In order to seize the initiative, commanders evaluate and accept prudent risks. Opportunities never last long. Unless commanders are willing to accept risk and then act, the adversary is likely to close the window of opportunity and exploit friendly inaction. Once they seize the initiative, Army forces exploit the opportunities it creates. Initiative requires constant effort to control tempo while maintaining freedom of action. The offensive mindset, with its focus on initiative, is central to the Army's operational concept and guides all leaders in the performance of their duty. It emphasizes opportunity created by action through full spectrum operations, whether offensive, defensive, stability, or civil support.

Combat Operations

In combat operations, commanders force the enemy to respond to friendly action. In the offense, it is about taking the fight to the enemy and never allowing enemy forces to recover from the initial shock of the attack. In the defense, it is about preventing the enemy from achieving success and then counterattacking to seize back the initiative. The object is not just to kill enemy personnel and destroy their equipment. It is to compel the enemy to react continuously and finally to be driven into untenable positions. Retaining the initiative pressures enemy commanders into abandoning their preferred options, accepting too much risk, or making costly mistakes. As enemy mistakes occur, friendly forces seize opportunities and create new avenues for exploitation. The ultimate goal is to break the enemy's will through relentless pressure.

Stability and Civil Support Operations

In stability and civil support operations, initiative is about improving civil conditions and applying combat power to prevent the situation from deteriorating. Commanders identify objectives that may be nonmilitary but are critical to achieving the end state. Such objectives may include efforts to ensure effective governance, reconstruction projects promoting social well-being, and consistent actions to improve public safety.

Seizing, retaining, and exploiting the initiative depends on individual initiative; the willingness to act in the absence of orders, when existing orders no longer fit the situation, or when unforeseen opportunities or threats arise. Military history contains many instances where a subordinate's action or inaction significantly affected the tactical, operational, or even strategic situation. When opportunity occurs, it is often fleeting. Subordinate leaders need to act quickly, even as they report the situation to their commanders. Individual initiative is the key component of mission command. Full spectrum operations depend on subordinate commanders exercising individual initiative and higher commanders giving them authority to do so.

II. Simultaneity and Synchronization

Simultaneity

Simultaneity means doing multiple things at the same time. It requires the ability to conduct operations in depth and to orchestrate them so that their timing multiplies their effectiveness. Commanders consider their entire area of operations, the enemy, the information environment, and civil conditions. Then they mount simultaneous operations that immobilize, suppress, or shock the enemy, nullifying the enemy's ability to conduct to conduct synchronized, mutually supporting actions. Army forces increase the depth of their operations through combined arms, advanced information systems, and joint capabilities. Because Army forces conduct operations across large areas, the enemy faces many potential friendly actions. Executing operations in depth is equally important in stability operations; commanders act to keep threats from operating outside the reach of friendly forces. In civil support operations and some stability operations, depth includes conducting operations that reach all citizens in the area of operations, bringing relief as well as hope.

Synchronization

Simultaneously executing the elements of full spectrum operations requires the synchronized application of combat power. Synchronization is the arrangement of military actions in time, space, and purpose to produce maximum relative combat power at a decisive place and time (JP 2-0). It is the ability to execute multiple related and mutually supporting tasks in different locations at the same time, producing greater effects than executing each in isolation. Synchronization is a means, not an end. Commanders balance it with agility and initiative; they never surrender the initiative for the sake of synchronization. Rather, they synchronize activities to best facilitate mission accomplishment. Excessive synchronization can lead to overcontrol, which limits the initiative of subordinates.

III. The Elements of Full Spectrum Operations

Ref: FM 3-0 Operations (2008), pp. 3-7 to 3-18 and fig. 3-2.

Full spectrum operations require simultaneous combinations of four elements—offense, defense, and stability or civil support.

A. Offensive Operations

Offensive operations are combat operations conducted to defeat and destroy enemy forces and seize terrain, resources, and population centers. They impose the commander's will on the enemy. In combat operations, the offense is the decisive element of full spectrum operations. Against a capable, adaptive enemy, the offense is the most direct and sure means of seizing, retaining, and exploiting the initiative to achieve decisive results. Executing offensive operations compels the enemy to react, creating or revealing weaknesses that the attacking force can exploit. Successful offensive operations place tremendous pressure on defenders, creating a cycle of deterioration that can lead to their disintegration.

Note: For discussion of offensive operations, see chap. 2, pp. 2-1 to 2-34.

Offensive Operations

Primary Tasks

- Movement to contact
- Attack
- Exploitation
- Pursuit

Purposes

- Dislocate, isolate, disrupt and destroy enemy forces
- Seize key terrain
- Deprive the enemy of resources
- Develop intelligence
- Deceive and divert the enemy
- Create a secure environment for stability operations

Defensive Operations

Primary Tasks

- Mobile defense
- Area defense
- Retrograde

Purposes

- Deter or defeat enemy offensive operations
- Gain time
- Achieve economy of force
- Retain key terrain
- Protect the populace, critical assets and infrastructure
- Develop intelligence

B. Defensive Operations

Defensive operations are combat operations conducted to defeat an enemy attack, gain time, economize forces, and develop conditions favorable for offensive or stability operations. The defense alone normally cannot achieve a decision. However, it can create conditions for a counteroffensive operation that lets Army forces regain the initiative. Defensive operations can also establish a shield behind which stability operations can progress. Defensive operations counter enemy offensive operations. They defeat attacks, destroying as much of the attacking enemy as possible. They also preserve control over land, resources, and populations. Defensive operations retain terrain, guard populations, and protect critical capabilities against enemy attacks. They can be used to gain time and economize forces so offensive tasks can be executed elsewhere.

Note: For discussion of defensive operations, see chap. 3, pp. 3-1 to 3-28.

C. Stability Operations

Stability operations encompass various military missions, tasks, and activities conducted outside the United States in coordination with other instruments of national power to maintain or reestablish a safe and secure environment, provide essential governmental services, emergency infrastructure reconstruction, and humanitarian relief (JP 3-0). Stability operations can be conducted in support of a host nation or interim government or as part of an occupation when no government exists. Stability operations involve both coercive and constructive military actions. They help to establish a safe and secure environment and facilitate reconciliation among local or regional adversaries. Stability operations can also help establish political, legal, social, and economic institutions and support the transition to legitimate local governance. It is essential that stability operations maintain the initiative by pursing objectives that resolve the causes of instability. Stability operations cannot succeed if they react only to enemy initiatives.

Note: For discussion of stability operations, see chap. 4, pp. 4-1 to 4-12.

Stability Operations

Primary Tasks

- Civil security
- Civil control
- Restore essential services
- Support to governance
- Support to economic and infrastructure development

Purposes

- Provide a secure environment
- Secure land areas
- Meet the critical needs of the populace
- Gain support for host-nation government
- Shape the environment for interagency and host-nation success

Civil Support Operations

Primary Tasks

- Provide support in response to disaster or terrorist attack
- Support civil law enforcement
- Provide other support as required

Purposes

- Save lives
- Restore essential services
- Maintain or restore law and order
- Protect infrastructure and property
- Maintain or restore local government
- Shape the environment for interagency success

D. Civil Support Operations

Civil support is Department of Defense support to U.S. civil authorities for domestic emergencies, and for designated law enforcement and other activities (JP 1-02). Civil support includes operations that address the consequences of natural or manmade disasters, accidents, terrorist attacks, and incidents within the United States and its territories. Army forces conduct civil support operations when the size and scope of events exceed the capabilities or capacities of domestic civilian agencies. The Army National Guard is usually the first military force to respond on behalf of state authorities. In this capacity, it functions under authority of Title 32, U.S. Code, or while serving on state active duty. The National Guard is suited to conduct these missions; however, the scope and level of destruction may require states to request assistance from Federal authorities.

Note: When published, FM 3-28 will discuss civil operations in detail.

IV. Lethal and Nonlethal Actions

Ref: FM 3-0 Operations (2008), pp. 3-4 to 3-8.

There is an inherent, complementary relationship between using lethal force and applying military capabilities for nonlethal purposes. Though each situation requires a different mix of violence and restraint, lethal and nonlethal actions used together complement each other and create dilemmas for opponents. Lethal actions are critical to accomplishing offensive and defensive missions.

A. Lethal Actions

Offensive and defensive operations place a premium on employing the lethal effects of combat power against the enemy. In these operations, speed, surprise, and shock are vital considerations. Historically, the side better able to combine them defeats its opponent rapidly while incurring fewer losses. Such victories create opportunities for exploitation. In some operations, the effects of speed, surprise, and shock are enough to collapse organized resistance. Such a collapse occurred in the offensive phase of Operation Iraqi Freedom in 2003.

Speed is swiftness of action. It allows a force to act before the enemy is ready or before the situation deteriorates further. Surprise is achieved by acting at a time, in a place, or using methods to which the enemy cannot effectively react or does not expect. Speed contributes to surprise. Shock results from applying overwhelming violence. Combat power applied with enough speed and magnitude to overwhelm the enemy produces it. Shock slows and disrupts enemy operations. It is usually transient, but while it lasts, shock may paralyze the enemy's ability to fight. Sometimes the psychological effects of threatening to use overwhelming violence can also produce shock.

B. Nonlethal Actions

Army forces employ a variety of nonlethal means. Stability operations often involve using military capabilities to perform such tasks as restoring essential services. Civil support operations are characterized by providing constructive support to civil authorities. However, demonstrating the potential for lethal action (by actions such as increased military presence in an area) often contributes to maintaining order during stability and some civil support operations. Other examples include such actions as pre-assault warnings and payments for collateral damage. Some nonlethal actions, such as information engagement, are common to all operations.

Opposing forces wage a continuous struggle in the information environment simultaneously with operations in the physical domains. Friendly actions in the information environment include attacking the enemy's command and control system, defending against electronic attacks, and protecting friendly information.

Nonlethal actions in combat include a wide range of intelligence-gathering, disruptive, and other activities. Furthermore, nonlethal means can mitigate the indirect effects on noncombatants of lethal actions directed against the enemy.

Stability and civil support operations emphasize nonlethal, constructive actions by Soldiers working among noncombatants. Civil affairs forces have a major role. In stability operations, they work with and through host-nation agencies and other civilian organizations to enhance the host-nation government's legitimacy. Nonlethal, constructive actions can persuade the local populace to withhold support from the enemy and provide information to friendly forces. Loss of popular support presents the enemy with two bad choices: stay and risk capture, or depart and risk exposure to lethal actions in less populated areas. Commanders focus on managing the local populace's expectations and countering rumors. The moral advantage provided by the presence of well-trained, well-equipped, and well-led forces can be a potent nonlethal capability. It creates fear and doubt in the minds of the enemy and may deter adversaries.

Chap 1

Tactical Mission Fundamentals

III. Tactical Mission Tasks

Ref: FM 3-90 Tactics, app. C. See also The Battle Staff SMARTbook.

Tactical mission tasks describe the results or effects the commander wants to achieve - the *what* and *why* of a mission statement. The commander is not limited to the tactical mission tasks listed in this section or FM 3-90; there is no definitive list.

Effects on Enemy Force

Block
Canalize
Contain
Defeat
Destroy
Disrupt
Fix
Interdict
Isolate
Neutralize
Penetrate
Turn

Actions by Friendly Forces

Assault
Attack-by-Fire
Breach
Bypass
Clear
Combat Search and Rescue
Consolidation & Reorganization
Control
Counterreconnaissance
Disengagement
Exfiltrate
Follow and Assume
Follow and Support
Linkup
Occupy
Reconstitution
Reduce
Retain
Secure
Seize
Support-by-Fire
Suppress

Types and Forms of Operations

Movement to Contact
Search and Attack

Attack
Ambush
Demonstration
Feint
Raid
Spoiling Attack

Exploitation

Pursuit

Offensive Maneuver
Envelopment
Frontal Attack
Infiltration
Penetration
Turning Movement

Area Defense

Mobile Defense

Retrograde Operations
Delay
Withdrawal
Retirement

Reconnaissance Operations
Zone
Area (including point)
Route
Recon in force
Forms of security
- Screen
- Guard
- Cover
- Area

Security Operations

Information Operations

Combined Arms Breach Opns

Passage of Lines

Relief in Place

River Crossing Operations

Troop Movement
Administrative Movement
Approach March
Road March

Purpose (in order to)

Divert
Enable
Deceive
Deny
Prevent
Open
Envelop
Surprise
Cause
Protect
Allow
Create
Influence
Support

A. Effects on Enemy Forces

Task	Symbol	Description
Block	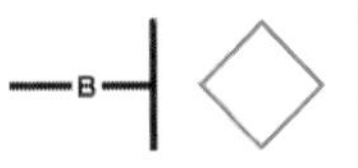	*Block* is a tactical mission task that denies the enemy access to an area or prevents his advance in a direction or along an avenue of approach.
	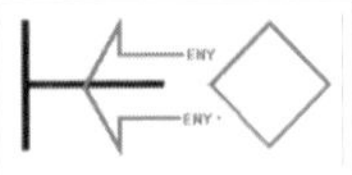	*Block* is also an engineer obstacle effect that integrates fire planning and obstacle effort to stop an attacker along a specific avenue of approach or prevent him from passing through an engagement area.
Canalize	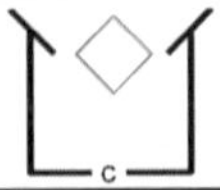	*Canalize* is a tactical mission task in which the commander restricts enemy movement to a narrow zone by exploiting terrain coupled with the use of obstacles, fires, or friendly maneuver.
Contain	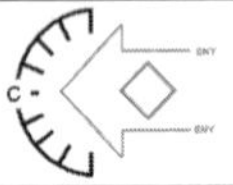	*Contain* is a tactical mission task that requires the commander to stop, hold, or surround enemy forces or to cause them to center their activity on a given front and prevent them from withdrawing any part of their forces for use elsewhere.
Defeat		*Defeat* occurs when an enemy has temporarily or permanently lost the physical means or the will to fight. The defeated force is unwilling or unable to pursue his COA, and can no longer interfere to a significant degree. Results from the use of force or the threat of its use.
Destroy		*Destroy* is a tactical mission task that physically renders an enemy force combat-ineffective until it is reconstituted. Alternatively, to destroy a combat system is to damage it so badly that it cannot perform any function or be restored to a usable condition without being entirely rebuilt.
Disrupt	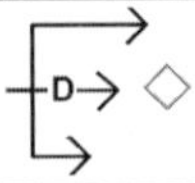	*Disrupt* is a tactical mission task in which a commander integrates direct and indirect fires, terrain, and obstacles to upset an enemy's formation or tempo, interrupt his timetable, or cause his forces to commit prematurely or attack in a piecemeal fashion.
	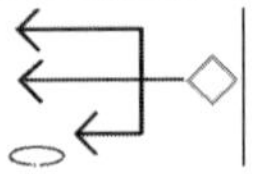	*Disrupt* is also an engineer obstacle effect that focuses fire planning and obstacle effort to cause the enemy to break up his formation and tempo, interrupt his timetable, commit breaching assets prematurely, and attack in a piecemeal effort.
Fix		*Fix* is a tactical mission task where a commander prevents the enemy from moving any part of his force from a specific location for a specific period. Fixing an enemy force does not mean destroying it. The friendly force has to prevent the enemy from moving in any direction.
	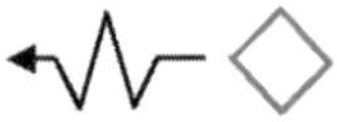	*Fix* is also an engineer obstacle effect that focuses fire planning and obstacle effort to slow an attacker's movement within a specified area, normally an engagement area.
Interdict	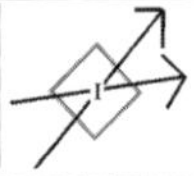	*Interdict* is a tactical mission task where the commander prevents, disrupts, or delays the enemy's use of an area or route. Interdiction is a shaping operation conducted to complement and reinforce other ongoing offensive or defensive
Isolate	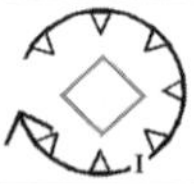	*Isolate* is a tactical mission task that requires a unit to seal off-both physically and psychologically-an enemy from his sources of support, deny him freedom of movement, and prevent him from having contact with other enemy forces.
Neutralize	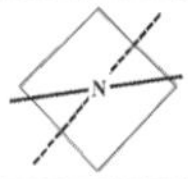	*Neutralize* is a tactical mission task that results in rendering enemy personnel or materiel incapable of interfering with a particular operation.
Turn	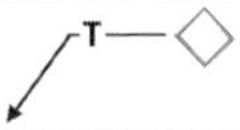	*Turn* is a tactical mission task that involves forcing an enemy element from one avenue of approach or movement corridor to another.
	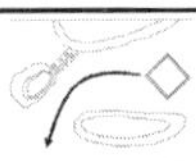	*Turn* is also a tactical obstacle effect that integrates fire planning and obstacle effort to divert an enemy formation from one avenue of approach to an adjacent avenue of approach or into an engagement area.

B. Actions by Friendly Forces

Task	Graphic	Definition
Attack by Fire		*Attack-by-fire* is a tactical mission task in which a commander uses direct fires, supported by indirect fires, to engage an enemy without closing with him to destroy, suppress, fix, or deceive him.
Breach	B	*Breach* is a tactical mission task in which the unit employs all available means to break through or secure a passage through an enemy defense, obstacle, minefield, or fortification.
Bypass	B	Bypass is a tactical mission task in which the commander directs his unit to maneuver around an obstacle, position, or enemy force to maintain the momentum of the operation while deliberately avoiding combat with an enemy force.
Clear	C	*Clear* is a tactical mission task that requires the commander to remove all enemy forces and eliminate organized resistance within an assigned area.
Control	*No graphic*	*Control* is a tactical mission task that requires the commander to maintain physical influence over a specified area to prevent its use by an enemy or to create conditions for successful friendly operations.
Counterrecon	*No graphic*	*Counterreconnaissance* is a tactical mission task that encompasses all measures taken by a commander to counter enemy reconnaissance and surveillance efforts.
Disengage	*No graphic*	*Disengage* is a tactical mission task where a commander has his unit break contact with the enemy to allow the conduct of another mission or to avoid decisive engagement.
Exfiltrate	*No graphic*	*Exfiltrate* is a tactical mission task where a commander removes soldiers or units from areas under enemy control by stealth, deception, surprise, or clandestine means.
Follow and Assume		*Follow and assume* is a tactical mission task in which a second committed force follows a force conducting an offensive operation and is prepared to continue the mission if the lead force is fixed, attritted, or unable to continue. The follow-and-assume force is not a reserve but is committed to accomplish specific tasks.
Follow and Support		*Follow and support* is a tactical mission task in which a committed force follows and supports a lead force conducting an offensive operation. The follow-and-support force is not a reserve but is a force committed to specific tasks.
Occupy	O	*Occupy* is a tactical mission task that involves moving a friendly force into an area so that it can control that area. Both the force's movement to and occupation of the area occur without enemy opposition.
Reduce	*No graphic*	*Reduce* is a tactical mission task that involves the destruction of an encircled or bypassed enemy force.
Retain	R	*Retain* is a tactical mission task in which the cdr ensures that a terrain feature controlled by a friendly force remains free of enemy occupation or use. The commander assigning this task must specify the area to retain and the duration of the retention, which is time- or event-driven.
Secure	S	*Secure* is a tactical mission task that involves preventing a unit, facility, or geographical location from being damaged or destroyed as a result of enemy action. This task normally involves conducting area security operations.
Seize	S	*Seize* is a tactical mission task that involves taking possession of a designated area by using overwhelming force. An enemy force can no longer place direct fire on an objective that has been seized.
Support by Fire		*Support-by-fire* is a tactical mission task in which a maneuver force moves to a position where it can engage the enemy by direct fire in support of another maneuvering force. The primary objective of the support force is normally to fix and suppress the enemy so he cannot effectively fire on the maneuvering force.

C. Mission Symbols

Counterattack (dashed axis)	CATK	A form of attack by part or all of a defending force against an enemy attacking force, with the general objective of denying the enemy his goal in attacking (FM 3-0).
Cover	C C	A form of security operation whose primary task is to protect the main body by fighting to gain time while also observing and reporting information and preventing enemy ground observation of and direct fire against the main body.
Delay	D	A form of retrograde [JP 1-02 uses *an operation*] in which a force under pressure trades space for time by slowing down the enemy's momentum and inflicting maximum damage on the enemy without, in principle, becoming decisively engaged (JP 1-02, see delaying operation).
Guard	G G	A form of security operations whose primary task is to protect the main body by fighting to gain time while also observing and reporting information and preventing enemy ground observation of and direct fire against the main body. Units conducting a guard mission cannot operate independently because they rely upon fires and combat support assets of the main body.
Penetrate		A form of maneuver in which an attacking force seeks to rupture enemy defenses on a narrow front to disrupt the defensive system (FM 3-0).
Relief in Place	RIP	A tactical enabling operation in which, by the direction of higher authority, all or part of a unit is replaced in an area by the incoming unit.
Retirement	R	A form of retrograde [JP 1-02 uses *operation*] in which a force out of contact with the enemy moves away from the enemy (JP 1-02).
Screen	S S	A form of security operations that primarily provides early warning to the protected force.
Withdraw	W	A planned operation in which a force in contact disengages from an enemy force (JP 1-02) [The Army considers it a form of retrograde.]

Ref: Mission symbols in the above chart are from FM 1-02 Operational Terms and Graphics, app. A.

Tactical Mission Fundamentals

IV. Battle Command

Ref: FM 3-0 Operations (2008), chap. 5 and FM 5-0, pp. 3-4 to 3-9. For complete discussion of battle command, see The Battle Staff SMARTbook.

Battle command is the art and science of understanding, visualizing, describing, directing, leading, and assessing forces to impose the commander's will on a hostile, thinking, and adaptive enemy. Battle command applies leadership to translate decisions into actions—by synchronizing forces and warfighting functions in time, space, and purpose—to accomplish missions. Battle command is guided by professional judgment gained from experience, knowledge, education, intelligence, and intuition. It is driven by commanders.

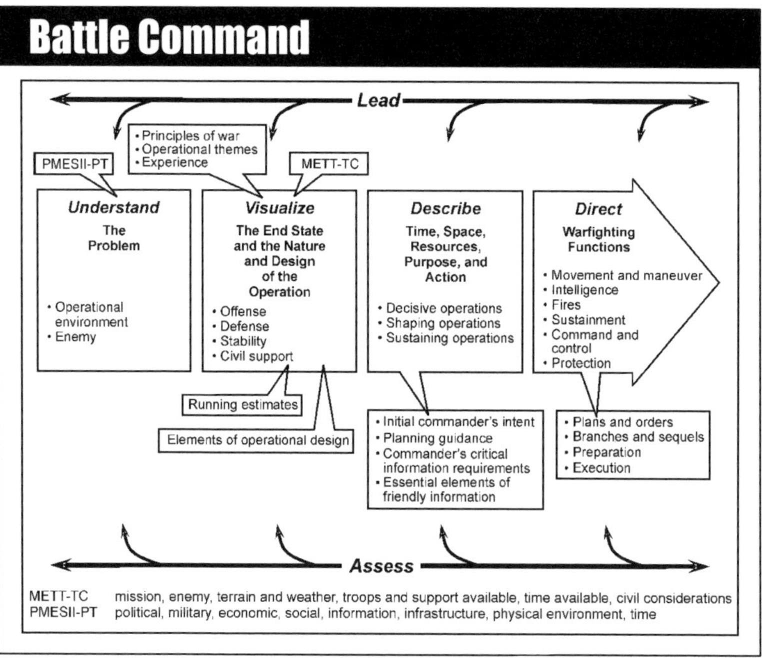

Ref: FM 3-0 Operations (2008), fig. 5-1, p. 5-3.

Understand, Visualize, Describe, Direct, Lead and Assess

Commanders understand, visualize, describe, direct, lead, and assess throughout the operations process. First, they develop a personal and in-depth understanding of the enemy and operational environment. Then they visualize the desired end state and a broad concept of how to shape the current conditions into the end state. Commanders describe their visualization through the commander's intent, planning guidance, and concept of operations in a way that brings clarity to an uncertain situation. They also express gaps in relevant information as commander's critical information requirements (CCIRs). Direction is implicit in command; commanders direct actions to achieve results and lead forces to mission accomplishment.

Effective battle command requires commanders to continuously assess and lead. Assessment helps commanders better understand current conditions and broadly describe future conditions that define success. They identify the difference between the two and visualize a sequence of actions to link them. Commanders lead by force of example and personal presence. Leadership inspires Soldiers (and sometimes civilians) to accomplish things that they would otherwise avoid. This often requires risk. Commanders anticipate and accept risk to create opportunities to seize, retain, and exploit the initiative and achieve decisive results.

Battle command encourages the leadership and initiative of subordinates through mission command. Commanders accept setbacks that stem from the initiative of subordinates. They understand that land warfare is chaotic and unpredictable and that action is preferable to passivity. They encourage subordinates to accept calculated risks to create opportunities, while providing intent and control that allow for latitude and discretion.

I. Understand

Understanding is fundamental to battle command. It is essential to the commander's ability to establish the situation's context. Analysis of the enemy and the operational variables provides the information senior commanders use to develop understanding and frame operational problems. To develop a truer understanding of the operational environment, commanders need to circulate throughout their areas of operations as often as possible, talking to the subordinate commanders and Soldiers conducting operations, while observing for themselves. These individuals will have a more finely attuned sense of the local situation, and their intuition may cause them to detect trouble or opportunity long before the staff might. This deepens commanders' understanding. It allows them to anticipate potential opportunities and threats, information gaps, and capability shortfalls. Understanding becomes the basis of the commander's visualization.

Numerous factors determine the commander's depth of understanding. These include the commander's education, intellect, experience, and perception. Intelligence, surveillance, and reconnaissance (ISR) is indispensable as is actual observation and listening to subordinates. Formulating CCIRs, keeping them current, determining where to place key personnel, and arranging for liaisons also contribute to understanding. Maintaining understanding is a dynamic ability; a commander's situational understanding changes as an operation progresses. Relevant information fuels understanding and fosters initiative. Greater understanding enables commanders to make better decisions. It allows them to focus their intuition on visualizing the current and future conditions of the environment and describe them to subordinates.

II. Visualize

Assignment of a mission provides the focus for developing the commander's visualization. Because military operations are fundamentally dynamic, this visualization must be continuous. Visualizing the desired end state requires commanders to clearly understand the operational environment and analyze the situation in terms of METT-TC. This analysis forms the basis of their situational understanding. Commanders consider the current situation and perform a mission analysis that assists in their initial visualization. They continually validate their visualization throughout the operation. To develop their visualization, commanders draw on several sources of knowledge and relevant information. These include—

- The elements of operational design appropriate to their echelon
- Input from the staff and other commanders
- Principles of war *(see p. 1-24)*
- Operational themes and related doctrine

- Running estimates
- The common operational picture
- Their experience and judgment
- Subject matter experts

Visualization allows commanders to develop their intent and planning guidance for the entire operation, not just the initial onset of action.

A. Commander's Visualization

Commander's visualization is the mental process of developing situational understanding, determining a desired end state, and envisioning the broad sequence of events by which the force will achieve that end state. It involves discussion and debate between commanders and staffs. During planning, commander's visualization provides the basis for developing plans and orders. During execution, it helps commanders determine if, when, and what to decide as they adapt to changing conditions. Commanders and staffs continuously assess the progress of operations toward the desired end state. They plan to adjust operations as required to accomplish the mission.

Subordinate, supporting, adjacent, and higher commanders communicate with one another to compare perspectives and visualize their environment. Commanders increase the breadth and depth of their visualizations by collaborating with other commanders and developing a shared situational understanding. Likewise, staff input, in the form of running estimates, focuses analysis and detects potential effects on operations. Commanders direct staffs to provide the information necessary to shape their visualization.

Commanders consider the elements of operational design as they frame the problem and describe their visualization. However, the utility and applicability of some elements are often limited at the tactical level. Commanders use the elements that apply to their echelon and situation.

B. Area of Influence

An area of influence is a geographical area wherein a commander is directly capable of influencing operations by maneuver and fire support systems normally under the commander's command or control (JP 1-02). The area of influence normally surrounds and includes the area of operations. Understanding the command's area of influence helps the commander and staff plan branches to the current operation that could require the force to use capabilities outside the area of operations.

C. Area of Interest

An area of interest is that area of concern to the commander, including the area of influence, areas adjacent thereto, and extending into enemy territory to the objectives of current or planned operations. This area also includes areas occupied by enemy forces who could jeopardize the accomplishment of the mission (JP 2-03). The area of interest for stability or civil support operations may be much larger than that associated with offensive and defensive operations.

D. Mission Variables: The Factors of METT-TC

METT-TC is a memory aid that identifies the mission variables: Mission, Enemy, Terrain and weather, Troops and support available, Time available, and Civil considerations. It is used in information management (the major categories of relevant information) and in tactics (the major variables considered during mission analysis). Mission analysis describes characteristics of the area of operations in terms of METT-TC, focusing on how they might affect the mission.

Note: See p. 1-31.

III. Describe

Ref: FM 3-0 Operations (2008), pp. 5-9 to 5-9.

After commanders visualize an operation, they describe it to their staffs and subordinates to facilitate shared understanding of the mission and intent. Commanders ensure subordinates understand the visualization well enough to begin planning. Commanders describe their visualization in doctrinal terms, refining and clarifying it as circumstances require. Commanders express their initial visualization in terms of—

- Initial commander's intent
- Planning guidance, including an initial concept of operations
- Information required for further planning (CCIRs)
- Essential elements of friendly information (EEFIs) that must be protected

1. Initial Commander's Intent

Commanders summarize their visualization in their initial intent statement. The purpose of the initial commander's intent is to facilitate planning while focusing the overall operations process. Commanders develop this intent statement personally. It is a succinct description of the commander's visualization of the entire operation, a clear statement of what the commander wants to accomplish. The initial commander's intent links the operation's purpose with the conditions that define the desired end state. Usually the intent statement evolves as planning progresses and more information becomes available.

The initial commander's intent statement focuses the staff during the operations process. The staff uses this statement to develop and refine courses of action that contribute to establishing conditions that define the end state. Planning involves developing lines of effort that link the execution of tactical tasks to end state conditions. A clear initial intent statement is essential to this effort.

2. Planning Guidance

Commanders provide planning guidance with their initial intent statement. Planning guidance conveys the essence of the commander's visualization. Guidance may be broad or detailed, depending on the situation. Effective planning guidance is essentially an initial concept of operations that includes priorities for each warfighting function. It reflects how the commander sees the operation unfolding. It broadly de-scribes when, where, and how the commander intends to employ combat power to accomplish the mission within the higher commander's intent.

Commanders use their experience and judgment to add depth and clarity to their planning guidance. They ensure staffs understand the broad outline of their visualization while allowing the latitude necessary to explore different options. This guidance provides the basis for a detailed concept of operations without dictating the specifics of the final plan. As with their intent, commanders may modify planning guidance based on staff and subordinate input and changing conditions.

3. Commander's Critical Information Requirements (CCIR)

A commander's critical information requirement is an information requirement identified by the commander as being critical to facilitating timely decisionmaking. The two key elements are friendly force information requirements and priority intelligence requirements (JP 3-0). A CCIR directly influences decisionmaking and facilitates the successful execution of military operations. Commanders decide whether to designate an information requirement as a CCIR based on likely decisions and their visualization of the course of the operation. A CCIR may support one or more decisions. During planning, staffs recommend information requirements for commanders to designate as CCIRs. During preparation and execution, they recommend changes to CCIRs based on assessment.

A CCIR is—

- Specified by a commander for a specific operation
- Applicable only to the commander who specifies it
- Situation dependent—directly linked to a current or future mission
- Focused on predictable events or activities
- Time-sensitive—the answer to a CCIR must be reported to the commander immediately by any means available
- Always promulgated by a plan or order

Commanders limit the number of CCIRs to focus the efforts of limited collection assets. Typically, commanders identify ten or fewer CCIRs. The fewer the CCIRs, the easier it is for staffs to remember, recognize, and act on each one. This helps staffs and subordinates identify information the commander needs immediately. The staff's first priority is to provide the commander with answers to CCIRs. While most staffs provide relevant information, a good staff expertly distills that information. It identifies answers to CCIRs and gets them to the commander immediately. It also identifies vital information that does not answer a CCIR but that the commander nonetheless needs to know. A good staff develops this acumen through training and experience. Designating too many CCIRs limits the staff's ability to immediately recognize and react to them. Excessive critical items reduce the focus of collection efforts.

The list of CCIRs constantly changes. Commanders add and delete individual requirements throughout an operation based on the information needed for specific decisions. Commanders determine their own CCIRs but may select some from staff nominations. Staff sections recommend the most important priority intelligence requirements (PIRs) and friendly force information requirements (FFIRs) for the commander to designate as CCIRs. Once approved, a CCIR falls into one of two categories: PIRs and FFIRs.

- **Priority Intelligence Requirement (PIR).** A priority intelligence requirement is an intelligence requirement, stated as a priority for intelligence support, that the commander and staff need to understand the adversary or the operational environment (JP 2-0). PIRs identify the information about the enemy, terrain and weather, and civil considerations that the commander considers most important. Lessons from recent operations show that intelligence about civil considerations may be as critical as intelligence about the enemy. Thus, all staff sections may recommend information about civil considerations as PIRs. The intelligence officer manages PIRs for the commander.
- **Friendly Force Information Requirement (FFIR).** A friendly force information requirement is information the commander and staff need to understand the status of friendly force and supporting capabilities (JP 3-0). FFIRs identify the information about the mission, troops and support available, and time available for friendly forces that the commander considers most important. In coordination with the staff, the operations officer manages FFIRs for the commander.

4. Essential Elements of Friendly Information (EEFI)

An essential element of friendly information is a critical aspect of a friendly operation that, if known by the enemy, would subsequently compromise, lead to failure, or limit success of the operation, and therefore should be protected from enemy detection. Although EEFIs are not CCIRs, they have the same priority. An EEFI establishes an element of information to protect rather than one to collect. EEFIs identify those elements of friendly force information that, if compromised, would jeopardize mission success.

EEFIs help commanders protect vital friendly information. Their identification is the first step in the operations security process and central to information protection. (FM 3-13 addresses the operations security process.) EEFIs are also key factors in formulating military deception operations. Operations security, information protection, and military deception all contribute to information superiority.

IV. Direct

Commanders direct all aspects of operations. This direction takes different forms during planning, preparation, and execution. Commanders make decisions and direct actions based on their situational understanding, which they maintain by continuous assessment.

A. Plans and Orders

Plans and orders are key tools used by commanders in directing operations. Under mission command, commanders direct with mission orders. Mission orders is a technique for developing orders that emphasizes to subordinates the results to be attained, not how they are to achieve them. It provides maximum freedom of action in determining how to best accomplish assigned missions. Mission orders synchronize subordinates' actions only as required for mission success. Constraints are appropriate when mission success requires closely synchronized action by multiple elements. Even then, commanders establish constraints in a manner that least limits subordinates' initiative.

When close coordination is necessary, commanders limit subordinates' freedom of action with control measures specified in plans and orders. Generally, subordinate commanders exercise full freedom of action within the concept of operations and commander's intent. Higher commanders may impose additional control over subordinates during a particular phase or mission. As soon as conditions allow, subordinates regain their freedom of action. Effective mission orders communicate to subordinates the situation, their commander's mission and intent, and the important tasks of each unit. The commander's intent and concept of operations set guidelines that ensure unity of effort while allowing subordinate commanders to exercise initiative.

Note: See pp. 1-37 to 1-44.

B. Commander's Intent

The commander's intent is a clear, concise statement of what the force must do and the conditions the force must establish with respect to the enemy, terrain, and civil considerations that represent the desired end state. The commander's intent succinctly describes what constitutes success in an operation. It includes the operation's purpose and the conditions that define the end state. It links the mission, concept of operations, and tasks to subordinate units. A clear commander's intent facilitates a shared understanding and focus on the overall conditions that represent mission accomplishment. During execution, the commander's intent spurs subordinates' initiative.

The commander's intent must be easy to remember and clearly understood two echelons down. The shorter the commander's intent, the better it serves these purposes. Typically, the commander's intent statement is three to five sentences long.

C. Concept of the Operations

After commanders visualize an operation, they describe it to their staffs and subordinates to facilitate shared understanding of the mission and intent. Commanders ensure subordinates understand the visualization well enough to begin planning. Commanders describe their visualization in doctrinal terms, refining and clarifying it as circumstances require. Commanders express their initial visualization in terms of—

- Initial commander's intent
- Planning guidance, including an initial concept of operations
- Information required for further planning (CCIRs)
- Essential elements of friendly information (EEFIs) that must be protected

Note: See facing page (p. 1-21).

Concept of Operations (Direct)

Ref: FM 3-0 Operations (2008) p. 5-11 to 5-12.

The concept of operations is a statement that directs the manner in which subordinate units cooperate to accomplish the mission and establishes the sequence of actions the force will use to achieve the end state. It is normally expressed in terms of decisive, shaping, and sustaining operations. The concept of operations expands on the commander's intent by describing how the commander wants the force to accomplish the mission. It states the principal tasks required, the responsible subordinate units, and how the principal tasks complement one another. Normally, the concept of operations projects the status of the force at the end of the operation.

Note: Small-unit commanders and leaders usually do not describe their concept of operations in terms of decisive, shaping, and sustaining operations; they simply assign tasks to subordinates using main effort as required. (FM 5-0 discusses the concept of operations in detail.)

1. Decisive Operations

The decisive operation is the operation that directly accomplishes the mission. It determines the outcome of a major operation, battle, or engagement. The decisive operation is the focal point around which commanders design the entire operation. Multiple units may be engaged in the same decisive operation. Units operating in non contiguous areas of operations may execute the tasks composing the higher headquarters' decisive operation simultaneously in different locations. Commanders visualize the decisive operation and then design shaping and sustaining operations around it.

2. Shaping Operations

A shaping operation is an operation at any echelon that creates and preserves conditions for the success of the decisive operation. Shaping operations establish conditions for the decisive operation through effects on the enemy, population (including local leaders), and terrain. Shaping operations may occur throughout the operational area and involve any combination of forces and capabilities. Shaping operations may occur before, during, or after the decisive operation begins. Some shaping operations, especially those executed simultaneously with the decisive operation, may be economy of force actions. However, if the force available does not permit simultaneous decisive and shaping operations, the commander sequences shaping operations around the decisive operation.

3. Sustaining Operations

A sustaining operation is an operation at any echelon that enables the decisive operation or shaping operations by generating and maintaining combat power. Sustaining operations differ from decisive and shaping operations in that they are focused internally (on friendly forces) rather than externally (on the enemy or environment). Sustaining operations cannot be decisive. They determine the limit of operational reach. At the tactical level, sustaining operations determine the tempo of the overall operation; they ensure the force is able to seize, retain, and exploit the initiative.

Main Effort

The concept of operations identifies a main effort unit if required; otherwise, the priorities of support go to the unit conducting the decisive operation. The main effort is the designated subordinate unit whose mission at a given point in time is most critical to overall mission success. It is usually weighted with the preponderance of combat power. Designating a main effort temporarily prioritizes resource allocation. Commanders may shift the main effort several times during an operation. A unit conducting a shaping operation may be designated as the main effort until the decisive operation commences. However, the unit with primary responsibility for the decisive operation becomes the main effort upon execution of the decisive operation.

The Six Warfighting Functions (Direct)

Ref: FM 3-0 Operations (2008), pp. 4-3 to 4-7.

The battlefield operational systems (BOS) or battlefield functional areas (BFA) have been replaced with six warfighting functions. The warfighting functions, when combined with a seventh element, leadership, are the elements of combat power.

Commanders use the warfighting functions to help them exercise battle command. A warfighting function is a group of tasks and systems (people, organizations, information, and processes) united by a common purpose that commanders use to accomplish missions and training objectives. Decisive, shaping, and sustaining operations combine all the warfighting functions to generate combat power. No warfighting function is exclusively decisive, shaping, or sustaining. The Army's warfighting functions are fundamentally linked to the joint functions.

Movement and Maneuver

The movement and maneuver warfighting function is the related tasks and systems that move forces to achieve a position of advantage in relation to the enemy. Direct fire is inherent in maneuver, as is close combat. The function includes tasks associated with force projection related to gaining a positional advantage over an enemy. The movement and maneuver warfighting function does not include administrative movements of personnel and materiel. These movements fall under the sustainment warfighting function.

FM 3-90 discusses maneuver and tactical movement. FMI 3-35 and FMs 100-17-1 and 100-17-2 discuss force projection. When published, FM 3-35 will supersede FMI 3-35.

Intelligence

The intelligence warfighting function is the related tasks and systems that facilitate understanding of the enemy, terrain, weather, and civil considerations.

FM 2-0 describes the intelligence warfighting function. Several unit-level manuals provide supplemental doctrine on surveillance and reconnaissance.

Fires

The fires warfighting function is the related tasks and systems that provide collective and coordinated use of Army indirect fires, joint fires, and command and control warfare through the targeting process.

When published, FM 3-09 will contain doctrine on fires. When revised, FM 3-13 will address command and control warfare.

Sustainment

The sustainment warfighting function is the related tasks and systems that provide support and services to ensure freedom of action, extend operational reach, and prolong endurance.

FM 4-0 describes the sustainment warfighting function.

Command and Control

The command and control warfighting function is the related tasks and systems that support commanders in exercising authority and direction.

FM 6-0 describes command and control warfighting doctrine.

Protection

The protection warfighting function is the related tasks and systems that preserve the force so the commander can apply maximum combat power.

When published, FM 3-10 will establish doctrine for protection. When revised, FM 3-13 will address information protection.

V. Lead

After commanders make decisions, they guide their forces throughout execution. Upon execution, commanders must provide the strength of character, moral courage, and will to follow through with their decisions.

Note: FM 6-22 discusses leadership actions during execution. For additional information, see The Leader's SMARTbook.

In many instances, a leader's physical presence is necessary to lead effectively. Advanced information systems provide detailed information that facilitates situational understanding and command and control; however, much of the art of command comes from intuition. Commanders carefully consider where they need to be, balancing the need to inspire Soldiers with that of maintaining an overall perspective of the entire operation. The commander's forward presence demonstrates a willingness to share danger. It also allows them to appraise for themselves the subordinate unit's condition, including leader and Soldier morale. Forward presence allows commanders to sense the human dimension of conflict, particularly when fear and fatigue reduce effectiveness. Then commanders need to lead by example, face-to-face with Soldiers.

VI. Assess

Assessment is the continuous monitoring and evaluation of the current situation, particularly the enemy, and progress of an operation. Commanders, assisted by their staffs and subordinate commanders, continuously assess the current situation and the progress of the operation and compare it with the concept of operations, mission, and commander's intent. Based on their assessment commanders direct adjustments, ensuring that the operation remains focused on the mission and commander's intent.

Assessment precedes and guides every operations process activity and concludes each operation or phase of an operation. It involves a comparison of forecasted outcomes to actual events. Assessment entails three tasks:

- Continuously assessing the enemy's reactions and vulnerabilities
- Continuously monitoring the situation and progress of the operation towards the commander's desired end state
- Evaluating the operation against measures of effectiveness and measures of performance

1. Measure of Performance

A measure of performance is a criterion used to assess friendly actions that is tied to measuring task accomplishment (JP 3-0). Measures of performance answer the question, "Was the task or action performed as the commander intended?" A measure of performance confirms or denies that a task has been properly performed.

2. Measure of Effectiveness

A measure of effectiveness is a criterion used to assess changes in system behavior, capability, or operational environment that is tied to measuring the attainment of an end state, achievement of an objective, or creation of an effect (JP 3-0). Measures of effectiveness focus on the results or consequences of actions taken. They answer the question, "Is the force doing the right things, or are additional or alternative actions required?" A measure of effectiveness provides a benchmark against which the commander assesses progress toward accomplishing the mission.

Cdrs and small unit leaders monitor the current situation for unexpected successes, failures, or enemy actions. As commanders assess the operation, they look for opportunities, threats, and acceptable progress. They accept risks, seize opportunities, and mitigate threats. Throughout the operation, commanders visualize, describe, and direct changes to the operation.

Principles of War and Operations (Visualize)

Ref: FM 3-0 Operations (2008), app. A.

The nine principles of war represent the most important nonphysical factors that affect the conduct of operations at the strategic, operational, and tactical levels. The Army published its original principles of war after World War I. In the following years, the Army adjusted the original principles modestly as they stood the tests of analysis, experimentation, and practice. The principles of war are not a checklist. While they are considered in all operations, they do not apply in the same way to every situation. Rather, they summarize characteristics of successful operations. Applied to the study of past campaigns, major operations, battles, and engagements, the principles of war are powerful analysis tools. Joint doctrine adds three principles of operations.

- **Objective.** Direct every military operation toward a clearly defined, decisive, and attainable objective.
- **Offensive.** Seize, retain, and exploit the initiative.
- **Mass.** Concentrate the effects of combat power at the decisive place and time.
- **Economy of Force.** Allocate minimum essential combat power to secondary efforts.
- **Maneuver.** Place the enemy in a disadvantageous position through the flexible application of combat power.
- **Unity of Command.** For every objective, ensure unity of effort under one responsible commander.
- **Security.** Never permit the enemy to acquire an unexpected advantage.
- **Surprise.** Strike the enemy at a time, place or in a manner for which he is unprepared.
- **Simplicity.** Prepare clear, uncomplicated plans and clear, concise orders to ensure thorough understanding.

Additional Principles of Joint Operations

In addition to these nine principles, JP 3-0 adds three principles of operations—perseverance, legitimacy, and restraint. Together with the principles of war, these twelve make up the principles of joint operations.

- **Perseverance.** Ensure the commitment necessary to attain the national strategic end state. Commanders prepare for measured, protracted military operations in pursuit of the desired national strategic end state. Some joint operations may require years to reach the desired end state. Resolving the underlying causes of the crisis may be elusive, making it difficult to achieve conditions supporting the end state.
- **Legitimacy.** Develop and maintain the will necessary to attain the national strategic end state. For Army forces, legitimacy comes from three important factors. First, the operation or campaign must be conducted under U.S. law. Second, the operation must be conducted according to international laws and treaties recognized by the United States, particularly the law of war. Third, the campaign or operation should develop or reinforce the authority and acceptance for the host-nation government by both the governed and the international community.
- **Restraint.** Limit collateral damage and prevent the unnecessary use of force. Restraint requires careful and disciplined balancing of security, the conduct of military operations, and the desired strategic end state. Excessive force antagonizes those friendly and neutral parties involved. Hence, it damages the legitimacy of the organization that uses it while potentially enhancing the legitimacy of any opposing party.

Chap 1 V. Troop Leading Procedures (TLP)

Ref: FM 5-0 Army Planning and Orders Production, chap. 4 and FM 3-21.10 The Infantry Rifle Company, chap. 2, section II. For complete discussion of the military decision making process (MDMP) to include troop leading procedures, see The Battle Staff SMARTbook.

Troop leading procedures (TLP) provide small unit leaders a framework for planning and preparing for operations. Leaders of company and smaller units use TLP to develop plans and orders. This section describes the eight steps of TLP and its relationship to the military decision making process (MDMP). The TLP is applicable to all types of small units.

Leaders project their presence and guidance through troop leading procedures. TLP is the process a leader goes through to prepare the unit to accomplish a tactical mission. It begins when the mission is received. (Photo by Jeong, Hae-jung).

TLP extend the MDMP to small unit level. The MDMP and TLP are similar but not identical. Commanders with a coordinating staff use the MDMP as their primary planning process. Company-level and smaller units do not have formal staffs and use TLP to plan and prepare for operations. This places the responsibility for planning primarily on the commander or small unit leader.

Troop leading procedures is a dynamic process used by small unit leaders to analysis a mission, develop a plan, and prepare for an operation. These procedures enable leaders to maximize available planning time while developing effective plans and adequately preparing their unit for an operation. TLP consist of the eight steps. The sequence of the TLP steps is not rigid. They are modified to meet the mission, situation, and available time. Some steps are done concurrently while others may go on continuously throughout the operations.

I. Performing Troop Leading Procedures

TLP provide small unit leaders a framework for planning and preparing for operations. This section discusses each step of TLP.

Army leaders begin TLP when they receive the initial WARNO or perceive a new mission. As each subsequent order arrives, leaders modify their assessments, update tentative plans, and continue to supervise and assess preparations. In some situations, the higher headquarters may not issue the full sequence of WARNOs; security considerations or tempo may make it impractical. In other cases, Army leaders may initiate TLP before receiving a WARNO based on existing plans and orders (contingency plans or be-prepared missions), and an understanding of the situation.

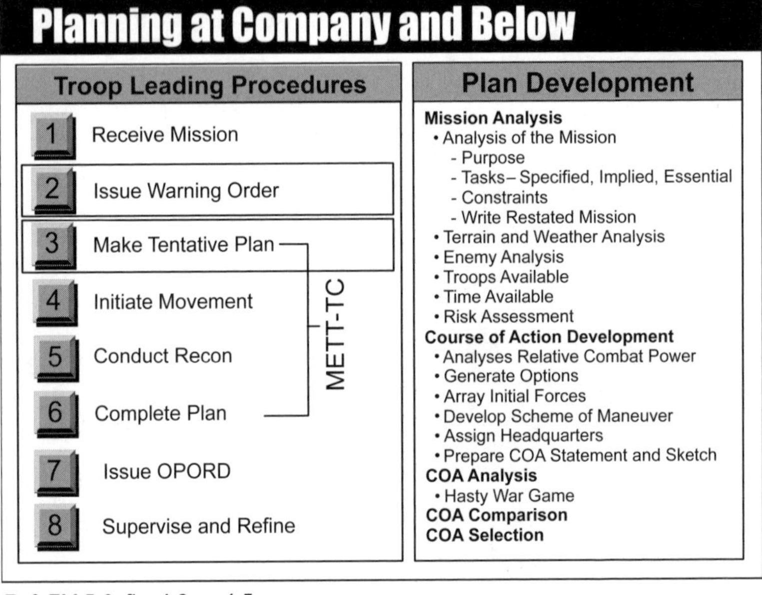

Ref: FM 5-0, fig. 4-3, p. 4-5.

1. Receive The Mission

Receipt of a mission may occur in several ways. It may begin with the initial WARNO from higher or when a leader receives an OPORD. Frequently, leaders receive a mission in a FRAGO over the radio. Ideally, they receive a series of WARNOs, the OPORD, and a briefing from their commander. Normally after receiving an OPORD, leaders are required to give a confirmation brief to their higher commander to ensure they understand the higher commander's concept of operations and intent for his unit.

Upon receipt of mission, Army leaders perform an initial assessment of the situation (METT-TC analysis) and allocate the time available for planning and preparation. (Preparation includes rehearsals and movement.) This initial assessment and time allocation form the basis of their initial WARNO. Army leaders issue the initial WARNO quickly to give subordinates as much time as possible to plan and prepare.

Ideally, a battalion headquarters issues at least three WARNOs to subordinates when conducting the MDMP. WARNOs are issued upon receipt of mission, completion of mission analysis, and when the commander approves a COA. WARNOs serve a function in planning similar to that of fragmentary orders (FRAGOs) during execution.

Troop Leading Procedures and the MDMP

Ref: FM 5-0, pp. 3-4 to 3-9.

TLP extend the MDMP to small unit level. The MDMP and TLP are similar but not identical. They are both linked by the basic problem solving methodology. Commanders with a coordinating staff use the MDMP as their primary planning process. Company-level and smaller units do not have formal staffs and use TLP to plan and prepare for operations. This places the responsibility for planning primarily on the commander or small unit leader.

Leaders use TLP when working alone to solve tactical problems or with a small group. For example, a company commander may use his executive officer, first sergeant, fire support officer, supply sergeant and communications sergeant to assist him during TLP.

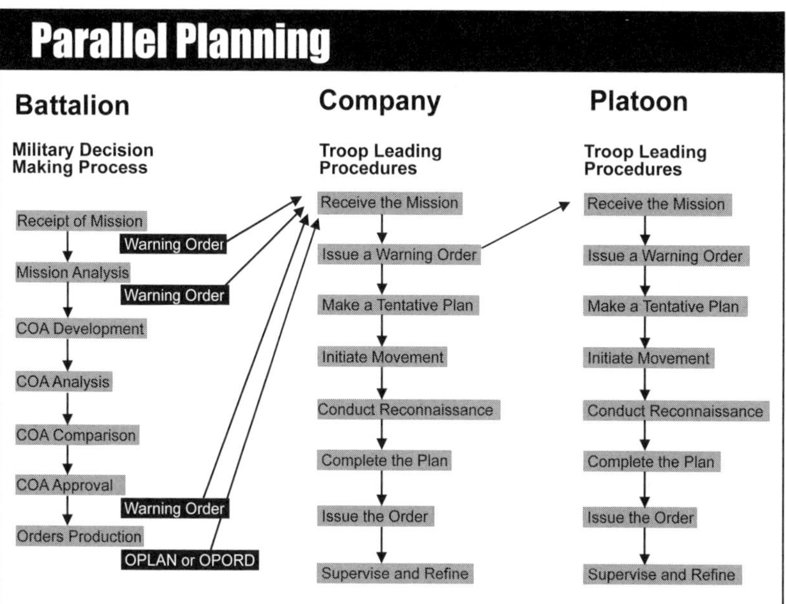

Ref: FM 5-0, fig. 4-2, p. 4-2.

Normally the first three steps (receive the mission, issue a WARNO, and make a tentative plan) of TLP occur in order. However, the sequence of subsequent steps is based on the situation. The tasks involved in some steps (for example, initiate movement and conduct reconnaissance) may occur several times. The last step, supervise and refine, occurs throughout.

There is a tension between executing current operations and planning for future operations. The small unit leader must balance both. If engaged in a current operation, there is less time for TLP. If in a lull, transition, or an assembly area, there is more time and therefore more time to do a thorough job of TLP. In some situations, time constraints or other factors may prevent Army leaders from performing each step of TLP as thoroughly as they would like. For example, during the step "make a tentative plan", small unit leaders often develop only one acceptable course of action (COA) vice multiple COAs. If time permits however, leaders may develop, compare, and analyze several COAs before arriving at a decision on which one to execute.

A. Perform an Initial Assessment

The initial assessment addresses the factors of mission, enemy, terrain and weather, troops and support available, time available, and civil considerations (METT-TC). The order and detail in which Army leaders analyze the factors of METT-TC is flexible. It depends on the amount of information available and the relative importance of each factor. For example, they may concentrate on the mission, enemy, and terrain, leaving weather and civil considerations until they receive more detailed information.

Often, Army leaders will not receive their final unit mission until the WARNO is disseminated after COA approval or after the OPORD. Effective leaders do not wait until their higher headquarters completes planning to begin their planning. Using all information available, Army leaders develop their unit mission as completely as they can. They focus on the mission, commander's intent, and concept of operations of their higher and next higher headquarters. They pick out the major tasks their unit will probably be assigned and develop a mission statement based on information they have received. At this stage, the mission may be incomplete. For example, an initial mission statement could be, "First platoon conducts an ambush in the next 24 hours." While not complete, this information allows subordinates to start preparations. Leaders complete a formal mission statement during TLP step 3 (make a tentative plan) and step 6 (complete the plan).

B. Allocate the Available Time

Based on what they know, Army leaders estimate the time available to plan and prepare for the mission. They begin by identifying the times at which major planning and preparation events, including rehearsals, must be complete. Reverse planning helps them do this. Army leaders identify the critical times specified by higher headquarters and work back from them, estimating how much time each event will consume.

Leaders ensure that all subordinate echelons have sufficient time for their own planning and preparation needs. A general rule of thumb for leaders at all levels is to use no more than one-third of the available time for planning and issuance of the OPORD. Leaders allocate the remaining two-thirds of it to subordinates.

2. Issue a Warning Order (WARNO)

As soon as Army leaders finish their initial assessment of the situation and available time, they issue a WARNO. Leaders do not wait for more information. They issue the best WARNO possible with the information at hand and update it as needed with additional WARNOs.

The WARNO contains as much detail as possible. It informs subordinates of the unit mission and gives them the leader's time line. Army leaders may also pass on any other instructions or information they think will help subordinates prepare for the new mission. This includes information on the enemy, the nature of the higher headquarters plan, and any specific instructions for preparing their units. The most important thing is that leaders not delay in issuing the initial WARNO. As more information becomes available, leaders can -- and should -- issue additional WARNOs.

Warning Order (WARNO)

Normally an initial WARNO issued below battalion level includes:

- Mission or nature of the operation
- Time and place for issuing the OPORD
- Units or elements participating in the operation
- Specific tasks not addressed by unit SOP
- Time line for the operation

Allocate Available Time

Based on what they know, Army leaders estimate the time available to plan and prepare for the mission. They begin by identifying the times at which major planning and preparation events, including rehearsals, must be complete. Reverse planning helps them do this. Army leaders identify the critical times specified by higher headquarters and work back from them, estimating how much time each event will consume. Critical times might include aircraft loading times, the line of departure (LD) time, or the start point (SP) time for movement. By working backwards, Army leaders arrive at the time available to plan and prepare for the operation.

Leaders ensure that all subordinate echelons have sufficient time for their own planning and preparation needs. A general rule of thumb for leaders at all levels is to use no more than one-third of the available time for planning and issuance of the OPORD. Leaders allocate the remaining two-thirds of it to subordinates.

Below is a sample time schedule for an infantry company. This tentative schedule is adjusted as TLP progresses.

0600 - Execute mission
0530 - Finalize or adjust the plan based on leader's recon
0400 - Establish the objective rallying point; begin leaders recon
0200 - Begin movement
2100 - Conduct platoon inspections
1900 - Conduct rehearsals
1800 - Eat meals (tray packs)
1745 - Hold backbriefs (squad leaders to platoon leaders)
1630 - Issue platoon OPORDs
1500 - Hold backbriefs (platoon leaders to company commander)
1330 - Issue company OPORD
1045 - Conduct reconnaissance
1030 - Update company WARNO
1000 - Receive battalion OPORD
0900 - Receive battalion WARNO; issue company WARNO

An example patrol timeline is below:

11:00 Patrol secures OBJ [END]
10:45 Patrol starts actions on OBJ
10:30 Patrol passes through release point
10:10 Patrol departs ORP
10:00 Leader's recon returns to ORP
09:30 Leader's recon departs ORP
09:15 Patrol occupies ORP
08:15 Patrol conducts passage of line through FLOT
08:00 PL links up with forward unit commander/guide
07:45 Patrol occupies AA
07:30 Patrol begins movement to AA.
07:15 Leaders conducts PCI
07:00 Patrol conducts rehearsals
06:30 PL issues OPORD
06:00 PL issues WARNO [START]

3. Make a Tentative Plan

Once they have issued the initial WARNO, Army leaders develop a tentative plan. This step combines MDMP steps 2 through 6: mission analysis, COA development, COA analysis, COA comparison, and COA approval. At levels below battalion, these steps are less structured than for units with staffs. Often, leaders perform them mentally. They may include their principal subordinates-especially during COA development, analysis, and comparison. However, Army leaders, not their subordinates, select the COA on which to base the tentative plan.

A. Mission Analysis

To frame the tentative plan, Army leaders perform mission analysis. This mission analysis follows the METT-TC format, continuing the initial assessment performed in TLP step 1. FM 6-0 discusses the factors of METT-TC.

Note: See facing page (p. 1-31) for discussion and an outline of METT-TC.

METT-TC

- M - Mission
- E - Enemy
- T - Terrain and Weather
- T - Troops and Support Available
- T - Time Available
- C - Civil Considerations

The product of this part of the mission analysis is the restated mission. The restated mission is a simple, concise expression of the essential tasks the unit must accomplish and the purpose to be achieved. The mission statement states who (the unit), what (the task), when (either the critical time or on order), where (location), and why (the purpose of the operation).

B. Course of Action Development

Mission analysis provides information needed to develop COAs. The purpose of COA development is simple: to determine one or more ways to accomplish the mission. At lower echelons, the mission may be a single task. Most missions and tasks can be accomplished in more than one way. However, in a time-constrained environment, Army leaders may develop only one COA. Normally, they develop two or more. Army leaders do not wait for a complete order before beginning COA development. They develop COAs as soon as they have enough information to do so. Usable COAs are suitable, feasible, acceptable, distinguishable, and complete. To develop them, leaders focus on the actions the unit takes at the objective and conducts a reverse plan to the starting point.

Note: See The Battle Staff SMARTbook for further discussion of COA Development.

COA Development

1. Analyze relative combat power
2. Generate options
3. Array forces
4. Develop the concept of operations
5. Assign responsibilities
6. Prepare COA statement and sketch

II. METT-TC (Mission Analysis)

Ref: FM 5-0, pp. 4-7 to 4-10.

To frame the tentative plan, Army leaders perform mission analysis following the METT-TC format, continuing the initial assessment performed in TLP step 1:

M - Mission

Army leaders analyze the higher headquarters WARNO or OPORD to determine how their unit contributes to the higher headquarters mission:

- Higher Headquarters Mission and Commander's Intent
- Higher Headquarters Concept of Operations
- Specified, Implied, and Essential Tasks
- Constraints

The product of this part of the mission analysis is the restated mission. The restated mission is a simple, concise expression of the essential tasks the unit must accomplish and the purpose to be achieved. The mission statement states who (the unit), what (the task), when (either the critical time or on order), where (location), and why (the purpose of the operation).

E - Enemy

With the restated mission as the focus, Army leaders continue the analysis with the enemy. For small unit ops, Army leaders need to know about the enemy's composition, disposition, strength, recent activities, ability to reinforce, and possible COAs.

T - Terrain and Weather

This aspect of mission analysis addresses the military aspects of terrain (OKOCA):

- Observation and Fields of Fire
- Key Terrain
- Obstacles
- Cover and Concealment
- Avenues of Approach

There are five military aspects of weather: visibility, winds, precipitation, cloud cover, and temperature/humidity (see FM 34-130). The analysis considers the effects on soldiers, equip., and supporting forces, such as air and artillery support.

Note: See pp. 1-32 to 1-33 for additional information on OCOKA.

T - Troops and Support Available

Perhaps the most important aspect of mission analysis is determining the combat potential of one's own force. Army leaders know the status of their soldiers' morale, their experience and training, and the strengths and weaknesses.

T - Time Available

Army leaders not only appreciate how much time is available; they understand the time-space aspects of preparing, moving, fighting, and sustaining. They view their own tasks and enemy actions in relation to time. They know how long it takes under such conditions to prepare for certain tasks (prepare orders, rehearsals, etc).

C - Civil Considerations

Civil considerations are how the man-made infrastructure, civilian institutions, and attitudes and activities of the civilian leaders, populations, and organizations within an area of operations influence the conduct of military operations (FM 6-0). Civil considerations are analyzed in terms of six factors **(ASCOPE)**: areas, structures, capabilities, organizations, people and events.

III. OCOKA - Military Aspects of the Terrain

Ref: FM 34-130 Intelligence Preparation of the Battlefield, pp. 2-10 to 2-21 .

Terrain analysis consists of an evaluation of the military aspects of the battlefield's terrain to determine its effects on military operations. The military aspects of terrain are often described using the acronym OCOKA.

O - Observation and Fields of Fire

Observation. Observation is the ability to see the threat either visually or through the use of surveillance devices. Factors that limit or deny observation include concealment and cover.

Fields of fire. A field of fire is the area that a weapon or group of weapons may effectively cover with fire from a given position. Terrain that offers cover limits fields of fire.

Terrain that offers both good observation and fields of fire generally favors defensive COAs.

The evaluation of observation and fields of fire allows you to:

- Identify potential engagement areas, or "fire sacks" and "kill zones"
- Identify defensible terrain and specific system or equipment positions
- Identify where maneuvering forces are most vulnerable to observation and fire

Evaluate observation from the perspective of electronic and optical line-of-sight (LOS) systems as well as unaided visual observation. Consider systems such as weapon sights, laser range finders, radars, radios, and jammers.

While ground based systems usually require horizontal LOS, airborne systems use oblique and vertical LOS. The same is true of air defense systems.

If time and resources permit, prepare terrain factor overlays to aid in evaluating observation and fields of fire. Consider the following:

- Vegetation or building height and density
- Canopy or roof closure
- Relief features, including micro-relief features such as defiles (elevation tinting techniques are helpful).
- Friendly and threat target acquisition and sensor capabilities
- Specific LOSs

C - Concealment and Cover

Concealment is protection from observation. Woods, underbrush, snowdrifts, tall grass, and cultivated vegetation provide concealment.

Cover is protection from the effects of direct and indirect fires. Ditches, caves, river banks, folds in the ground, shell craters, buildings, walls, and embankments provide cover.

The evaluation of concealment and cover aids in identifying defensible terrain, possible approach routes, assembly areas, and deployment and dispersal areas. Use the results of the evaluation to:

- Identify and evaluate AAs
- Identify defensible terrain and potential battle positions
- Identify potential assembly and dispersal areas

O - Obstacles

Obstacles are any natural or man-made terrain features that stop, impede, or divert military movement.

An evaluation of obstacles leads to the identification of mobility corridors. This in turn helps identify defensible terrain and AAs. To evaluate obstacles:

- Identify pertinent obstacles in the AI
- Determine the effect of each obstacle on the mobility of the evaluated force
- Combine the effects of individual obstacles into an integrated product

If DMA products are unavailable, and time and resources permit, prepare terrain factor overlays to aid in evaluating obstacles. Some of the factors to consider are:

- Vegetation (tree spacing/diameter)
- Surface drainage (stream width, depth, velocity, bank slope, & height)
- Surface materials (soil types and conditions that affect mobility)
- Surface configuration (slopes that affect mobility)
- Obstacles (natural and man-made; consider obstacles to flight as well as ground mobility)
- Transportation systems (bridge classifications and road characteristics such as curve radius, slopes, and width)
- Effects of actual or projected weather such as heavy precipitation or snow

K - Key Terrain

Key terrain is any locality or area the seizure, retention, or control of which affords a marked advantage to either combatant. Key terrain is often selected for use as battle positions or objectives. Evaluate key terrain by assessing the impact of its seizure, by either force, upon the results of battle.

A common technique is to depict key terrain on overlays and sketches with a large "K" within a circle or curve that encloses and follows the contours of the designated terrain. On transparent overlays use a color, such as purple, that stands out.

In the offense, key terrain features are usually forward of friendly dispositions and are often assigned as objectives. Terrain features in adjacent sectors may be key terrain if their control is necessary for the continuation of the attack or the accomplishment of the mission. If the mission is to destroy threat forces, key terrain may include areas whose seizure helps ensure the required destruction. Terrain that gives the threat effective observation along an axis of friendly advance may be key terrain if it is necessary to deny its possession or control by the threat.

In the defense, key terrain is usually within the AO and within or behind the selected defensive area.

Some examples of such key terrain are:

- Terrain that gives good observation over AAs to and into the defensive position
- Terrain that permits the defender to cover an obstacle by fire
- Important road junctions or communication centers that affect the use of reserves, sustainment, or LOCs

Additional Considerations:

- **Key terrain varies with the level of command.** For example, to an army or theater commander a large city may afford marked advantages as a communications center. To a division commander the high ground which dominates the city may be key terrain while the city itself may be an obstacle.
- **Terrain which permits or denies maneuver may be key terrain.**
- **Major obstacles are rarely key terrain features.** The high ground dominating a river rather than the river itself is usually the key terrain feature for the tactical commander. An exception is an obstacle such as a built-up area which is assigned as an objective.
- **Key terrain is decisive** terrain if it has an **extraordinary impact** on the mission.
- **Decisive terrain is rare and will not be present in every situation.**

A - Avenue of Approach (AA)

An Avenue of Approach (AA) is an air or ground route that leads an attacking force of a given size to its objective or to key terrain in its path.

During offensive operations, the evaluation of AAs leads to a recommendation on the best AAs to the command's objective and identification of avenues available to the threat for withdrawal or the movement of reserves.

During the defense, identify AAs that support the threat's offensive capabilities and avenues that support the movement and commitment of friendly reserves.

C. Analyze Courses of Action (Wargame)

For each COA, Army leaders think through the operation from start to finish. They compare each COA with the enemy's most probable COA. At small unit level, the enemy's most probable COA is what the enemy is most likely to do, given what friendly forces are doing at that instant. The leader visualizes a set of actions and reactions. The object is to determine what can go wrong and what decision the leader will likely have to make as a result.

D. Compare COAs and Make a Decision

Army leaders compare COAs by weighing the advantages, disadvantages, strengths, and weaknesses of each, as noted during the wargame. They decide which COA to execute based on this comparison and on their professional judgment. They take into account:

- Mission accomplishment
- Time to execute the operation
- Risk
- Results from unit reconnaissance
- Subordinate unit tasks and purposes
- Casualties incurred
- Posturing the force for future operations

4. Initiate Movement

Army leaders initiate any movement necessary to continue mission preparation or position the unit for execution, sometimes before making a tentative plan. They do this as soon as they have enough information to do so, or when the unit is required to move to position itself for a task. This is also essential when time is short. Movements may be to an assembly area, a battle position, a new AO, or an attack position. They may include movement of reconnaissance elements, guides, or quartering parties. Army leaders often initiate movement based on their tentative plan and issue the order to subordinates in the new location.

5. Conduct Reconnaissance

Whenever time and circumstances allow, Army leaders personally observe the AO for the mission. No amount of intelligence preparation of the battlefield (IPB) can substitute for firsthand assessment of METT-TC from within the AO. Unfortunately, many factors can keep leaders from performing a personal reconnaissance. The minimum action necessary is a thorough map reconnaissance, supplemented by imagery and intelligence products. In some cases, subordinates or other elements (such as scouts) may perform the reconnaissance for the leader while the leader completes other TLP steps.

Army leaders use the results of the wargame to identify information requirements. Reconnaissance operations seek to confirm or deny information that supports the tentative plan. They focus first on information gaps identified during mission analysis. Army leaders ensure their leader's reconnaissance complements the higher headquarters reconnaissance plan. The unit may conduct additional reconnaissance operations as the situation allows. This step may also precede making a tentative plan if there is not enough information available to begin planning. Reconnaissance may be the only way to develop the information required for planning.

6. Complete the Plan

During this step, Army leaders incorporate the result of reconnaissance into their selected COA to complete the plan or order. This includes preparing overlays, refining the indirect fire target list, coordinating combat service support and command and control requirements, and updating the tentative plan as a result of the reconnaissance. At lower levels, this step may entail only confirming or updating information contained in the tentative plan. If time allows, Army leaders make final coordination with adjacent units and higher headquarters before issuing the order.

7. Issue the Order

Small unit orders are normally issued verbally and supplemented by graphics and other control measures. The order follows the standard five-paragraph format OPORD format. Typically, Army leaders below company level do not issue a commander's intent. They reiterate the intent of their higher and next higher commander.

Note: See pp. 1-37 to 1-44 for a sample order formats.

The ideal location for issuing the order is a point in the AO with a view of the objective and other aspects of the terrain. The leader may perform a leader's reconnaissance, complete the order, and then summon subordinates to a specified location to receive it. Sometimes security or other constraints make it infeasible to issue the order on the terrain; then Army leaders use a sand table, detailed sketch, maps, and other products to depict the AO and situation.

8. Supervise and Refine

Throughout TLP, Army leaders monitor mission preparations, refine the plan, perform coordination with adjacent units, and supervise and assess preparations. Normally unit SOPs state individual responsibilities and the sequence of preparation activities. Army leaders supervise subordinates and inspect their personnel and equipment to ensure the unit is ready for the mission.

Army leaders refine their plan based on continuing analysis of their mission and updated intelligence. Most important, Army leaders know that they create plans to ensure all their subordinates focus on accomplishing the same mission within the commander's intent. If required, they can deviate from the plan and execute changes based on battlefield conditions and the enemy. Army leaders oversee preparations for operations. These include inspections, coordination, reorganization, fire support and engineer activities, maintenance, resupply, and movement. The requirement to supervise is continuous; it is as important as issuing orders. Supervision allows Army leaders to assess their subordinates' understanding of their orders and determine where additional guidance is needed. It is crucial to effective preparation.

Rehearsals

Note: See pp. 1-51 to 1-54 for a complete discussion of rehearsals.

A crucial component of preparation is the rehearsal. Rehearsals allow Army leaders to assess their subordinates' preparations. They may identify areas that require more supervision. Army leaders conduct rehearsals to:

- Practice essential tasks
- Identify weaknesses or problems in the plan
- Coordinate subordinate element actions
- Improve soldier understanding of the concept of operations
- Foster confidence among soldiers

IV. Composite Risk Management (CRM)

Ref: FM 5-19 Composite Risk Management. For more complete discussion of CRM and CRM steps, see The Leader's SMARTbook (3rd Revised Edition), chap. 6.

Composite Risk Management (CRM) is a decisionmaking process used to mitigate risks associated with all hazards that have the potential to injure or kill personnel, damage or destroy equipment, or otherwise impact mission effectiveness.

Composite Risk Management

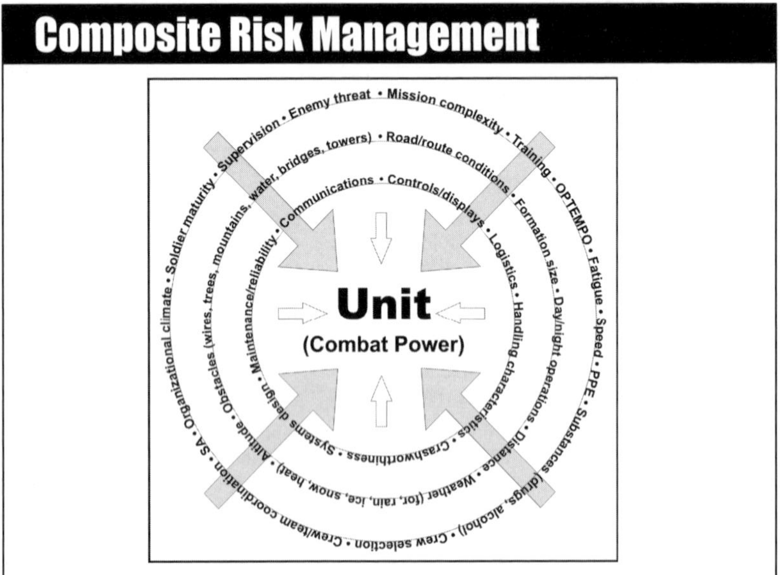

Ref: FM 5-19, fig. 1-1, p. 1-1.

1. Identify hazards

A hazard is a condition with the potential to cause injury, illness, or death of personnel; damage to or loss of equipment or property; or mission degradation. Hazards exist in all environments—combat operations, stability operations, base support operations, training, garrison activities, and off-duty activities. The factors of mission, enemy, terrain and weather, troops and support available, time available, and civil considerations (METT-TC) serve as a standard format for identification of hazards, on-duty or off-duty.

2. Assess hazards to determine risk

This process is systematic in nature and uses charts, codes and numbers to present a methodology to assess probability and severity to obtain a standardized level of risk. Hazards are assessed and risk is assigned in terms of probability and severity of adverse impact of an event/occurrence.

3. Develop controls and make risk decisions

The process of developing and applying controls and reassessing risk continues until an acceptable level of risk is achieved or until all risks are reduced to a level where benefits outweigh the potential cost.

4. Implement controls

Leaders and staffs ensure that controls are integrated into SOPs, written and verbal orders, mission briefings, and staff estimates.

5. Supervise and evaluate

Tactical Mission Fundamentals

VI. Combat Orders

Ref: FM 3-21.8 The Infantry Rifle Platoon and Squad, pp. 5-4 to 5-5 and FM 5-0 Army Planning and Orders Production, app. G. For more complete discussion of plans and orders, see The Battle Staff SMARTbook.

Combat orders are the means by which the small unit leader receives and transmits information from the earliest notification that an operation will occur through the final steps of execution. WARNOs, OPORDs, and FRAGOs are absolutely critical to mission success. In a tactical situation, the small unit leaders work with combat orders on a daily basis, and they must have precise knowledge of the correct format for each type of order. At the same time, they must ensure that every Soldier in the unit understands how to receive and respond to the various types of orders.

Plans and orders are the means by which commanders express their visualization, commander's intent, and decisions. They focus on results the commander expects to achieve. Plans and orders form the basis commanders use to synchronize military operations. They encourage initiative by providing the "what" and "why" of a mission, and leave the how to accomplish the mission to subordinates. They give subordinates the operational and tactical freedom to accomplish the mission by providing the minimum restrictions and details necessary for synchronization and coordination.

The OPORD provides the troops with the essential information required to conduct the operation and to carry out the commander's intent. This format allows the team to see the big picture and orient on key information. (Photo by Jeong, Hae-jung).

Plans and orders:

- Permit subordinate commanders to prepare supporting plans and orders
- Implement instructions derived from a higher commander's plan or order
- Focus subordinates' activities
- Provide tasks and activities, constraints, and coordinating instructions necessary for mission accomplishment
- Encourage agility, speed, and initiative during execution
- Convey instructions in a standard, recognizable, clear, and simple format

The amount of detail provided in a plan or order depends on several factors, to include the experience and competence of subordinate commanders, cohesion and tactical experience of subordinate units, and complexity of the operation. Commanders balance these factors with their guidance and commander's intent, and determine the type of plan or order to issue. To maintain clarity and simplicity, plans and orders include annexes only when necessary and only when they pertain to the entire command. Annexes contain the details of support and synchronization necessary to accomplish the mission.

At the small unit level, orders are normally issued verbally and supplemented by graphics and other control measures. The order follows the standard five-paragraph format OPORD format. Typically, Army leaders below company level do not issue a commander's intent. They reiterate the intent of their higher and next higher commander.

There are three types of orders of primary importance at the small unit level: the warning order (WARNO); the operation order (OPORD); and the fragmentary order (FRAGO).

The following information reflects a generic, standard form for each type of combat order. In many cases, we simply cut and paste the information into the format. However, some of this information will be generated from the vision of the commander.

Remember that when developing an order to consider two levels up and plan one level down. For example, a platoon leader will plan for the fires and maneuvers of his squads…while keeping in mind the overall mission of the company and battalion.

I. Warning Order (WARNO)

The WARNO serves as a notice of an upcoming mission and OPORD. It's also important because it allows troops to prepare mentally and physically. Experienced troops and leaders know from the mission statement what tasks will likely be required. They begin to ready any special equipment as well as their standard equipment. The troops also prepare themselves mentally, going over the tasks or lessons learned from previous experience and conducting battle drills or task rehearsals. Finally, the troops can pace themselves to some extent, getting sleep and food prior to the mission.

The warning order is a preliminary notice of an order or action which is to follow. It helps subordinate units and staffs prepare for new missions. WARNOs increase subordinates' planning time, provide details of the impending operations, and detail events that accompany preparation and execution.
The WARNO provides answers to the following questions:

- Who is involved in the mission?
- What is the task to be accomplished?
- Why are we performing this mission?
- When is the start time and location of the OPORD?

At a minimum, the WARNO states the situation, the mission, and coordinating instructions--such as the time and place of the OPORD. This allows subordinate leaders to prepare troops and equipment for the mission. (Photo by Jeong, Hae-jung).

A WARNO informs recipients of tasks they must do now or notifies them of possible future tasks. However, a WARNO does not authorize execution other than planning unless specifically stated. A WARNO follows the OPORD format. It may include some or all of the following:

- Series numbers, sheet numbers and names, editions, and scales of maps required (if changed from the current OPORD)
- The enemy situation and significant intelligence events
- The higher headquarters' mission
- Mission or tasks of the issuing headquarters
- The commander's intent statement
- Orders for preliminary actions, including intelligence, surveillance, and reconnaissance (ISR) operations
- Coordinating instructions (estimated timelines, orders group meetings, and the time to issue the OPORD)
- Service support instructions, any special equipment needed, regrouping of transport, or preliminary unit movement

II. Operations Order (OPORD)

An operation order is a directive issued by a commander to subordinate commanders for the purpose of effecting the coordinated execution of an operation (JP 1-02). It is the detailed plan of the mission, including the scheme of fire and maneuver, and the commander's intent. All Soldiers need to understand what is expected of them, what their specific role is in the mission, and how each fits into the "bigger picture." Rehearsals of actions on the objective allow each troop to see that big picture and where everyone will be physically located.

Traditionally called the five paragraph field order, an OPORD contains, as a minimum, descriptions of the following:

- Task organization
- Situation
- Mission
- Execution
- Administrative and logistic support
- Command and signal for the specified operation
- OPORDs always specify an execution date and time

Much of paragraphs 1, 2, 4, and 5 of the OPORD are "cut and paste." However, that's not the case for Paragraph 3 – Execution. Paragraph 3a – Concept of the Operation is the very heart of the OPORD because it details the overall scheme of fire and maneuver. It answers the question, "How are we going to achieve this?"

The commander issues the OPORD and orients the OPORD to the terrain. Ideally, the order is given while standing on the terrain. This may be possible in the case of the defense, but is highly unlikely for any other type of combat operation. In those cases, a terrain model (or at least a topographical map) is used.

The commander's intent is the soul of the operation. The commander's intent answers the questions, "What are we going to do…and why are we doing this?" This is the most critical information of any mission—what, why, and how. Through the **commander's intent** statement, the commander explains in very concise terms what it is he or she expects to achieve. There is an art to this statement because it includes subtle nuances that must be understood by every troop on the mission.

Note: See pp. 1-18 and 1-20 for further discussion of commander's intent.

III. Fragmentary Order (FRAGO)

The FRAGO is an adjustment to an existing OPORD. There are many reasons an order might need adjusting. Most commonly, a FRAGO is issued due to a significant change in the situation on the ground or for clarifying instructions.

It is issued after an OPORD to change or modify that order or to execute a branch or a sequel to that order.

FRAGOs differ from OPORDs only in the degree of detail provided. They address only those parts of the original OPORD that have changed. FRAGOs refer to previous orders and provide brief and specific instructions.

FRAGOs include all five OPORD paragraph headings. After each heading, state either new information or "no change." As such, this information depends on the specifics of the tactical situation. FRAGO may include:

- Updates to the enemy or friendly situation
- Changes to the scheme of maneuver
- Coordinating and clarifying instructions
- Expanding the mission tasks (branches and sequels)

Techniques for Issuing Orders

Ref: FM 5-0 Army Planning and Orders Production, app. G, p. G-7.

There are several techniques for issuing orders: verbal, written, or electronically produced using matrices or overlays. The five-paragraph format is the standard for issuing combat orders. Orders may be generated and disseminated by electronic means to reduce the amount of time needed to gather and brief the orders group. When available preparation time or resources are constrained, commanders may use the matrix method of issuing orders.

At the small unit level, orders are normally issued verbally and supplemented by graphics and other control measures. The order follows the standard five-paragraph format OPORD format. Typically, Army leaders below company level do not issue a commander's intent. They reiterate the intent of their higher and next higher commander.

1. Verbal Orders

Verbal orders are used when operating in an extremely time-constrained environment. They offer the advantage of being passed quickly, but risk important information being overlooked or misunderstood. Verbal orders are usually followed up by written FRAGOs.

2. Graphics

Plans and orders generally include both text and graphics. Graphics convey information and instructions through military symbols (see FM 1-02). They complement the written portion of a plan or an order and promote clarity, accuracy, and brevity. The Army prefers depicting information and instructions graphically when possible. However, the mission statement and the commander's intent are always in writing.

3. Overlays

An overlay graphically portrays the location, size, and activity (past, current, or planned) of depicted units more consistently and accurately than text alone. An overlay enhances a viewer's ability to analyze the relationships of units and terrain. A trained viewer can attain a vision of a situation as well as insight into the identification of implied tasks, relationships, and coordination requirements that the written plan or order may not list or readily explain. Overlay graphics may be used on stand-alone overlays or overprinted maps. The issuing headquarters is responsible for the accuracy of control measures and for transposing graphics to and from the map scale used by subordinate headquarters.

4. Overlay Orders

An overlay order is a technique used to issue an order (normally a FRAGO) that has abbreviated instructions written on an overlay. Overlay orders combine a five-paragraph order with an operation overlay. Commanders may issue an overlay order when planning and preparation time is severely constrained and they must get the order to subordinate commanders as soon as possible. Commanders issue overlay orders by any suitable graphic method. An overlay order may consist of more than one overlay. A separate overlay or written annex can contain the service support coordination and organizations.

The Operations Order (OPORD) - A Small Unit Perspective

Editor's Note: This is an abbreviated OPORD sample based on small unit information needs. For a more complete OPORD (and WARNO/FRAGO) discussion and format, see The Battle Staff SMARTbook or FM 5-0 Army Planning and Order Production.

Much of paragraphs 1, 2, 4, and 5 of the OPORD are "cut and paste." However, that's not the case for Paragraph 3 – Execution. Paragraph 3a – Concept of the Operation is the very heart of the OPORD because it details the overall scheme of fire and maneuver. It answers the question, "How are we going to achieve this?"

The commander issues the OPORD and orients the OPORD to the terrain. Ideally, the order is given while standing on the terrain. This may be possible in the case of the defense, but is highly unlikely for any other type of combat operation. In those cases, a terrain model (or at least a topographical map) is used.

Paragraph 1 - SITUATION

a. Enemy forces and battlefield conditions.

(1) Weather and sunlight/moonlight data

(2) Terrain using factors of OCOKA

(3) Enemy forces

Uniform identification

Unit identification

Recent activities

Strengths/weaknesses

Current location

Most probable COA

b. Friendly forces

(1) The larger unit's mission and commander's intent

(2) Adjacent unit missions and locations

(3) Identify fire support unit

(4) Identify other supporting units

Paragraph 2 - MISSION

Identify the task to be completed by the_unit

Paragraph 3 - EXECUTION

Commander's Intent

Purpose

Key tasks

End state

Note: See pp. 1-18 and 1-20 for complete discussion of Commander's Intent.

a. Concept of the operation

(1) Scheme of maneuver

(2) Fires

(3) Engineer support

b. Tasks to maneuver units

(1) Task for each element

(2) Purpose for each element

c. Tasks to combat support units

d. Coordinating instructions

(1) Movement instructions

SP Time and location

Order of march

Route of march

Rendezvous time and location (AA, ERP, ORP)

LOA and PL

(2) Passage of lines

Linkup time and location

Passage point location

(3) Priority Intelligence Requirements (PIR)

(4) Troop safety

RFL and weapons control status

Paragraph 4 - <u>SERVICE SUPPORT</u> [or <u>ADMINISTRATION & LOGISTICS</u>]

a. Concept of support

Location of combat field supply

Location of aid station

Scheme of support

b. Materiel and services

(1) Supply

(2) Transportation

(3) Service

(4) Maintenance

c. Medical evacuation procedures

d. Coordination for civilian personnel and EPW

Paragraph 5 - <u>COMMAND & SIGNAL</u>

a. Command

(1) Location of leaders

(2) Succession of command

b. Signal

(1) SOI/CEOI in effect

(2) Radio communications restrictions

Listening silence and time frame
Alternate frequencies and condition for frequency change

(3) Visual and pyrotechnic signals

(4) Brevity codes specific to the operation

(5) Electronic protection, including COMSEC guidelines and procedures

On Point

Plans are the basis for any mission. To develop a plan (concept of the operation), the small unit leader summarizes how best to accomplish his mission within the scope of the commander's intent one and two levels up. The leader uses TLP to turn the concept into a fully developed plan and to prepare a concise, accurate operation order (OPORD). He assigns additional tasks (and outlines their purpose) for subordinate elements, allocates available resources, and establishes priorities to make the concept work.

Soldiers spell out the need and plan in terms of a "purpose" which is relayed through a "combat order". The WARNO alerts the unit of an upcoming mission. The OPORD provides greater detail, and most significantly includes the commander's intent and the scheme of the operation's fires and maneuver—the what, why, and how. The FRAGO allows the commander to adjust the mission once the OPORD has been issued.

As a practical matter, too much information can be a bad thing. Conversely, more information is always good. Both of these statements are correct. It's a paradox. While it is true that more information is good because an informed troop possesses the essential situational awareness to be successful on the battlefield.

While a 2-hour OPORD can be common at the company or battalion level, its rare at the platoon and squad level. Time plays a major factor in issuing the OPORD. Typically, a squad leader has about 15 minutes to issue the OPORD to his squad. If they have another 15 minutes, they can conduct a shoulder-to-shoulder rehearsal.

Tactical Mission Fundamentals

VII. Preparation & PCI

Ref: FM 6-0 Mission Command, chap. 6; FM 3-21.8 The Infantry Rifle Platoon and Squad, p. D-23, and FM 7-1 Battle Focused Training, fig. 5-47, p. 5-46.

I. Preparation

Preparation is activities by the unit before execution to improve its ability to conduct the operation including, but not limited to, the following: plan refinement, rehearsals, reconnaissance, coordination, inspections, and movement. Preparation occurs when a command is not executing an operation. When not executing operations, commanders prepare their forces for them. These preparations include such activities as training and maintaining personnel and equipment. Preparation for a specific operation starts with receiving a WARNO and ends when execution begins.

Note: See following pages (pp. 1-46 to 1-47) for a listing of preparation activities, all of which involve actions at various levels by units, soldiers and staffs.

II. The Pre-Combat Inspection (PCI)

Pre-combat checks are detailed final checks that units conduct immediately before and during the execution of training and operations. These checks are usually included in unit SOPs. They are normally conducted as part of troop leading procedures and can be as simple or as complex as the training or operation dictates. Pre-combat checks start in garrison and many are completed in the assembly area or in the training location; for example, applying camouflage, setting radio frequencies and distributing ammunition.

Subordinate leaders MUST conduct an inspection of their troops prior to each combat mission. The PCI is an essential part of every mission. The objective of the PCI is to confirm the combat readiness of the unit. (Photo by Jeong, Hae-jung).

Preparation Activities

Ref: FM 6-0 Mission Command, pp. 6-13 to 6-18.

Preparation consists of the following activities, all of which involve actions by staffs, units, and soldiers:

Assessment During Preparation

Assessment during preparation involves monitoring the progress of readiness to execute the operation and helps staffs refine plans. It evaluates preparations against criteria of success established during planning to determine variances. It forecasts their significance for the success of the operation. Commanders continue commander's visualization. Staffs continue running estimates begun during planning.

Reconnaissance Operations

During preparation, commanders take every opportunity to improve their situational understanding about the enemy and environment. Reconnaissance is often the most important part of this activity, providing data that contribute to answering the CCIR. As such, commanders conduct it with the same care as any other operation. They normally initiate reconnaissance operations before completing the plan.

Reconnaissance is not a static, one-time effort that achieves a goal and stops. As reconnaissance forces gather information, the staff modifies the collection plan to account for new information and to redirect ISR efforts. Commanders and staffs continuously review intelligence products and synchronize their reconnaissance efforts within the ISR plan. They focus on the most important remaining gaps, emphasizing the established or revised CCIR.

Security Operations

Security operations during preparation prevent surprise and reduce uncertainty through security operations (see FM 3-90), local security, and operations security (OPSEC; see FM 3-13). These are all designed to prevent enemies from discovering the friendly force's plan and to protect the force from unforeseen enemy actions. Security elements direct their main effort toward preventing the enemy from gathering essential elements of friendly information (EEFI). As with reconnaissance, security is a dynamic effort that anticipates and thwarts enemy collection efforts. When successful, security operations provide the force time and maneuver space to react to enemy attacks.

Force Protection

Force protection consists of those actions taken to prevent or mitigate hostile actions against DoD personnel (to include family members), resources, facilities, and critical information. These actions conserve the force's fighting potential so it can be applied at the decisive time and place and incorporates the coordinated and synchronized offensive and defensive measures to enable the effective employment of the joint force while degrading opportunities for the enemy. Force protection does not include actions to defeat the enemy or protect against accidents, weather, or disease (FM 3-0). Force protection employs a combination of active and passive measures to deter, defeat, or mitigate hostile actions against friendly forces. It is not a discrete mission assigned to a single unit, but a continuous process performed by all commands.

Revising and Refining the Plan

Plans are not static; commanders adjust them based on new information. During preparation, enemies are also acting and the friendly situation is evolving: Assumptions prove true or false. Reconnaissance confirms or denies enemy actions and dispositions. The status of friendly units changes. As these and other aspects of the situation change, commanders determine whether the new information invalidates the plan, requires adjustments to the plan, or validates the plan with no further changes. They adjust the plan or prepare a new one, if necessary.

Coordination and Liaison

Coordination is the action necessary to ensure adequately integrated relationships between separate organizations located in the same area. Coordination may include such matters as fire support, emergency defense measures, area intelligence, and other situations in which coordination is considered necessary (Army-Marine Corps). Coordination takes place continuously throughout operations and fall into two categories: external and internal. Available resources and the need for direct contact between sending and receiving headquarters determine when to establish liaison. The earlier liaison is established, the more effective the coordination.

Rehearsals

A rehearsal is a session in which a unit or staff practices expected actions to improve performance during execution. Rehearsals occur during preparation.

Note: See pp 1-51 to 1-54 for additional information on rehearsals.

Task Organizing

Task organizing is the process of allocating available assets to subordinate commanders and establishing their command and support relationships (FM 3-0). Receiving commands act to integrate units that are assigned, attached, under operational control (OPCON), or placed in direct support under a task organization.

Training

Training develops the teamwork, trust, and mutual understanding that commanders need to exercise mission command and forces need to achieve unity of effort. During repetitive, challenging training, commanders enhance their tactical skills and learn to develop, articulate, and disseminate their commander's intent. They hone command skills during rehearsals, which also help to reinforce their command's common understanding of tactics, techniques, and procedures (TTP).

Troop Movement

Troop movement is the movement of troops from one place to another by any available means (FM 3-90). Troop movements to position or reposition units for execution occur during preparation. Troop movements include assembly area reconnaissance by advance parties and route reconnaissance.

Pre-operation Checks and Inspections

Unit preparation includes completing pre-combat checks and inspections. These ensure that soldiers, units, and systems are as fully capable and ready to execute as time and resources permit. This preparation includes precombat training that readies soldiers and systems to execute the mission.

Logistic Preparation

Resupplying, maintaining, and issuing special supplies or equipment occurs during preparation. So does any repositioning of logistic assets. In addition, there are many other possible activities. These may include identifying and preparing forward bases, selecting and improving lines of communications, and identifying resources available in the area and making arrangements to acquire them. Commanders direct OPSEC measures to conceal preparations and friendly intentions.

Integrating New Soldiers and Units

Commanders and staffs ensure that new soldiers are assimilated into their units and new units into the force in a posture that allows them to contribute effectively. They also prepare new units and soldiers to perform their roles in the upcoming operation.

Conducting the PCI

Ref: FM 3-19 Military Police Leader's Handbook, appendix E.

The pre-combat inspection (PCI), or preoperation checks and inspections as FM 6-0 refers to them, is one of these critical preparation activities. Unit preparation includes completing precombat checks and inspections. These ensure that soldiers, units, and systems are as fully capable and ready to execute as time and resources permit. This preparation includes pre-combat training that readies soldiers and systems to execute the mission.

PCI is essential in that it checks:

1. Each troop's equipment necessary for mission accomplishment
2. Each troop's understanding of the mission purpose (commander's intent)
3. Each troop's understanding of how their task contributes to the mission

That means the PCI looks at equipment, asks questions regarding the commander's intent, and asks questions regarding the rehearsal. In this manner, the PCI protects the unit from missing any of critical steps of TLP.

The PCI is typically conducted in two stages. First, subordinate leaders conduct a PCI prior to movement to the AA to check equipment. Second, the PL conducts a PCI after the rehearsal to check equipment and mission knowledge.

The PCI is best achieved with a checklist. This keeps us from missing important key equipment and situational awareness.

Soldiers are inspected for what to bring and what *not* to bring. This will differ greatly depending on their role in the patrol. Every military unit must be able to shoot, move, and communicate. Those are the three basic Soldier skills. The PCI makes sure that each Soldier can do this.

A. Uniform and Gear

- Check that the troop is wearing the proper uniform and camouflage
- Check that boots are serviceable, comfortable, and appropriate
- Check that rain and cold weather gear is carried if needed
- Check water canteens and bladders are full and the troop is hydrated
- Check that first aid kits are present and complete
- Check that ID tags are worn, as well as special medical tags (allergies)
- Check that all specialty equipment is carried in either the LBE or rucksack
- Check all leaders for appropriate maps and compass/GPS
- Check all leaders for communication devices
- Check for secured gear by having the troop jump up and down

B. Communication Devices

- Check that extra batteries, antenna, mic, and basic radio kit are present
- Check that the radio is set to the proper channel and/or frequency
- Check the SOI/CEOI and ensure that each troop knows the call signs and code
- Check that all field phones are serviceable, clean, and in watertight containers
- Check for whistles, flares, color panels, and other communication devices

C. Weapon Systems

- Check that each weapon system is assigned to the appropriate troop
- Check that each weapon is serviceable, clean, and zeroed.
- Check that ammunition is serviceable and plentiful for each weapon
- Check that lubrication is present, as well as field cleaning kits
- Check optical devices (day and night) are serviceable
- Check that extra batteries are carried for optical devices

D. Specialty Equipment

- Check for first aid kits
- Check for protective gear—body armor, eye wear, kneepads, etc
- Check for screening smoke canisters
- Check for wire breaching/marking equipment if appropriate
- Check for mines/explosives if appropriate
- Check for anti-armor weapons if appropriate
- Check for rappelling/climbing/crossing gear if appropriate
- Check for pioneering tools if appropriate

E. Mission Knowledge

Small unit leaders should conduct a confirmation brief after issuing the oral OPORD to ensure subordinates know the mission, the commander's intent, the concept of the operation, and their assigned tasks. Confirmation briefs can be conducted face-to-face or by radio, depending on the situation. Face-to face-is the desired method, because all section and squad leaders are together to resolve questions, and it ensures that each leader knows what the adjacent squad is doing.

1. Commander's Intent

- Check that each troop understands the mission purpose
- Check that each troop understands the key tasks we must achieve
- Check that each troop understands the end state of success

2. Mission Tasks

- Check that each troop understands the mission statement
- Check that each troop understands their assigned task(s)
- Check that each troop knows how to identify the enemy
- Check that each troop knows the expected light, weather, and terrain conditions
- Check that each troop knows where other friendly troops are located
- Check that each troop knows his leader, and SOI/CEOI information

Commanders must allocate sufficient time for subordinate leaders to execute pre-combat checks and inspections to standard.

- OPORD briefed. Leaders and soldiers know what is expected of them
- Safety checks and briefings completed
- All required TADSS are on hand and operational; for example, MILES equipment zeroed
- Before-operations PMCS completed on vehicles, weapons, communications, and NBC equipment
- Leaders and equipment inspected; for example, compasses, maps, strip maps, and binoculars
- Soldiers and equipment inspected and camouflaged; for example, weapons, ID cards, driver's licenses
- Soldier packing lists checked and enforced
- Medical support present and prepared
- Communications checks completed
- Ammunition (Class V) drawn, accounted for, prepared, and issued
- Vehicle load plans checked and confirmed; cargo secured
- Rations (Class I) drawn and issued
- Quartering party briefed and dispatched
- OPFOR personnel deployed and ready to execute their OPORD

On Point

Mission failure is often due to equipment malfunction or a lack of mission knowledge. This is completely preventable. US military studies have shown that the PCI is conducted in only 40 percent of missions.

Leaders are responsible for ensuring that the combat vehicles and Soldiers in their unit are prepared to begin combat operations. A single item can doom the mission to failure. Leaders must conduct PCI. It takes only a few minutes. Subordinate leaders check each troop's equipment and specialty equipment prior to moving to the AA. After rehearsals, personally check every Soldier's equipment a second time and check each Soldier's knowledge of the mission.

Tactical Mission Fundamentals

VIII. Rehearsals

Ref: FM 6-0 Mission Command: Command and Control of Army Forces, app. F. For complete discussion of rehearsals, see The Battle Staff SMARTbook.

A rehearsal is a session in which a staff or unit practices expected actions to improve performance during execution. Rehearsing key combat actions before execution allows participants to become familiar with the operation and to translate the relatively dry recitation of the tactical plan into visual impression. This impression helps them orient themselves to their environment and other units when executing the operation. Moreover, the repetition of combat tasks during the rehearsal leaves a lasting mental picture of the sequence of key actions within the operation. This section contains guidelines for conducting rehearsals. It describes rehearsal types and techniques. It lists responsibilities of those involved.

For units to be effective and efficient in combat, rehearsals need to become habitual in training. All commands at every level should routinely train and practice a variety of rehearsal types and techniques. (Photo by Jeong, Hae-jung).

Rehearsals allow staff officers, subordinate commanders, and other leaders to practice executing the course of action (COA) the commander chose at the end of the military decisionmaking process (MDMP). Rehearsals are the commander's tool. Commanders use them to ensure staffs and subordinates understand the commander's intent and the concept of operations. Rehearsals also synchronize operations at times and places critical to successful mission accomplishment.

Local standing operating procedures (SOPs) should identify appropriate rehearsal types, techniques, and standards for their execution. Leaders at all levels conduct periodic after-action reviews (AARs) to ensure that units conduct rehearsals to standard and that substandard performance is corrected. AARs also provide opportunities to incorporate lessons learned into existing plans and orders, or into subsequent rehearsals.

I. Rehearsal Techniques

Ref: FM 6-0 Mission Command, pp. F-3 to F-7.

Generally, six techniques are used for executing rehearsals.

A. Full-dress Rehearsal

A full-dress rehearsal produces the most detailed understanding of the operation. It involves every participating soldier and system. If possible, organizations execute full-dress rehearsals under the same conditions-weather, time of day, terrain, and use of live ammunition-that the force expects to encounter during the actual operation.

- **Time**. Full-dress rehearsals are the most time consuming of all rehearsal types. For companies and smaller units, the full-dress rehearsal is the most effective technique for ensuring all involved in the operation understand their parts. However, brigade and task force commanders consider the time their subordinates need to plan and prepare when deciding whether to conduct a full-dress rehearsal.
- **Echelons involved**. A subordinate unit can perform a full-dress rehearsal as part of a larger organization's reduced-force rehearsal.
- **OPSEC**. Moving a large part of the force may attract enemy attention. Commanders develop a plan to protect the rehearsal from enemy surveillance and reconnaissance. One method is to develop a plan, including graphics and radio frequencies, that rehearses selected actions but does not compromise the actual OPORD. Commanders take care to not confuse subordinates when doing this.
- **Terrain**. Terrain management for a full-dress rehearsal can be difficult if it is not considered during the initial array of forces. The rehearsal area must be identified, secured, cleared, and maintained throughout the rehearsal.

B. Reduced-force Rehearsal

A reduced-force rehearsal involves only key leaders of the organization and its subordinate units. It normally takes fewer resources than a full-dress rehearsal. The commander first decides the level of leader involvement. The selected leaders then rehearse the plan while traversing the actual or similar terrain. A reduced-force rehearsal may be used to prepare key leaders for a full-dress rehearsal.

- **Time**. A reduced-force rehearsal normally requires less time than a full-dress rehearsal. Commanders consider the time their subordinates need to plan and prepare when deciding whether to conduct a reduced-force rehearsal.
- **Echelons involved**. A small unit can perform a full-dress rehearsal as part of a larger organization's reduced-force rehearsal.
- **OPSEC**. A reduced-force rehearsal is less likely to present an OPSEC vulnerability than a full-dress rehearsal because the number of participants is smaller. However, the number of radio transmissions required is the same as for a full-dress rehearsal and remains a consideration.
- **Terrain**. Terrain management for the reduced-force rehearsal can be just as difficult as for the full-dress rehearsal. The rehearsal area must be identified, secured, cleared, and maintained throughout the rehearsal.

C. Terrain-model Rehearsal

The terrain-model rehearsal takes less time and fewer resources than a full-dress or reduced-force rehearsal. (A terrain-model rehearsal takes a proficient brigade from one to two hours to execute to standard.) It is the most popular rehearsal technique. An accurately constructed terrain model helps subordinate leaders visualize the commander's intent and concept of operations. When possible, commanders place the terrain model where it overlooks the actual terrain of the area of operations (AO).

- **Time**. Often, the most time-consuming part of this technique is constructing the terrain model.
- **Echelons involved**. Because a terrain model is geared to the echelon conducting the rehearsal, multiechelon rehearsals using this technique are difficult.
- **OPSEC**. This rehearsal can present an OPSEC vulnerability if the area around the site is not secured. The collection of troops and vehicles can draw enemy attention.
- **Terrain**. Terrain management is less difficult than with the previous techniques. An optimal location overlooks the terrain where the operation will be executed.

D. Sketch-map Rehearsal

Commanders can use the sketch-map technique almost anywhere, day or night. The procedures are the same as for a terrain-model rehearsal, except the commander uses a sketch map in place of a terrain model. Effective sketches are large enough for all participants to see as each participant walks through execution of the operation. Participants move markers on the sketch to represent unit locations and maneuvers.

- **Time**. Sketch-map rehearsals take less time than terrain-model rehearsals and more time than map rehearsals.
- **Echelons involved**. Because a sketch map is geared to the echelon conducting the rehearsal, multiechelon rehearsals using this technique are difficult.
- **OPSEC**. This rehearsal can present an OPSEC vulnerability if the area around the site is not secured. The collection of troops and vehicles can draw enemy attention.
- **Terrain**. This technique requires less space than a terrain model rehearsal. A good site is easy for participants to find, yet concealed from the enemy. An optimal location overlooks the terrain where the unit will execute the operation.

E. Map Rehearsal

A map rehearsal is similar to a sketch-map rehearsal, except the commander uses a map and operation overlay of the same scale used to plan the operation.

- **Time**. The most time-consuming part is the rehearsal itself. A map rehearsal is normally the easiest technique to set up, since it requires only maps and current operational graphics.
- **Echelons involved**. Because a map is geared to the echelon conducting the rehearsal, multiechelon rehearsals using this technique are difficult.
- **OPSEC**. This rehearsal can present an OPSEC vulnerability if the area around the site is not secured. The collection of troops and vehicles can draw enemy attention.
- **Terrain**. This technique requires the least space. An optimal location overlooks the terrain where the operations will be executed, but is concealed from the enemy.

F. Network Rehearsal (WAN/LAN)

Network rehearsals can be executed over wide-area networks (WANs) or local-area networks (LANs). Commanders and staffs execute network rehearsals by talking through critical portions of the operation over communications networks in a sequence the commander establishes. Only the critical parts of the operation are rehearsed.

- **Time**. If the organization does not have a clear SOP and if all units are not up on the net, this technique can be very time consuming.
- **Echelons involved**. This technique lends itself to multiechelon rehearsals. Participation is limited only by commander's desires and the availability of INFOSYSs.
- **OPSEC**. If a network rehearsal is executed from current unit locations, the volume of the communications transmissions and potential compromise of information through enemy monitoring can present an OPSEC vulnerability.
- **Terrain**. If a network rehearsal is executed from unit locations, terrain considerations are minimal.

II. Rehearsals - Company Level & Smaller

Ref: FM 5-0 Army Planning and Orders Production, pp. 4-14 to 4-16.

Company and smaller-sized units use five types of rehearsals:

A. Confirmation Brief

Immediately after receiving the order, subordinate leaders brief their superior on the order they just received. They brief their understanding of the commander's intent, the specific tasks they have been assigned and their purposes, and the relationship of their tasks to those of other elements conducting the operation. They repeat any important coordinating measures specified in the order.

B. Backbrief

The backbrief differs from the confirmation brief in that subordinate leaders are given time to complete their plan. Backbriefs require the fewest resources and are often the only option under time-constrained conditions. Subordinate leaders explain their actions from start to finish of the mission. Backbriefs are performed sequentially, with all leaders going over their tasks. When time is available, backbriefs can be combined with other types of rehearsals. If possible, backbriefs are performed overlooking subordinates' AOs, after they have developed their own plans.

C. Combined Arms Rehearsal

A combined arms rehearsal requires considerable resources, but provides the most planning and training benefit. There are two types:

- **Reduced Force.** Circumstances may prohibit a rehearsal with all members of the unit. Unit leaders and other key individuals may perform a reduced force rehearsal, while most of their subordinates continue to prepare for the operation. Often, smaller scale replicas of terrain or buildings substitute for the actual AO. Army leaders not only explain their plans, but also walk through their actions or move replicas across the rehearsal area or sand table. This is called a "rock drill." It reinforces the backbrief given by subordinates, since everyone can see the concept of operations and sequence of tasks.
- **Full Dress**. The preferred rehearsal technique is a full dress rehearsal. Army leaders rehearse their subordinates on terrain similar to the AO, initially under good light conditions, and then in limited visibility. Small unit actions are repeated until executed to standard. Full dress rehearsals help soldiers to clearly understand what is expected of them. It helps them gain confidence in their ability to accomplish the mission. Supporting elements, such as aviation crews, meet soldiers and rehearse with them. An important benefit is the opportunity to synchronize the operation. The unit may conduct full dress rehearsals. They also may be conducted and supported by the higher HQ.

D. Support Rehearsals

At any point in TLP, units may rehearse their support for an operation. For small units, this typically involves coordination and procedure drills for aviation, fire, combat service, engineer support, or causality evacuation. Support rehearsals and combined arms rehearsals complement preparations for the operation.

E. Battle Drills or SOP Rehearsal

A battle drill is a collective action rapidly executed without applying a deliberate decision making process. A battle drill or SOP rehearsal ensures that all participants understand a technique or a specific set of procedures. Throughout preparation, units rehearse battle drills and SOP actions.

IX. The After Action Review (AAR)

Ref: FM 7-1 Battle Focused Training, app. C and FM 3-21.8 (FM 7-8) The Infantry Rifle Platoon and Squad, pp. 1-34 to 1-35. For more complete discussion of after action reviews, see The Battle Staff SMARTbook or The Leader's SMARTbook.

After action reviews (AARs) are a professional discussion of an event that enables soldiers and units to discover for themselves what happened, and why. They provide candid insights into strengths and weaknesses from various perspectives, and feedback. They focus directly on the training objectives.

AARs are a key part of the training process, but they are not cure-alls for unit-training problems. Leaders must still make on-the-spot corrections and take responsibility for training soldiers and units. (Photo by Jeong, Hae-jung).

The goal of the AAR is to improve soldier, leader, and unit performance. The result is a more cohesive and proficient fighting force.

Because soldiers and leaders participating in an AAR actively discover what happened and why, they learn and remember more than they would from a critique alone. A critique gives only one viewpoint and frequently provides little opportunity for discussion of events by participants. The climate of the critique-focusing only on what is wrong-prevents candid discussion of training events and stifles learning and team building.

The purpose of the AAR is to provide the feedback essential to correcting training deficiencies. Feedback should be direct and on-the-spot. In collective training, such as an STX, it may not be possible to interrupt the exercise to correct a soldier who is performing an individual task improperly. This is why an AAR should be planned at the completion of each mission or phase to provide immediate feedback to the soldiers being trained.

I. Types Of After Action Reviews

There are two types of AARs: formal and informal. A formal AAR is resource-intensive and involves the planning, coordination, and preparation of the AAR site; supporting training aids; and support personnel. Informal AARs require less preparation and planning.

Types of After Action Reviews

Formal Reviews	Informal Reviews
Have external observers and controllers (OCs)	Conducted by internal chain of command
Take more time	Take less time
Use more complex training aids	Use simple training aids
Are scheduled beforehand	Are conducted when needed
Are conducted where best supported	Are conducted at the training site

Ref: FM 25-20, fig. 1-3, p. 1-4 (not included in FM 7-1).

A. Formal

Leaders plan formal AARs at the same time that they finalize the near-term training plan (6 to 8 weeks before execution). Formal AARs require more planning and preparation than informal AARs. They require site reconnaissance and selection, coordination for training aids (terrain models, map blow-ups, etc.), and selection, setup, and maintenance of the AAR site.

During formal AARs, the AAR facilitator (unit leader or OC) provides an exercise overview, and focuses the discussion of events on the training objectives. At the end, the facilitator reviews key points and issues, and summarizes strengths and weaknesses discussed during the AAR.

B. Informal

Leaders and OCs use informal AARs as on-the-spot coaching tools while reviewing soldier and unit performances during training. The informal AAR is extremely important, as all soldiers are involved. For example, after destroying an enemy observation post (OP) during a movement to contact, a squad leader conducts an informal AAR to make corrections and reinforce strengths. Using nothing more than pinecones to represent squad members, the squad leader and squad members discuss the contact from start to finish. The squad quickly-

- Evaluates their performance against the Army standard
- Identifies their strengths and weaknesses
- Decides how to improve their performance when training continues

Informal AARs provide immediate feedback to soldiers, leaders, and units during training. Ideas and solutions the leader gathers during informal AARs can be immediately put to use as the unit continues its training.

II. Steps in the After Action Review (AAR)

Ref: FM 7-0 Training the Force, pp. 6-4 to 6-5.

The AAR, whether formal or informal, provides feedback for all training. It is a structured review process that allows participating soldiers, leaders, and units to discover for themselves what happened during the training, why it happened, and how it can be done better. The AAR is a professional discussion that requires the active participation of those being trained. The AAR is not a critique and has the following advantages over a critique:

- Focuses directly on key METL derived training objectives
- Emphasizes meeting Army standards rather than pronouncing judgment of success or failure
- Uses "leading questions" to encourage participants to self-discover important lessons from the training event
- Allows a large number of individuals and leaders to participate so more of the training can be recalled and more lessons learned can be shared

The AAR consists of four parts-

1. Review what was supposed to happen (training plans)

The evaluator, along with the participants, reviews what was supposed to happen based on the commander's intent for the training event, unit-training plan, training objectives, and applicable T&EOs.

2. Establish what happened

The evaluator and the participants determine what actually happened during performance of the training task. A factual and indisputable account is vital to the effectiveness of the discussion that follows. For force-on-force training, OPFOR members assist in describing the flow of the training event and discuss training outcomes from their points of view.

3. Determine what was right or wrong with what happened

The participants establish the strong and weak points of their performance. The evaluator plays a critical role in guiding the discussions so conclusions reached by participants are doctrinally sound, consistent with Army standards, and relevant to the wartime mission.

4. Determine how the task should be done differently the next time

The evaluator assists the chain of command undergoing the training to lead the group in determining exactly how participants will perform differently the next time the task is performed.

Leaders understand that not all tasks will be performed to standard and in their initial planning, allocate time and other resources for retraining. Retraining allows the participants to apply the lessons learned during the AAR and implement corrective action. Retraining should be conducted at the earliest opportunity to translate observation and evaluation into training to standard. Commanders must ensure that units understand that training is incomplete until the Army standard is achieved.

The AAR is often "tiered" as a multiechelon leader development technique. Following an AAR with all participants, senior trainers may use the AAR for an extended professional discussion with selected leaders. These discussions usually include a more specific AAR of leader contributions to the observed training results.

III. AARs - A Small Unit Perspective

Ideally, the AAR is conducted by an outside source, such as an observer/controller. If there is no outside source, the AAR is moderated by the appropriate Army leader. A representation of the terrain covered in the mission is essential. This can be a terrain model, a map, or even video and photographs of the mission. The point is to get everyone thinking on the same sheet of music in terms of where and when.

An after-action review (AAR) is an assessment conducted after an event or major activity that allows participants to learn what and why something happened, and most importantly, how the unit can improve through change. This professional discussion enables units and their leaders to understand why things happened during the progression of an operation, and to learn from that experience. This learning is what enables units and their leaders to adapt to their operational environment. The AAR does not have to be performed at the end of the activity. Rather, it can be performed after each identifiable event (or whenever feasible) as a live learning process.

The AAR is a professional discussion that includes the participants and focuses directly on the tasks and goals. While it is not a critique, the AAR has several advantages over a critique:

- It does not judge success or failure
- It attempts to discover why things happened
- It focuses directly on the tasks and goals that were to be accomplished
- It encourages participants to raise important lessons in the discussion
- More Soldiers participate so more of the project or activity can be recalled and more lessons can be learned and shared

Be sure to include everyone's perspective, not just the leader's.

1. The Plan - Review What Was Supposed to Happen

This phase details "what was supposed to happen." In fact, it is nothing more than a restatement of the operation order (OPORD) in a concise form. The patrol leader (PL) stands in front of the team and quickly restates the commander's intent and the scheme of maneuver.

Remember this is not "what I think might have happened" or "what I really wished had happened." There should be no conjecture or grandstanding at this point. It's simply a restatement of the plan in as much detail as necessary, and no more.

For the first phase, the plan, it is a good idea to begin an AAR by asking each of the element leaders what mission they were tasked to do and to let them answer in their own words. The leader will listen to the clarity of focus from each of these subordinate leaders for their grasp of the mission as a whole and the understanding of their element's role in the mission.

2. The Performance - Establish What Happened

The second phase of the AAR details "what really happened." Those team members who were on the ground and taking part in the action state this part of the AAR. The PL is generally discouraged from speaking during this phase unless they have a unique perspective or information that is of use.

The point isn't to put ego on the line and taking up time arguing or finger pointing, yet the patrol has to get a realistic measure of their performance. This can be a painful, even embarrassing process. But why didn't the mission go off just as planned? Or did it? That is what patrol is looking for in this phase of the AAR—the gap between the plan and the actual performance.

For the second phase, the performance, the initial movement is a good place to start within the execution of the mission. Did the patrol hit their start time? How about the time hacks for phase lines or reaching their objective rally point (ORP)? If not, this may explain any "accordion" effect in the time frames or the physical movement of the formation.

Actions in the ORP must be addressed. Was a leader's recon forward of the ORP required? Were the plans finalized in the ORP and, if so, did the leaders feel confident that the members of their element understood these plans? Often, when plans are changed in the ORP, the lines of communication tend to have gaps. Only with clearly delineated responsibilities and element integrity can these communication barriers be overcome.

Actions on the objective (OBJ) include all considerations from the release point—that magical place on the map where the commander relinquishes control to his subordinate leaders—up to the point of reconsolidation. To list every consideration would be too much information for this single chapter, but most issues fall within each element's ability to "shoot, move, and communicate." More exactly, this refers to the ability of each element to engage the enemy within their sectors of fire, to move toward and across the OBJ, and to coordinate these efforts with friendly elements to their flanks and rear. Most of the AAR is spent focusing on the actions on the OBJ and with good reason. It is on the objective that efforts are either realized in success or lost in defeat.

3. The Issues - Determine What Was Right or Wrong

Once the patrol members have established the gap between the plan and the performance, they set out to identify the reasons for the discrepancy. In truth, Soldiers usually stumble across and identify the issues during the performance phase. However, it will be necessary to restate these issues so that everyone can see the big picture. This responsibility typically falls to the observer-controller during training, but may be executed by the PL in lieu of an observer.

Combat leaders identify the issues in the third phase. It is a good idea to allow some venting—whether negative or positive. Even though a moderator may lose some control of the flow of information, it is a good idea to invite everyone to speak his mind during this phase.

A technique, known as "nut shelling," requires everyone to make a concise statement on the exercise, if time permits. To begin, simply single out the most vocal member of the group and ask the Soldier what they think needs to be the focus of future training (or more simply, what was the most significant thing to go wrong with the mission). Then ask the next troop what was one thing they saw that was well executed or coordinated. Move around the group, alternating these two simple questions back and forth. Listen closely for consensus on these areas. A neat variation of this technique is to make those troops most vocal about negative issues give a positive observation of the mission and to ask the most positive troops to give a negative observation of the mission.

4. The Fix - Determine What Should Be Done Differently

The last step of the AAR is to identify who—by name—is responsible for correcting the deficiencies that contributed to the gap between the plan and the performance. Do not make the mistake of assuming that all of the responsibility falls to the PL. Subordinate leaders and even experienced troops can lead training or take responsibility for equipment operation/procurement. The PL assigns these tasks accordingly.

Finally, before the AAR draws to a close, identify those individuals who will be responsible for **the fix** of each issue. Often this means an individual is assigned a leadership role in training the troops on the identified task or deficiency. Just as common is to fix or acquire necessary equipment. Sometimes, a fix simply means to research the problem and report back to the team and/or leaders with the findings.

On Point

Leaders are responsible for training their units and making their units adapt. The AAR is one of the primary tools used to accomplish this. It does this by providing feedback, which should be direct and on the spot. Each time an incorrect performance is observed, it should be immediately corrected so it does not interfere with future tasks. During major events or activities, it is not always easy to notice incorrect performances. An AAR should be planned at the end of each activity or event. In doing so, feedback can be provided, lessons can be learned, and ideas and suggestions can be generated to ensure the next project or activity will be an improved one.

To maximize the effectiveness of AARs, leaders should plan and rehearse before training begins. After-action review planning is a routine part of unit near-term planning (six to eight weeks out). During planning, leaders assign OC responsibilities and identify tentative times and locations for AARs. This ensures the allocation of time and resources to conduct AARs and reinforces the important role AARs play in realizing the full benefit of training.

Because soldiers and leaders participating in an AAR actively discover what happened and why, they learn and remember more than they would from a critique alone. A critique only gives one viewpoint and frequently provides little opportunity for discussion of events by participants. Soldier observations and comments may not be encouraged. The climate of the critique, focusing only on what is wrong, prevents candid discussion of training events and stifles learning and team building.

The art of an AAR is in obtaining mutual trust so people will speak freely. Problem solving should be practical and Soldiers should not be preoccupied with status, territory, or second guessing "what the leader will think." There is a fine line between keeping the meeting from falling into chaos where little is accomplished, to people treating each other in a formal and polite manner that masks issues (especially with the leader).

The AAR facilitator should—

- Remain unbiased throughout the review
- Ask open-ended questions to draw out comments from all
- Do not allow personal attacks
- Focus on learning and continuous improvement
- Strive to allow others to offer solutions rather than offering them yourself
- Find solutions and recommendations to make the unit better

To avoid turning an AAR into a critique or lecture—

- Ask why certain actions were taken
- Ask how Soldiers reacted to certain situations
- Ask when actions were initiated
- Ask leading and thought-provoking questions
- Exchange "war stories" (lessons learned)
- Ask Soldiers to provide their own point of view on what happened
- Relate events to subsequent results
- Explore alternative courses of actions that might have been more effective
- Handle complaints positively
- When the discussion turns to errors made, emphasize the positive and point out the difficulties of making tough decisions
- Summarize
- Allow junior leaders to discuss the events with their Soldiers in private
- Follow up on needed actions

Offensive Operations

FM 3-0 Operations (2008), pp. 3-7 to 3-10 and FM 3-90 Tactics, chap. 3.

Offensive operations are combat operations conducted to defeat and destroy enemy forces and seize terrain, resources, and population centers. They impose the commander's will on the enemy. In combat operations, the offense is the decisive element of full spectrum operations. Against a capable, adaptive enemy, the offense is the most direct and sure means of seizing, retaining, and exploiting the initiative to achieve decisive results. Executing offensive operations compels the enemy to react, creating or revealing weaknesses that the attacking force can exploit. Successful offensive operations place tremendous pressure on defenders, creating a cycle of deterioration that can lead to their disintegration. This was the case in early 2003 in Iraq, when coalition operations led to the collapse of the Iraqi military and ultimately the Baathist regime of Saddam Hussein.

Offensive operations are combat operations conducted to defeat and destroy enemy forces and seize terrain, resources, and population centers. They impose the commander's will on the enemy. (Photo by Jeong, Hae-jung).

Effective offensive operations capitalize on accurate intelligence regarding the enemy, terrain and weather, and civil considerations. Commanders maneuver their forces to advantageous positions before making contact. However, commanders may shape conditions by deliberately making contact to develop the situation and mislead the enemy. In the offense, the decisive operation is a sudden, shattering action against enemy weakness that capitalizes on speed, surprise, and shock. If that operation does not destroy the enemy, operations continue until enemy forces disintegrate or retreat to where they are no longer a threat.

I. Primary Offensive Tasks

At the operational level, offensive operations defeat enemy forces that control important areas or contest the host-nation government's authority. The joint force conducts operations throughout the depth of its operational area. Army forces attack using ground and air maneuver to achieve objectives that conclude the campaign or move it to a subsequent phase. In expeditionary campaigns and major operations, operational maneuver includes deploying land forces to positions that facilitate joint force offensive action. Operational-level offensives in counterinsurgency may be conducted to eliminate insurgent sanctuaries. Counterinsurgencies usually combine offensive and stability tasks to achieve decisive results.

In offensive operations, a force often transitions from one offensive task to another without pausing. For example, an attack can lead to exploitation and then pursuit, or to exploitation followed by another attack as enemy forces rally. Army forces perform the following primary offensive tasks.

A. Movement to Contact

A movement to contact develops the situation and establishes or regains contact. It also creates favorable conditions for subsequent tactical actions. Forces executing this task seek to make contact with the smallest friendly force feasible. On contact, the commander has five options: attack, defend, bypass, delay, or withdraw. Movements to contact include search and attack and cordon and search operations.

Note: See pp. 2-7 to 2-12.

B. Attack

An attack destroys or defeats enemy forces, seizes and secures terrain, or both. Attacks require maneuver supported by direct and indirect fires. They may be either decisive or shaping operations. Attacks may be hasty or deliberate, depending on the time available for planning and preparation. Commanders execute hasty attacks when the situation calls for immediate action with available forces and minimal preparation. They conduct deliberate attacks when there is more time to plan and prepare. Success depends on skillfully massing the effects of all the elements of combat power.

Note: See pp. 2-13 to 2-18.

C. Exploitation

Exploitation rapidly follows a successful attack and disorganizes the enemy in depth. Exploitations seek to expand an attack to the point where enemy forces have no alternatives but to surrender or flee. Commanders of exploiting forces receive the greatest possible latitude to accomplish their missions. They act with great aggressiveness, initiative, and boldness. Exploitations may be local or major. Local exploitations take advantage of tactical opportunities, foreseen or unforeseen. Division and higher headquarters normally conduct major exploitations using mobile forces to transform tactical success into a pursuit.

Note: See pp. 2-19 to 2-22.

D. Pursuit

A pursuit is designed to catch or cut off a hostile force attempting to escape with the aim of destroying it. Pursuits often follow successful exploitations. However they can develop at any point when enemy forces are beginning to disintegrate or disengage. Pursuits occur when the enemy fails to organize a defense and attempts to disengage. If it becomes apparent that enemy resistance has broken down entirely and enemy forces are fleeing, a force can transition to a pursuit from any type of offensive or defensive operation. Pursuits require speed and decentralized control.

Note: See pp. 2-23 to 2-28.

II. Purposes of Offensive Operations

Ref: FM 3-0 Operations (2008), pp. 3-9 to 3-10.

Seizing, retaining, and exploiting the initiative is the essence of the offense. Offensive operations seek to throw enemy forces off balance, overwhelm their capabilities, disrupt their defenses, and ensure their defeat or destruction by synchronizing and applying all of the elements of combat power. An offensive ends when it destroys or defeats the enemy, reaches a limit of advance, or approaches culmination. Army forces conclude an offense in one of four ways: consolidating gains through stability operations, resuming the attack, transitioning to the defense, or preparing for future operations.

Army forces conduct offensive operations for the following purposes:

1. Dislocate, Isolate, Disrupt, and Destroy Enemy Forces

Well-executed offensive operations dislocate, isolate, disrupt, and destroy enemy forces. If destruction is not feasible, offensive operations compel enemy forces to retreat. Offensive maneuver seeks to place the enemy at a positional disadvantage. This allows friendly forces to mass overwhelming effects while defeating parts of the enemy force in detail before the enemy can escape or be reinforced. When required, friendly forces close with and destroy the enemy in close combat. Ultimately, the enemy surrenders, retreats in disorder, or is eliminated altogether.

2. Seize Key Terrain

Offensive maneuver may seize terrain that provides the attacker with a decisive advantage. The enemy either retreats or risks defeat or destruction. If enemy forces retreat or attempt to retake the key terrain, they are exposed to fires and further friendly maneuver.

3. Deprive the Enemy of Resources

At the operational level, offensive operations may seize control of major population centers, seats of government, production facilities, and transportation infrastructure. Losing these resources greatly reduces the enemy's ability to resist. In some cases, Army forces secure population centers or infrastructure and prevent irregular forces from using them as a base or benefitting from the resources that they generate.

4. Develop Intelligence

Enemy deception, concealment, and security may prevent friendly forces from gaining necessary intelligence. Some offensive operations are conducted to develop the situation and discover the enemy's intent, disposition, and capabilities.

5. Deceive and Divert the Enemy

Offensive operations distract enemy ISR. They may cause the enemy to shift reserves away from the friendly decisive operation.

6. Create a Secure Environment for Stability Operations

Stability operations cannot occur if significant enemy forces directly threaten or attack the local populace. Offensive operations destroy or isolate the enemy so stability operations can proceed. Offensive operations against insurgents help keep them off balance. These actions may force insurgents to defend their bases, thus keeping them from attacking.

III. Forms of Maneuver

Ref: FM 3-90 Tactics, pp. 3-11 to 3-32.

The forms of maneuver are envelopment, turning movement, frontal attack, penetration, and infiltration. The commander generally chooses one form on which he builds a course of action (COA). The higher commander rarely specifies the specific form of offensive maneuver. However, his guidance and intent, along with the mission that includes implied tasks, may impose constraints such as time, security, and direction of attack that narrow the forms of offensive maneuver to one alternative.

A. Envelopment

The envelopment is a form of maneuver in which an attacking force seeks to avoid the principal enemy defenses by seizing objectives to the enemy rear to destroy the enemy in his current positions. At the tactical level, envelopments focus on seizing terrain, destroying specific enemy forces, and interdicting enemy withdrawal routes. Envelopments avoid the enemy front, where he is protected and can easily concentrate fires. Single envelopments maneuver against one enemy flank; double envelopments maneuver against both. Either variant can develop into an encirclement.

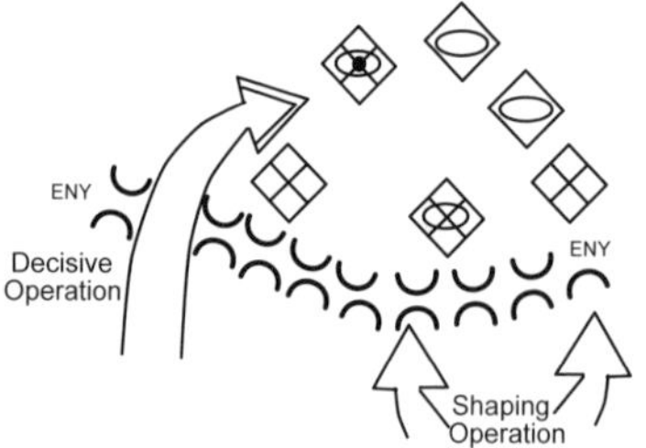

An envelopment avoids enemy strength by maneuver around or overenemy defenses. The decisive operation is directed against the enemy flanks or rear.

To envelop the enemy, commanders find or create an assailable flank. Sometimes the enemy exposes a flank by advancing, unaware of friendly locations. In other conditions, such as a fluid battle involving forces in noncontiguous AOs, a combination of air and indirect fires may create an assailable flank by isolating the enemy on unfavorable terrain.

An envelopment may result in an encirclement. Encirclements are operations where one force loses its freedom of maneuver because an opposing force is able to isolate it by controlling all ground lines of communications. An offensive encirclement is typically an extension of either a pursuit or envelopment. A direct pressure force maintains contact with the enemy, preventing his disengagement and reconstitution. Meanwhile, an encircling force maneuvers to envelop the enemy, cutting his escape routes and setting inner and outer rings. The outer ring defeats enemy attempts to break through to his encircled force. The inner ring contains the encircled force. All available means, including obstacles, should be used to contain the enemy. Then friendly forces use all available fires to destroy him. Encirclements often occur in nonlinear offensive operations.

B. Turning Movement

A turning movement is a form of maneuver in which the attacking force seeks to avoid the enemy's principal defensive positions by seizing objectives to the rear and causing the enemy to move out of current positions or divert major forces to meet the threat. A major threat to his rear forces the enemy to attack or withdraw rearward, thus "turning" him out of his defensive positions. Turning movements typically require greater depth than other maneuver forms. Deep fires take on added importance. They protect the enveloping force and attack the enemy.

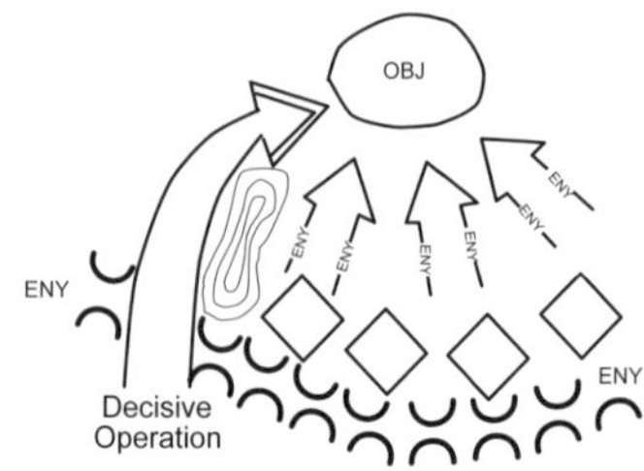

A turning movement attacks the enemy rear to "turn" him out of position and force him to fight to the rear of his flanks.

C. Infiltration

An infiltration is a form of maneuver in which an attacking force conducts undetected movement through or into an area occupied by enemy forces to occupy a position of advantage in the enemy rear while exposing only small elements to enemy defensive fires. The need to avoid being detected and engaged may limit the size and strength of infiltrating forces. Infiltration rarely defeats a defense by itself. Cdrs direct infiltrations to attack lightly defended positions or stronger positions from the flank and rear, to secure key terrain to support the decisive operation, or to disrupt enemy sustaining operations.

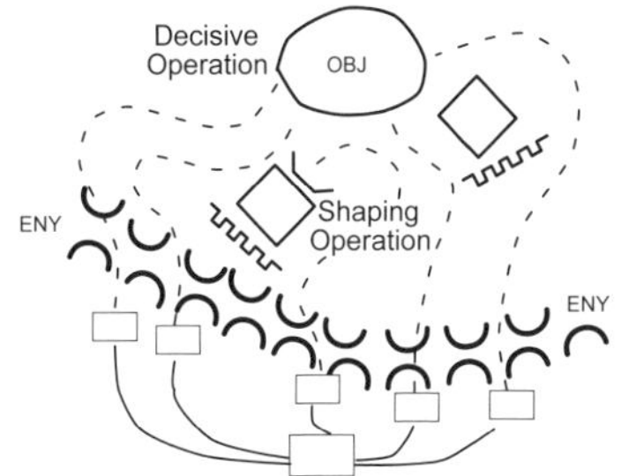

An infiltration uses covert movement of forces through enemy lines to attack position in the enemy rear.

D. Penetration

A penetration is a form of maneuver in which an attacking force seeks to rupture enemy defenses on a narrow front to disrupt the defensive system. It is used when enemy flanks are not assailable or time does not permit another form of maneuver. Successful penetrations create assailable flanks and provide access to enemy rear areas. Penetrations frequently are directed into the front of the enemy defense, and risk more friendly casualties than envelopments, turning movements and infiltrations.

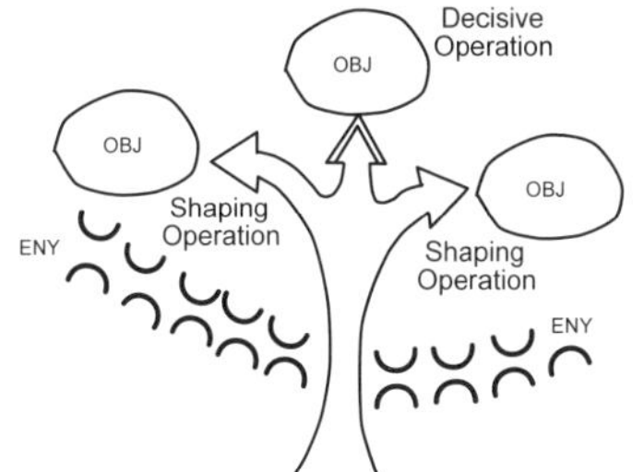

A penetration has three stages: initial rupture, rolling up the flanks, and continuing the attack to secure a deep objective.

E. Frontal Attack

A frontal attack is a form of maneuver in which an attacking force seeks to destroy a weaker enemy force or fix a larger enemy force in place over a broad front. At the tactical level, an attacking force can use a frontal attack to rapidly overrun a weaker enemy force. A frontal attack strikes the enemy across a wide front and over the most direct approaches. Commanders normally use it when they possess overwhelming combat power and the enemy is at a clear disadvantage. Commanders mass the effects of direct and indirect fires, shifting indirect and aerial fires just before the assault. Success depends on achieving an advantage in combat power throughout the attack.

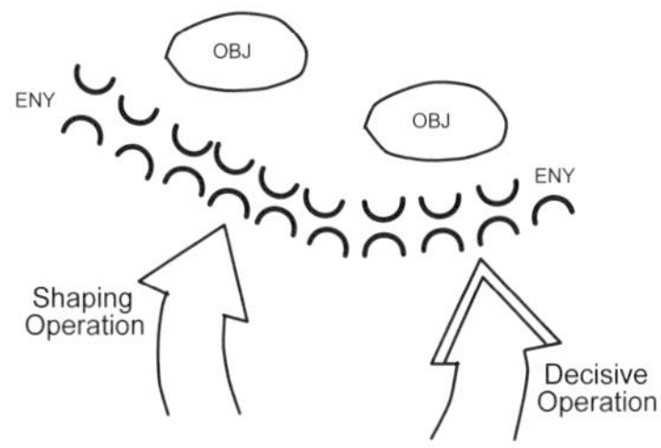

A frontal attack is conducted across a wide front over the most direct approach.

The frontal attack is frequently the most costly form of maneuver, since it exposes the majority of the attackers to the concentrated fires of the defenders. As the most direct form of maneuver, however, the frontal attack is useful for overwhelming light defenses, covering forces, or disorganized enemy resistance. It is often the best form of maneuver for hasty attacks and meeting engagements, where speed and simplicity are essential to maintain tempo and the initiative. Commanders may direct a frontal attack as a shaping operation and another form of maneuver as the decisive operation. Commanders may also use the frontal attack during an exploitation or pursuit. Commanders of large formations conducting envelopments or penetrations may direct subordinate elements to conduct frontal attacks as either shaping operations or the decisive operation.

IV. Characteristics of Offensive Operations

Surprise, concentration, tempo, and audacity characterize the offense. Effective offensive operations capitalize on accurate intelligence and other relevant information regarding enemy forces, weather, and terrain. The commander maneuvers his forces to advantageous positions before contact. Security operations and defensive information operations keep or inhibit the enemy from acquiring accurate information about friendly forces. Contact with enemy forces before the decisive operation is deliberate, designed to shape the optimum situation for the decisive operation.

A. Surprise

In the offense, commanders achieve surprise by attacking the enemy at a time or place he does not expect or in a manner for which he is unprepared. Estimating the enemy commander's intent and denying him the ability to gain thorough and timely situational understanding is necessary to achieve surprise. Unpredictability and boldness help gain surprise. The direction, timing, and force of the attack also help achieve surprise. Surprise delays enemy reactions, overloads and confuses his command and control (C2) systems, induces psychological shock in enemy soldiers and leaders, and reduces the coherence of the defense. By diminishing enemy combat power, surprise enables attackers to exploit enemy paralysis and hesitancy.

B. Concentration

Concentration is the massing of overwhelming effects of combat power to achieve a single purpose. Commanders balance the necessity for concentrating forces to mass effects with the need to disperse them to avoid creating lucrative targets. Advances in ground and air mobility, target acquisition, and long-range precision fires enable attackers to rapidly concentrate effects. C2 systems provide reliable relevant information that assists commanders in determining when to concentrate forces to mass effects.

C. Tempo

Controlling or altering tempo is necessary to retain the initiative. At the operational level, a faster tempo allows attackers to disrupt enemy defensive plans by achieving results quicker than the enemy can respond. At the tactical level, a faster tempo allows attackers to quickly penetrate barriers and defenses and destroy enemy forces in depth before they can react.

D. Audacity

Audacity is a simple plan of action, boldly executed. Commanders display audacity by developing bold, inventive plans that produce decisive results. Commanders demonstrate audacity by violently applying combat power. They understand when and where to take risks and do not hesitate as they execute their plan. Commanders dispel uncertainty through action; they compensate for lack of information by seizing the initiative and pressing the fight. Audacity inspires soldiers to overcome adversity and danger.

Offensive Operations

I. Movement to Contact

Ref: FM 3-90 Tactics, chap 4; FM 3-21.10 The Infantry Rifle Company, chap 4 and FM 3-21.8 The Infantry Rifle Platoon and Squad, pp. 7-18 to 7-24.

Movement to contact is a type of offensive operation designed to develop the situation and establish or regain contact. A commander conducts this type of offensive operation when the tactical situation is not clear or when the enemy has broken contact. A properly executed movement to contact develops the combat situation and maintains the commander's freedom of action after contact is gained. This flexibility is essential in maintaining the initiative.

Purposeful and aggressive movement, decentralized control, and the hasty deployment of combined arms formations from the march to attack or defend characterize the movement to contact. The fundamentals of a movement to contact are—

- Focus all efforts on finding the enemy
- Make initial contact with the smallest force possible, consistent with protecting the force
- Make initial contact with small, mobile, self-contained forces to avoid decisive engagement of the main body on ground chosen by the enemy. This allows the commander maximum flexibility to develop the situation
- Task-organize the force and use movement formations to deploy and attack rapidly in any direction
- Keep forces within supporting distances to facilitate a flexible response
- Maintain contact regardless of the course of action (COA) adopted once contact is gained

Meeting Engagement

The movement to contact results in a meeting engagement. A meeting engagement is the combat action that occurs when a moving element engages a stationary or moving enemy at an unexpected time and place. Meeting engagements are characterized by—

- Limited knowledge of the enemy
- Minimum time available for the leader to conduct actions on contact
- Rapidly changing situation
- Rapid execution of battle and crew drills

A meeting engagement is a combat action that occurs when a moving force engages an enemy at an unexpected time and place. Conducting an MTC results in a meeting engagement. The enemy force may be either stationary or moving. Such encounters often occur in small-unit operations when reconnaissance has been ineffective. The force that reacts first to the unexpected contact generally gains an advantage over its opponent. However, a meeting engagement may also occur when the opponents are aware of each other and both decide to attack immediately to obtain a tactical advantage or seize key or decisive terrain. A meeting engagement may also occur when one force attempts to deploy into a hasty defense while the other force attacks before its opponent can organize an effective defense. Acquisition systems may discover the enemy before the security force can gain contact. No matter how the force makes contact, seizing the initiative is the overriding imperative.

I. MTC - Organization

A movement to contact is organized with an offensive covering force or an advance guard as a forward security element and a main body as a minimum. Based on the factors of METT-TC, the commander may increase his security forces by having an offensive covering force and an advance guard for each column, as well as flank and rear security (normally a screen or guard).

The MTC may use multiple teams to find the enemy. When a team makes contact, they report the information. The commander decides when to commit the body of the main force.

A movement to contact is conducted using one of two techniques: approach march, or search and attack. The approach march technique is used when the enemy is expected to deploy using relatively fixed offensive or defensive formations, and the situation remains vague. The search and attack technique is used when the enemy is dispersed, when he is expected to avoid contact or quickly disengage and withdraw, or when the higher unit needs to deny him movement in an area of operation.

1. Search and Attack

Search and attack is a technique for conducting a MTC; this technique shares many of the same characteristics of an area security mission. Conducted primarily by Infantry forces and often supported by heavy forces, a commander employs this form of a MTC when the enemy is operating as small, dispersed element, or when the task is to deny the enemy the ability to move within a given area. The battalion is the echelon that normally conducts a search and attack. *(Note: See also p.2-12)*

2. Approach-March Technique

A unit normally uses this technique when it conducts a MTC as part of a battalion. Depending on its location in the formation and its assigned mission, the company can act as the advance guard, move as part of the battalion main body, or provide flank or rear guards for the battalion. *(Note: See also p.2-12)*

Prompt execution of battle drills at platoon level and below, and standard actions on contact for larger units can give that initiative to the friendly force.

II. Planning & Preparation

Small units (e.g., an infantry company) normally conducts MTC as part of a battalion or larger element; however, based on the METT-TC factors, it can conduct the operation independently. As an example, the company may conduct MTC prior to occupation of a screen line. Because the enemy situation is not clear, the company moves in a way that provides security and supports a rapid buildup of combat power against enemy units once they are identified. Two techniques for conducting a MTC are the search-and-attack technique and the approach-march technique. If no contact occurs, the company might be directed to conduct consolidation on the objective. The Infantry company commander analyzes the situation and selects the proper tactics to conduct the mission. He reports all information rapidly and accurately and strives to gain and maintain contact with the enemy. He retains freedom of maneuver by moving the company in a manner that--

- Ensures adequate force protection measures are always in effect
- Makes enemy contact (ideally visual contact) with the smallest element possible (ideally, a reconnaissance and surveillance [R&S] element). The commander plans for any forms of contact to identify enemy locations
- Rapidly develops combat power upon enemy contact
- Provides all-round security for the unit
- Supports the battalion concept

The higher commander will task-organize the subordinate units into reconnaissance (finding, fixing, and finishing) elements. He will assign specific tasks and purposes to his search and attack elements. It is important to note that within the concept of find, fix, and finish, all platoons could be the reconnaissance element. Depending on the size of the enemy they find, they could end up executing a reconnaissance mission, become the fixing element, or find that they are able to finish the enemy. Planning considerations for organizing include—

- The factors of METT-TC
- The requirement for decentralized execution.
- The requirement for mutual support. (The platoon leader must be able to respond to contact with his rifle squads or to mutually support another platoon within the company.)
- The Soldier's load. (The leader should ask, "Does the Soldier carry his rucksack, cache it, or leave it at a central point? How will the rucksacks be linked up with the Soldier?")
- Resupply and CASEVAC
- The employment of key weapons
- The requirement for patrol bases

III. Conducting the MTC - A Small Unit Perspective

1. From the assembly area (AA) the commander conducts a final communication check with the teams and dispatches them forward of the main body. The commander starts movement of the main body, keeping a distance great enough to avoid becoming absorbed when a team engages the enemy—and yet close enough to respond quickly with the reserve force.

2. Each team seeks visual contact with the enemy, being careful not to become engaged in a firefight. If the team enters a firefight with the enemy, the patrol leader (PL) loses the mobility necessary to develop the situation and collect intelligence for the commander of the MTC. If the team becomes decisively engaged, the PL reports this situation back to the commander.

3. The commander assesses the information coming from any force in contact with the enemy to determine if the main body should be committed to attacking the enemy, or if the team can effectively attack the enemy force, or if the enemy body should simply be bypassed.

Information is relayed back to the commander who remains with the main body of the MTC. The forces continue to develop the situation and send timely reports. (Photo by Jeong, Hae-jung).

4. The team in contact with the enemy acts as a shaping operation—meaning that the team doesn't conduct the main attack. Instead, the team fixes the enemy using an attack by fire to suppress and isolate the enemy force until the reserve force maneuvers to destroy the enemy. Alternatively, the team can be instructed to attack and destroy any smaller enemy force that would present a threat to the main body's flank or rear if bypassed. Even in this case, the team functions as a shaping operation within the force protection framework.

5. If the commander determines the detected enemy needs to be eliminated by the main body, he directs or leads the reserve force to crush the fixed enemy. This becomes the decisive operation—meaning it becomes the main attack. It consumes the attention and resources of the MTC until the engagement is concluded. If necessary, the commander pulls the other teams into the attack, attempting to isolate each subsequent enemy force so the enemy cannot coordinate their actions.

Once the commander has determined that a force is in contact with a key enemy element, the main body of the MTC is committed to the battle. The force fixes the enemy position, while the main body attacks aggressively. (Photo by Jeong, Hae-jung).

6. Once the engagement concludes, the commander again dispatches his teams forward and continues the movement—either to clear an axis of movement, or to defeat an identified enemy force. In any case, it is critical that the team seek and maintain visual contact with the enemy force and continues to develop the situation for the MTC commander.

7. The commander of the MTC looks for signs of culmination. That may come by means of hitting the established boundaries of his area of operation (AO) and limit of advance (LOA). Or the enemy may no longer be putting up resistance—such as fleeing and the number of engagements has drastically fallen. Or, the troops of the MTC may have become exhausted. In any case, at the sign of culmination, the commander must reconsolidate the friendly forces and assume a 360-degree security posture.

Offensive Operations

On Point

An Infantry company normally conducts MTC as part of a battalion or larger element; however, based on the METT-TC factors, it can conduct the operation independently. As an example, the company may conduct MTC prior to occupation of a screen line. Because the enemy situation is not clear, the company moves in a way that provides security and supports a rapid buildup of combat power against enemy units once they are identified. Two techniques for conducting a MTC are the search-and-attack technique and the approach-march technique. If no contact occurs, the company might be directed to conduct consolidation on the objective. The Infantry company commander analyzes the situation and selects the proper tactics to conduct the mission. He reports all information rapidly and accurately and strives to gain and maintain contact with the enemy.

Search and Attack

Search and attack is a technique for conducting a MTC; this technique shares many of the same characteristics of an area security mission (FM 3-0). Conducted primarily by Infantry forces and often supported by heavy forces, a commander employs this form of a MTC when the enemy is operating as small, dispersed element, or when the task is to deny the enemy the ability to move within a given area. The battalion is the echelon that normally conducts a search and attack. A brigade will assist its subordinate battalions by ensuring the availability of indirect fires and other support.

A commander conducts a search and attack for one or more of the following purposes:

- Protect the force--prevent the enemy from massing to disrupt or destroy friendly military or civilian operations, equipment, property, and key facilities.
- Collect information--gain information about the enemy and the terrain to confirm the enemy COA predicted by the IPB process. Help generate SA for the company and higher headquarters.
- Destroy the enemy and render enemy units in the AO combat ineffective.
- Deny the area--prevent the enemy from operating unhindered in a given area such as in any area he is using for a base camp or for logistics support.

Approach-March Technique

The Infantry company normally uses this technique when it conducts a MTC as part of the battalion. Depending on its location in the formation and its assigned mission, the company can act as the advance guard, move as part of the battalion main body, or provide flank or rear guards for the battalion. When planning for an approach-march MTC, the company commander needs certain information from the battalion commander. With this information, the company commander develops his scheme of maneuver and fire support plan. He provides this same information to the platoon leaders. As a minimum, he needs to know:

- The company's mission
- The friendly and enemy situations
- The route (axis of advance) and the desired rate of movement
- The control measures to be used
- The company's actions on contact
- The fire support plan
- The company's actions upon reaching the march objective, if one is used

Offensive Operations

II. Attack

Ref: FM 3-90 Tactics, chap 5 and FM 3-21.10 (FM 7-10) The Infantry Rifle Company, chap 4. Note: See also chap. 6 for discussion of special purpose attacks: the ambush, raid and swarming attacks.

An attack is an offensive operation that destroys or defeats enemy forces, seizes and secures terrain, or both. When the commander decides to attack or the opportunity to attack occurs during combat operations, the execution of that attack must mass the effects of overwhelming combat power against selected portions of the enemy force with a tempo and intensity that cannot be matched by the enemy. The resulting combat should not be a contest between near equals.

The support team masses together combat power in weaponry. Machineguns, grenade launchers, and rockets are employed to suppress enemy defenses while the assault team moves forward to destroy key positions. (Dept. of Army photo by Arthur McQueen).

Platoons and squads normally conduct an attack as part of the Infantry company. An attack requires detailed planning, synchronization, and rehearsals to be successful. The company commander designates platoon objectives with a specific mission for his assault, support, and breach elements. To ensure synchronization, all leaders must clearly understand the mission, with emphasis on the purpose, of peer and subordinate elements. Leaders must also know the location of their subordinates and adjacent units during the attack.

Hasty vs. Deliberate Attacks

In addition to having different forms based on their purposes, attacks are characterized as hasty, or deliberate. The primary difference between the hasty and deliberate attack is the planning and coordination time available to allow the full integration and synchronization of all available combined arms assets.

I. Attack - Organization

The attack force breaks into two teams, the support team and the assault team. If the enemy is specifically known to have prior warning to our attack and is known to have the available resources to conduct spoiling attacks, the combat leader may also form a security team for protecting the flanks from an enemy spoiling attack. Otherwise, the attack uses just the support and assault teams.

The assault team includes a breach team. The breach team has the job of moving forward to neutralize the enemy's obstacles. They use defilades and smoke to obscure their activity. (Photo by Jeong, Hae-jung.)

A. Assault Team

The assault team includes an internal breach team that is tasked with the responsibility of cutting a path through the enemy's forward obstacles. This team typically consists of a 2-man security team and a 2-man engineer team. The breach team carries specialized equipment for cutting through wire, neutralizing land mines, and marking the path once they have created the breach in the enemy's obstacles. In most cases, the breach team will require ample amounts of smoke canisters to mask their activity.

B. Support Team

The support team employs mass casualty producing weapons and may also have an internal sub-team to conduct a feign attack. The feign attack is coordinated to advance at the same time as the breach team advances. The feign attack serves to pull attention away from the breach team to confuse the enemy as to the true location of the main assault force.

Like the breach team, the feign attack team employs smoke canisters and high rates of fire to make their attack look convincing—though the feign attack team does not attempt to pass through enemy obstacles. Instead, the feign attack remains just outside the enemy's obstacles and conducts an attack by fire to augment the support team fires.

II. Planning & Preparation

In an attack, friendly forces seek to place the enemy in a position where he can easily be defeated or destroyed. The commander seeks to keep the enemy off-balance while continually reducing the enemy's options. In an attack the commander focuses the maneuver effects, supported by the other warfighting functions (formerly labeled "battlefield operating systems"), on those enemy forces that prevent him from accomplishing his mission and seizing his objective.

Fire superiority is that degree of dominance in the fires of one force over another that permits that force to conduct maneuver at a given time and place without prohibitive interference by the enemy. The force must gain and maintain fire superiority at critical points during the attack. Having fire superiority allows the commander to maneuver his forces without prohibitive losses. The commander gains fire superiority by using a variety of tactics, techniques, and procedures. Achieving fire superiority requires the commander to take advantage of—

- The range and lethality of available weapon systems
- Offensive information operations to prevent the enemy commander from synchronizing the effects of his available combat power.
- Movement to place the enemy in a position of disadvantage where his weapons can be destroyed, one or more at a time, with little risk to friendly systems

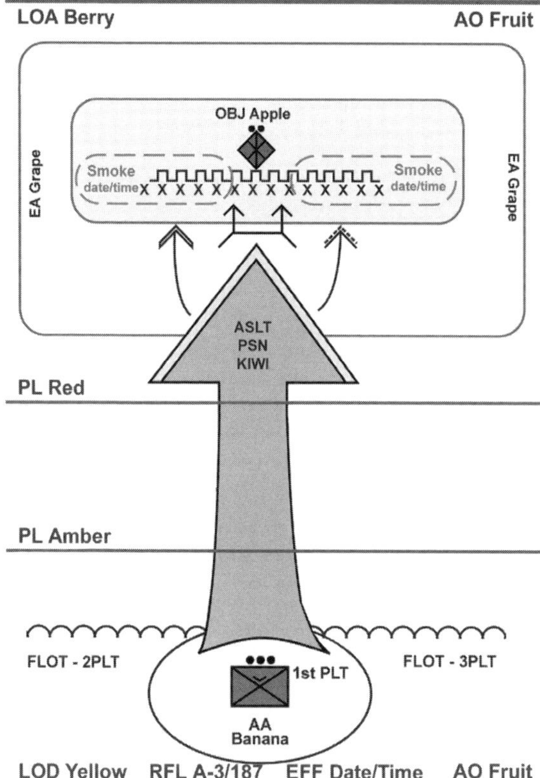

The progression of an attack takes the patrol from the assembly area through an attack lane up to the assault position. The support team deploys first, then the assault team and feign attack.

III. Conducting the Attack - A Small Unit Perspective

In the event a patrol is tasked to conduct an attack, the patrol may go through a 9-step process for the planning and execution of actions on the objective.

In the attack, the a small unit maneuvers along lines of least resistance using the terrain for cover and concealment. This indirect approach affords the best chance to achieve surprise on the enemy force. In the attack, the unit maneuvers along lines of least resistance using the terrain for cover and concealment. This indirect approach affords the best chance to achieve surprise on the enemy force.

1. Move to the Assault Position

An assault position is the last covered and concealed position before the OBJ. It differs from an ORP in that our patrol will *not* return to the assault position. We are not required to stop in the assault position; however, it is common to wait here so that friendly units and supporting fires can be synchronized against the enemy target. A leader's recon of the objective is optional, but with good intelligence, this is not required.

2. Form the Attack

At the designated time, the PL forms the patrol into its attack formation and order of march. This is the start of the attack. The attack will bypass any obstacles that have not been specifically assigned—unless they present a threat. The attack force passes through danger areas maintaining attack formation. Only as large a force as necessary is exposed to achieve each task. This conceals the size and intent of attack force.

3. Identify the Objective

The pointman determines the direction and distance of the OPFOR position (the OBJ). The PL leads the support team to its assigned position. This position allows the support team to observe the OPFOR defensive line and employ suppressive fires if the enemy detects the attack force.

4. Engage the Objective

The support team *does not* indiscriminately fire upon the OPFOR position if the attack still has the element of surprise! The assault's breach team moves up to the objective to neutralize the enemy's obstacles. If at any time the attack force is detected, the support team employs suppressive fire against enemy positions and may dispatch a feign attack.

5. Breach Obstacles

Using a defilade or similar cover, the assault's breach team moves forward. If the support team is not firing, the breach team uses stealth in approaching its objective. If suppressive fires are already underway, the breach team employs smoke to mask their movement. Simultaneously, the support team's feign attack employs a smoke screen at another point along the enemy's defensive line and attacks by fire. This will confuse the enemy as to the location of the breach team. The breach team uses visual tape during the day, or lights at night, to mark the breach of the enemy's obstacles.

6. Exploit the Breach

The breach team signals the assault leader once they have opened a path through the obstacles. Using the breach team as near side security, and moving under the cover fire of the support team, the entire assault team moves quickly through the breach.

Once the breach team opens a path through the enemy obstacles, the rest of the assault team moves forward to destroy key enemy positions. The support team coordinates suppressive fires during this time. (Photo by Jeong, Hae-jung.)

7. Clear the Objective

The assault team uses a high volume of fire and a small maneuver force to clear the first couple of fighting positions. Fireteams are assigned specific tasks, such as taking out bunkers or providing for left and right security. The support team continues to shift fires as the assault team clears more enemy fighting positions. The support team must keep the OPFOR suppressed and unable to form a counterattack. When the assault team clears enough of the enemy positions, the assault leader signals for the support team to move through the breach and join the assault team. Now the attack force assaults assigned targets, such as the OPFOR CP and communications nodes, or the attack may continue against the enemy's exposed flanks.

8. Reconsolidate and Reorganize

To regain the patrol's mass and strength, the PL forms the patrol into a 180° security position on the far side of the OBJ and prepares for a counterattack. Element leaders use liquid, ammo, casualties, equipment (LACE) considerations to account for personnel, ensure key weapon systems are manned, and redistribute ammunition, water, medical supplies, and batteries. The PL reports to higher command the progress of the attack and coordinates for supporting resources. Friendly casualties are evacuated, as are EPWs, according to the OPORD. In truth, reconsolidation and reorganization may occur even before all the objectives have been accomplished. It is an ongoing task and may be conducted multiple times.

9. Continue the Mission

After seizing the OBJ, the attack force prepares to transform into a new mission. The patrol might be required to defend, withdraw, or begin an exploitation or pursuit.

On Point

The attack is a primary form of offensive operation that seeks to impose our will through either a decisive defeat of an enemy force or by seizing essential terrain or facilities. This requires mass, mobility, and the element of surprise.

The massing of combat power (troops, weapons, and fires) is a luxury that the defense does not have. The defense must distribute its combat power over the larger area it intends to defend. True, these resources are coordinated to support one another, but there isn't a great deal of flexibility in the defense's use of combat power unless the defense is willing to surrender valuable territory or facilities.

Hasty or Deliberate

No clear distinction exists between hasty and deliberate attacks, because they are similar. However, the main difference between the two is the extent of planning and preparation conducted by the attacking force. Attacks range along a continuum defined at one end by FRAGOs, which direct the rapid execution of battle drills by forces immediately available. At the other end of the continuum, the company moves into a deliberate attack from a reserve position or assembly area with detailed knowledge of the enemy (a task organization designed specifically for the attack) and a fully rehearsed plan. Most attacks fall somewhere between these two ends of the continuum.

Characteristics of the Offense

The characteristics of the offense are surprise, tempo, concentration, and audacity. Due to the nature of modern offensive operations, flexibility is included in the following discussion of the offense. For each mission, the commander decides how to apply these characteristics to focus the effects of his combat power against enemy weakness. Detailed planning is critical to achieve a synchronized and effective operation. Instead of 'fighting the plan,' commanders should exploit enemy weaknesses.

The following considerations will help avoid common mistakes during the attack:

- Use stealth until contact has been made
- Do not break the attack formation for danger areas
- Bypass all unassigned obstacles
- Use only the force necessary to complete a task
- React with violence once contact has been made

The patrol leader (PL) uses the commander's intent to develop the attack plan. The principals of Mission, Enemy, Terrain & weather, Time available, Troops available, and Civilians on the battlefield (METT-TC) are considered and influence the attack plan's scheme of maneuver and fire support. Control measures are implemented to ensure that friendly fire incidents do not occur.

Maneuver Control Measures

Using a map overlay, the patrol leader identifies the maneuver control measures including the assembly area (AA), the line of departure (LD), the axis of advance, phase lines, the assault position, the objective (OBJ), and the limit of advance (LOA). Furthermore, the larger area of operations (AO) is indicated, giving special attention to any friendly unit's location and activity.

Fire Control Measures

Using a map overlay, the patrol leader identifies the fire control measures including the engagement area (EA), target reference points (TRP), the direction of fire, and the restrictive fire line (RFL). In addition to those terrain-based fire control measures, the patrol leader delineates the threat-based fire control measures. At a minimum, these include the engagement priorities, rules of engagement (ROE), and weapon safety postures.

Offensive Operations

III. Exploitation

Ref: FM 3-90 Tactics, chap 6 and FM 3-21.10 (FM 7-10) The Infantry Rifle Company, p. 4-3.

Exploitation is a type of offensive operation that usually follows a successful attack and is designed to disorganize the enemy in depth. Commanders at all echelons exploit successful offensive actions. Attacks that succeed in annihilating a defending enemy are rare. Failure to aggressively exploit success at every turn may give the enemy time to reconstitute an effective defense by shifting his forces or by regaining the initiative through a counterattack. The commander designs his exploitation to maintain pressure on the enemy, compound and take advantage of his disorganization, shatter his will to resist, and seize decisive or key terrain.

Exploitations are conducted at the battalion level and higher. Exploitations seek to disintegrate enemy forces to where they have no alternative but surrender or flight. Companies and platoons may conduct movements to contact or attack as part of a higher unit's exploitation.

Exploitation operations seek to gain key terrain, and enemy facilities or resources. The seizure of weapon and ammunition caches is a legitimate goal of the exploitation. (Photo by Jeong, Hae-jung.)

Exploitation is the primary means of translating tactical success into operational advantage. It reinforces enemy force disorganization and confusion in the enemy's command and control (C2) system caused by tactical defeat. It is an integral part of the concept of the offense. The psychological effect of tactical defeat creates confusion and apprehension throughout the enemy C2 structure and reduces the enemy's ability to react. Exploitation takes advantage of this reduction in enemy capabilities to make permanent what would be only a temporary tactical effect if exploitation were not conducted. Exploitation may be decisive.

Conducting the Exploitation - A Small Unit Perspective

Commanders at all echelons exploit successful offensive actions. Attacks that succeed in annihilating a defending enemy are rare. Failure to aggressively exploit success at every turn may give the enemy time to reconstitute an effective defense by shifting his forces or by regaining the initiative through a counterattack. Therefore, every offensive operation not restricted by higher authority or lack of resources should be followed without delay by bold exploitation. The commander designs his exploitation to maintain pressure on the enemy, compound and take advantage of his disorganization, shatter his will to resist, and seize decisive or key terrain.

The expressed intention of the exploitation is to seize land or structures. Exploitation forces do this by capitalizing on the success of the prior mission—thereby making the exploitation mission an opportunistic venture. By following up tactical success with further tactical success, operational gains are achieved.

Exploitations are conducted at the battalion level and higher. Companies and platoons may conduct movements to contact or attack as part of a higher unit's exploitation.

I. Organization

The forces conducting an attack are also the forces that initially exploit that attack's success. Typically, the commander does not assign a subordinate unit the mission of exploitation before starting a movement to contact (MTC) or an attack. The commander reorganizes his unit internally to reflect the existing factors of METT-TC when the opportunity to exploit success occurs. He uses fragmentary orders (FRAGOs) to conduct actions on contact. If a commander needs additional resources to support the exploitation, he requests them from the appropriate headquarters. The additional resources may include intelligence, surveillance, and reconnaissance (ISR) assets to help identify targets for attack, as well as attack helicopters and controlled munitions, such as the Army tactical missile system, to attack identified targets. Each exploitation force should be large enough to protect itself from those enemy forces it expects to encounter. It should also be a reasonably self-sufficient combined arms force capable of operations beyond the supporting range of the main body.

The units that create an opportunity to exploit should not be expected to perform the exploitation to an extended depth. If the commander plans to exploit with a specific subordinate unit, he must specify the degree of damage or risk to that force he is willing to accept in the course of the current operation. If the initially attacking units incur significant losses of combat power, the commander should replace them as soon as possible. When the exploiting force's combat power weakens because of fatigue, disorganization, or attrition, or when it must hold ground or resupply, the commander should continue the exploitation with a fresh force. In both cases, the replacement force should have a high degree of tactical mobility so it can conduct the exploitation.

II. Planning & Preparation

The commander's ability to deny the enemy options by proactive use of his battlefield operating systems is critical to a successful exploitation. He does this by arranging his battlefield operating systems within his opponent's time and space relationship in accordance with the factors of METT-TC.

The commander must plan for the decentralized execution of an exploitation. His commander's intent is especially important because subordinates must be able to exercise initiative in a rapidly changing, fluid situation. The commander must state the purpose of the exploitation, which may be to force the retrograde of enemy forces from an area, encircle enemy forces so they cannot withdraw, or destroy enemy artillery and other fire support systems. The intent must describe the desired end state. That intent will also determine his decisive and shaping operations and guide the designation of his main effort at any given point.

A clear commander's intent provides subordinates with guidance on how to integrate their operations into the overall operations of the higher headquarters. Only subordinates who can act quickly can seize all opportunities to damage the enemy or accelerate the tempo of operations. A commander should place minimal restrictions on his subordinates. These may include clear instructions regarding the seizure of key terrain and the size of enemy forces that may be bypassed. Reliable, secure communications between the exploiting force, the follow and support force, and the commander facilitate coordination that can maximize the impact of the exploitation. However, all subordinates should have a clear picture of the desired end state to conduct operations that support it, even if communications are lost.

Planning for an exploitation begins during the preparation phase of all offensive operations. To avoid losing critical time during the transition from an MTC or an attack to an exploitation, the commander tentatively identifies forces, objectives, and AOs for subordinate units before the offensive operation begins. When the opportunity to exploit occurs, brigade and higher echelon commanders should initiate the exploitation, either as a branch of or a sequel to the existing operation. The commander's plan should attempt to avoid driving the enemy back in the direction of his own sustaining base.

III. Execution

Exploitation requires physical and mental aggressiveness to combat the friction of limited visibility, fatigue, bad weather, dangers of fratricide, and extended operations. It requires bold and aggressive reconnaissance, prompt use of firepower, and rapid employment of previously uncommitted units. Exploiting forces maneuver swiftly toward their objectives, sever escape routes, and strike at enemy command posts, communications nodes, reserves, artillery, and CS units to prevent the enemy from reorganizing an effective defense.

The exploitation is planned as a branch or a sequel to another combat operation. As such, it is difficult to detail the exact execution because much depends on the primary operation. However, exploitation has the intended goal of seizing enemy terrain, facilities, or resources. The exact target of the exploitation may not become clear until the first operation has achieved its objectives.

1. The commander and subordinate leaders must know what lies ahead. As the exploitation is conducted, small pockets of enemy resistance are commonly bypassed—because the destruction of the enemy force is *not* the objective. Instead, the exploitation focuses on the seizure of property. The force bypasses anything that does not present a threat to the rear or flanks.

2. If an obstacle cannot be bypassed, the commander may choose to isolate the enemy with disruptive fires and continue to press the exploitation. The commander may also choose to destroy the enemy precisely as done in a MTC. In any case, the commander does not want to leave an enemy force behind that would be capable of striking either the exploitation force or our sustainment force.

3. At some point a unit conducting an exploitation reaches a culminating point or transitions to a pursuit. Culmination can occur for the variety of reasons, such as friendly losses or the enemy's commitment of his reserve. The commander, when he makes an assessment that his force is approaching culmination, should transition to another type of operation. On the other hand, a pursuit enables the commander to complete his destruction of the enemy.

On Point

The exploitation is a follow-on form of attack. It seeks to gain territory, key facilities or enemy resources, such as supply caches. However, exploitation is not a primary form of attack. That means that the exploitation will always follow a successful attack, movement to contact (MTC), or defense. The force conducting such operations will be required to transform into the exploitation. It may be planned as a branch or sequel to any mission.

Defined Objective

The exploitation requires a defined objective, such as terrain or facility. Additionally, like the MTC, exploitation forces rely on the experience of the combat leader to know when to bypass the enemy, when to engage the enemy, and how to recognize signs of culmination—the point at which the mission will bear no more success.

The conduct of exploitation is very similar in organization and conduct as the MTC. However, whereas the MTC is dedicated to a given axis of advance or targets the enemy force, the exploitation seeks a specific objective at a given geographical location. This means that bypassing the enemy is not only acceptable, but in most cases it is preferred.

Branch or Sequel

Exploitation is planned only as a branch or sequel to another combat operation. It is not a primary form of offensive operations. Primary operations (attack, MTC, or defense) must be prepared to transition quickly into the exploitation. This requires well-informed subordinate leaders.

Exploitation is the primary means of translating tactical success into operational advantage. It reinforces enemy force disorganization and confusion in the enemy's command and control (C2) system caused by tactical defeat. It is an integral part of the concept of the offense. The psychological effect of tactical defeat creates confusion and apprehension throughout the enemy C2 structure and reduces the enemy's ability to react. Exploitation takes advantage of this reduction in enemy capabilities to make permanent what would be only a temporary tactical effect if exploitation were not conducted. Exploitation may be decisive.

Transition

Local exploitation by the committed force follows a successful attack. A unit conducts a local exploitation when it capitalizes on whatever tactical opportunities it creates in the course of accomplishing its assigned offensive mission. Whenever possible, the lead attacking unit transitions directly to the exploitation after accomplishing its mission in a local exploitation. If this is not feasible, the commander can pass fresh forces (follow and assume) into the lead. The commander acts quickly to capitalize on local successes. Although such local exploitations may appear insignificant, their cumulative effects can be decisive. Subordinate commanders, working within a higher commander's intent, can use their initiative to launch an exploitation. When a commander initiates a local exploitation, he informs his higher headquarters to keep that commander informed of his intentions. This prevents the inadvertent disruption of the higher echelon's battle or campaign and allows the higher headquarters to assess the possibility.

Offensive Operations

IV. Pursuit

Ref: FM 3-90 Tactics, chap 7 and FM 3-21.10 (FM 7-10) The Infantry Rifle Company, p. 4-3.

The pursuit is a follow-on form of attack, or counterattack when conducted from a defense. Pursuits are normally conducted at the brigade or higher level. A pursuit typically follows a successful exploitation. Ideally, it prevents a fleeing enemy from escaping and then destroys him. Companies and platoons will participate in a larger unit's exploitation and may conduct attacks as part of the higher unit's operation. Therefore, it must be planned as a branch or a sequel of other operations. The primary operation must be prepared to transition into a pursuit at an appropriate time.

The pursuit seeks to find, fix, and finish a fleeing enemy force. To do this, an enveloping force moves quickly forward along a parallel route of the escaping enemy and suppresses the enemy in their escape routes. (Photo by Jeong, Hae-jung).

Unlike an exploitation, which may focus on seizing key or decisive terrain instead of the enemy force, the pursuit always focuses on destroying the fleeing enemy force. This is seldom accomplished by directly pushing back the hostile forces on their lines of communication (LOCs). The commander in a pursuit tries to combine direct pressure against the retreating forces with an enveloping or encircling maneuver to place friendly troops across the enemy's lines of retreat. This fixes the enemy in positions where he can be defeated in detail. If it becomes apparent that enemy resistance has broken down entirely and the enemy is fleeing the battlefield, any type of offensive operation can transition to a pursuit.

Pursuit operations begin when an enemy force attempts to conduct retrograde operations. At that point, it becomes most vulnerable to the loss of internal cohesion and complete destruction. A pursuit aggressively executed leaves the enemy trapped, unprepared, and unable to defend, faced with the options of surrendering or complete destruction. The rapid shifting of units, continuous day and night movements, hasty attacks, containment of bypassed enemy forces, large numbers of prisoners, and a willingness to forego some synchronization to maintain contact with and pressure on a fleeing enemy characterize this type of offensive operation. Pursuit requires swift maneuver and attacks by forces to strike the enemy's most vulnerable areas. A successful pursuit requires flexible forces, initiative by commanders at all levels, and the maintenance of a high operational tempo during execution.

The enemy may conduct a retrograde when successful friendly offensive operations have shattered his defense. In addition, the enemy may deliberately conduct a retrograde when—

- He is reacting to a threat of envelopment
- He is adjusting his battlefield dispositions to meet changing situations
- He is attempting to draw the friendly force into fire sacks, kill zones, or engagement areas
- He is planning to employ weapons of mass destruction

I. Organization

Normally, the commander does not organize specifically for a pursuit ahead of time, although he may plan for a pursuit as a branch or sequel to his offensive operation. Therefore, he must be flexible to react when the situation presents itself. The commander's maneuver and sustainment forces continue their ongoing activities while he readjusts their priorities to better support the pursuit. He acquires additional support from his higher headquarters in accordance with the factors of METT-TC.

For most pursuits, the commander organizes his forces into security, direct-pressure, encircling, follow and support, and reserve forces.

Given sufficient resources, there can be more than one encircling force. The follow and support force polices the battlefield to prevent the dissipation of the direct-pressure force's combat power. Appendix B addresses the duties of a follow and support force. The reserve allows the commander to take advantage of unforeseen opportunities or respond to enemy counterattacks.

There are two basic organizational options in conducting a pursuit; each involves a direct-pressure force. The first is a frontal pursuit that employs only a direct-pressure force. The second is a combination that uses a direct-pressure force and an encircling force. The combination pursuit is generally more effective. Either the direct-pressure force or the encircling force can conduct the decisive operation in a combination pursuit.

A. Frontal Pursuit

In a frontal pursuit, the commander employs only a direct-pressure force to conduct operations along the same retrograde routes used by the enemy. The commander chooses this option in two situations. The first is when he cannot create an encircling force with enough mobility to get behind the enemy force. The second is when he cannot create an encircling force capable of sustaining itself until it links up with the direct-pressure force. Either situation can occur because of restrictive terrain or because an enemy withdraws in a disciplined, cohesive formation and still has significant available combat power.

B. Combination Pursuit

In the pursuit, the most decisive effects result from combining the frontal pursuit with encirclement. In the combination pursuit, the direct-pressure force initiates a frontal pursuit immediately on discovering the enemy's initiation of a retrograde operation. This slows the tempo of the enemy's withdrawal (or fixes him in his current position if possible), and may destroy his rear security force. The direct-pressure force's actions help to set the conditions necessary for the success of the encircling force's operation by maintaining constant pressure. The encircling force conducts an envelopment or a turning movement to position itself where it can block the enemy's escape and trap him between the two forces, which leads to complete annihilation.

II. Planning & Preparation

The commander anticipates an enemy retrograde operation as either a branch or a sequel to the plan. The plan should identify possible direct-pressure, encircling, follow and support, and reserve forces and issue on-order or be-prepared missions to these forces. The commander should employ the maximum number of available combat troops in the pursuit. He bases the details of his plan on the enemy's anticipated actions, the combat formation of the attacking troops, and the amount of planning time available. The commander also considers—

- Possible routes the enemy might use to conduct his retrograde operations
- Availability of his intelligence, surveillance, and reconnaissance assets to detect enemy forces and acquire targets in depth
- Scheme of maneuver
- Availability and condition of pursuit routes
- Availability of forces to keep the pressure on the enemy until his destruction is complete
- Critical terrain features
- Use of reconnaissance and security forces
- Allocation of precision-guided munitions and aviation support
- Availability of CS and CSS resources

Pursuit planning must address the possibility of defending temporarily during operational pauses while making preparations to continue the pursuit or to consolidate gains. However, the use of an operational pause generally results in the abandonment of the pursuit because the enemy is able to use that time to organize a coherent defense.

The commander must specifically address how to detect the enemy retrograde operations; otherwise, the enemy may succeed in breaking contact. The commander relies on active reconnaissance, an understanding of enemy tactics, and knowledge of the current tactical situation. He must watch for signs that indicate the enemy is preparing to conduct a retrograde, such as when the enemy—

- Lacks the capability to maintain his position or cohesion
- Conducts limited local counterattacks
- Intensifies his reconnaissance and intelligence efforts
- Increases the amount of rearward movements and changes the type of elements conducting them, especially by fire support and reserves
- Prepares his facilities, installations, equipment, and supply stock-piles for demolition and destruction
- Decreases fire in intensity and effectiveness through the AO
- Increases his fires in one or more individual sectors of the front, which does not appear to be in accordance with the developing situation, and at a time when the amount of defensive fires seems to be decreasing

III. Conducting the Pursuit - A Small Unit Perspective

Pursuits are normally conducted at the brigade or higher level. A pursuit typically follows a successful exploitation. Ideally, it prevents a fleeing enemy from escaping and then destroys him. Companies and platoons will participate in a larger unit's exploitation and may conduct attacks as part of the higher unit's operation.

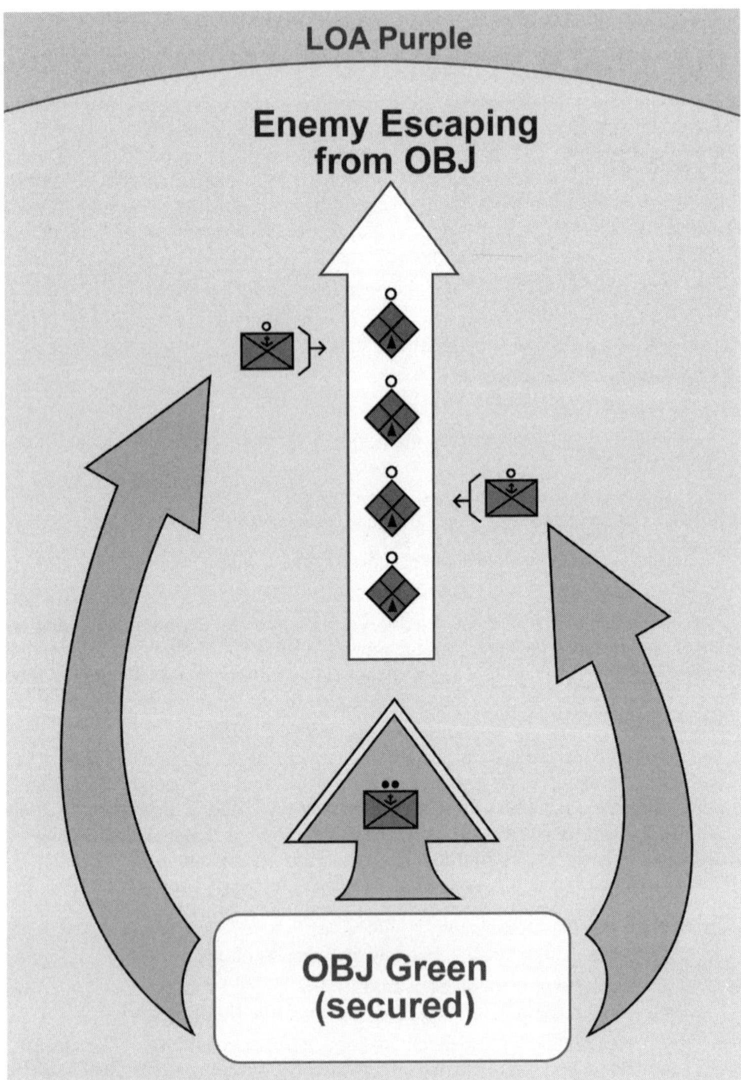

The pursuit deploys teams forward to envelop and fix the enemy in their escape route. The suppressed enemy cannot coordinate a defense, and the main force defeats them in detail. (Ref: FM 3-90, chap 7, fig. 7-2).

The pursuit is planned as a branch or a sequel to another combat operation. It is virtually impossible to detail the execution because much depends on the status of the enemy forces after the primary operation concludes. However, pursuit has the intended goal of destroying or capturing the enemy force.

Once the commander initiates a pursuit, he continues pursuing the enemy until a higher commander terminates the pursuit. Conditions under which a higher commander may terminate a pursuit include the following—

- The pursuing force annihilates or captures the enemy and resistance ceases
- The pursuing force fixes the enemy for follow-on forces
- The high commander makes an assessment that the pursuing force is about to reach a culminating point

The main body maneuvers aggressively while the enveloping force still has the enemy fixed. The main body attacks and defeats in detail each pocket of enemy. This process continues until culmination. (Photo by Jeong, Hae-jung).

1. The commander and subordinate leaders must know approximately where the enemy escape routes are located. A fixing force (typically the reserve of any combat operation) must move deep into enemy territory to identify the enemy's route of escape and relay this information back to the main force. The fixing force will suppress the enemy in individual pockets within the escape routes to prevent the enemy from coordinating an effective response with adjacent enemy units. The main force will aggressively maneuver up to and destroy the trapped, isolated enemy. Then the process repeats in order to trap and destroy as many enemy troops as possible.

2. The pursuit is focused on the destruction of the enemy force. As such, the pursuit force bypasses any terrain or facilities that do not present a threat to their rear or flanks. Do not leave an enemy force behind that would be capable of delaying the fixing force or the main force of the pursuit.

3. The commander must look for signs of culmination. As the enemy is pursued, they often are falling back on their own resources. For example, they could be falling back to designated rally points—which theoretically offer them defensive positions.

On Point

The pursuit is the classic "hammer and anvil" maneuver. The pursuit force must have some idea of where the enveloping force is, as well as where the enemy force is, before they can begin swinging the hammer of the main force.

When the commander initiates a pursuit, he often creates the encircling force from uncommitted or reserve elements. Normally, these forces do not have fire support assets allocated to them. The commander must plan how to redistribute his fire support assets to properly support the encircling force. Attack helicopters and close air support are well suited to support the encircling force.

A pursuit is often conducted as a series of encirclements in which successive portions of the fleeing enemy are intercepted, cut off from outside support, and captured or destroyed. The direct-pressure force conducts a series of hasty attacks to destroy the enemy's rear security force, maintain constant pressure on the enemy's main body, and slow the enemy's withdrawal. At every opportunity, the direct-pressure force fixes, slows down, and destroys enemy elements, provided such actions do not interfere with its primary mission of maintaining constant pressure on the enemy's main body. The direct pressure force can bypass large enemy forces if it can hand them off to follow and support units, or if they do not pose a risk to the direct-pressure force.

Mobility and Countermobility

Engineer mobility and countermobility assets are instrumental in sustaining the rate of advance and hindering the enemy's withdrawal. Engineers prepare the route of advance and support the lateral dispersion of units transitioning to the pursuit and the movement of the reserve. During the pursuit, the commander must plan for his engineers to provide assault bridging and emergency road repairs to sustain the tempo of the pursuit. The commander also plans to use his engineer assets to block any bypassed enemy's withdrawal routes by using antitank and command-operated mines, demolitions, and obstacles.

Risk

Conducting a pursuit is a calculated risk. Once the pursuit begins, the commander maintains contact with the enemy and pursues retreating enemy forces without further orders. The commander maintains the pursuit as long as the enemy appears disorganized and friendly forces continue to advance.

Transition

A pursuit often transitions into other types of offensive and defensive operations. If the enemy attempts to reorganize, forces conducting a pursuit execute hasty attacks. They conduct an exploitation to capitalize on the success of these attacks and then move back into pursuit. Forces conducting a pursuit may also transition into a defensive operation if the pursuing force reaches a culminating point. This usually occurs when the enemy introduces strong reinforcements to prepare for a counteroffensive.

V. Small Unit Offensive Tactical Tasks

Ref: FM 3-21.8 (FM 7-8) The Infantry Rifle Platoon and Squad, pp. 7-31 to 7-36.

Tactical tasks are specific activities performed by units as they conduct tactical operations or maneuver. At the platoon level, these tasks are the warfighting actions the platoon may be called on to perform in battle. This section provides discussion and examples of some common actions and tasks the platoon may perform during a movement to contact, a hasty attack, or a deliberate attack. It is extremely important to fully understand the purpose behind a task (what) because the purpose (why) defines what the platoon must achieve as a result of executing its mission. A task can be fully accomplished, but if battlefield conditions change and the platoon is unable to achieve the purpose, the mission is a failure.

Note: The situations used in this section to describe the platoon leader's role in the conduct of tactical tasks are examples only. They are not applicable in every tactical operation, nor are they intended to prescribe any specific method or technique the platoon must use in achieving the purpose of the operation. Ultimately, it is up to the commander or leader on the ground to apply both the principles discussed here, and his knowledge of the situation. An understanding of his unit's capabilities, the enemy he is fighting, and the ground on which the battle is taking place are critical when developing a successful tactical solution.

Task	Graphic	Description
Seize	S	*Seize* is a tactical mission task that involves taking possession of a designated area by using overwhelming force. An enemy force can no longer place direct fire on an objective that has been seized.
Suppress	No graphic provided in FM 3-90.	*Suppress* is a tactical mission task that results in the temporary degradation of the performance of a force or weapon system below the level needed to accomplish its mission.
Support by Fire		*Support-by-fire* is a tactical mission task in which a maneuver force moves to a position where it can engage the enemy by direct fire in support of another maneuvering force. The primary objective of the support force is normally to fix and suppress the enemy so he cannot effectively fire on the maneuvering force.
Clear	C	*Clear* is a tactical mission task that requires the commander to remove all enemy forces and eliminate organized resistance within an assigned area.
Attack by Fire		*Attack-by-fire* is a tactical mission task in which a commander uses direct fires, supported by indirect fires, to engage an enemy without closing with him to destroy, suppress, fix, or deceive him.

Tactical mission tasks describe the results or effects the commander wants to achieve - the what and why of a mission statement. For a more complete listing of tactical mission tasks, see pp. 1-11 to 1-14.

I. Seize

Seizing involves gaining possession of a designated objective by overwhelming force. Seizing an objective is complex. It involves closure with the enemy, under fire of the enemy's weapons to the point that the friendly assaulting element gains positional advantage over, destroys, or forces the withdrawal of the enemy.

A platoon may seize prepared or unprepared enemy positions from either an offensive or defensive posture. Examples include the following:

- A platoon seizes the far side of an obstacle as part of a company breach or seizes a building to establish a foothold in an urban environment
- A platoon seizes a portion of an enemy defense as part of a company deliberate attack
- A platoon seizes key terrain to prevent its use by the enemy

There are many inherent dangers in seizing an objective. They include the requirement to execute an assault, prepared enemy fires, a rapidly changing tactical environment, and the possibility of fratricide when friendly elements converge. These factors require the platoon leader and subordinate leaders to understand the following planning considerations.

Developing a clear and current picture of the enemy situation is very important. The platoon may seize an objective in a variety of situations, and the platoon leader will often face unique challenges in collecting and disseminating information on the situation. For example, if the platoon is the seizing element during a company deliberate attack, the platoon leader should be able to develop an accurate picture of the enemy situation during the planning and preparation for the operation. He must be prepared to issue modifications to the platoon as new intelligence comes in or as problems are identified in rehearsals.

In another scenario, the platoon leader may have to develop his picture of the enemy situation during execution. He must rely more heavily on reports from units in contact with the enemy and on his own development of the situation. In this type of situation, such as when the platoon is seizing an enemy combat security outpost during a movement to contact, the platoon leader must plan on relaying information as it develops. He uses clear, concise FRAGOs to explain the enemy situation, and gives clear directives to subordinates.

II. Suppress

The platoon maneuvers to a position on the battlefield where it can observe the enemy and engage him with direct and indirect fires. The purpose of suppressing is to prevent the enemy from effectively engaging friendly elements with direct or indirect fires. To accomplish this, the platoon must maintain orientation both on the enemy force and on the friendly maneuver element it is supporting. During planning and preparation, the platoon leader should consider—

- Conducting a line-of-sight analysis during his terrain analysis to identify the most advantageous positions from which to suppress the enemy
- Planning and integrating direct and indirect fires
- Determining control measures (triggers) for lifting, shifting, or ceasing direct fires
- Determining control measures for shifting or ceasing indirect fires
- Planning and rehearsing actions on contact
- Planning for large Class V expenditures. (The company commander and the platoon leader must consider a number of factors in assessing Class V require-

ments including the desired effects of the platoon direct fires; the composition, disposition, and strength of the enemy force; and the time required to suppress the enemy.)

- Determining when and how the platoon will reload ammunition during the fight while still maintaining suppression for the assaulting element

III. Support by Fire

The platoon maneuvers to a position on the battlefield from where it can observe the enemy and engage him with direct and indirect fires. The purpose of support by fire is to prevent the enemy from engaging friendly elements.

To accomplish this task, the platoon must maintain orientation both on the enemy force and on the friendly maneuver element it is supporting. The platoon leader should plan and prepare by—

- Conducting line-of-sight analysis to identify the most advantageous support-by-fire positions
- Conducting planning and integration for direct and indirect fires
- Determining triggers for lifting, shifting, or ceasing direct and indirect fires
- Planning and rehearsing actions on contact
- Planning for large Class V expenditures, especially for the weapons squad and support elements, because they must calculate rounds per minute. (The platoon leader and weapons squad leader must consider a number of factors in assessing Class V requirements, including the desired effects of platoon fires; the time required for suppressing the enemy; and the composition, disposition, and strength of the enemy force.)

A comprehensive understanding of the battlefield and enemy and friendly disposition is a crucial factor in all support-by-fire operations. The platoon leader uses all available intelligence and information resources to stay abreast of events on the battlefield. Additional considerations may apply. The platoon may have to execute an attack to secure the terrain from where it will conduct the support by fire. The initial support-by-fire position may not afford adequate security or may not allow the platoon to achieve its intended purpose. This could force the platoon to reposition to maintain the desired weapons effects on the enemy. The platoon leader must ensure the platoon adheres to these guidelines:

- Maintain communication with the moving element
- Be prepared to support the moving element with both direct and indirect fires
- Be ready to lift, shift, or cease fires when masked by the moving element
- Scan the area of operations and prepare to acquire and destroy any enemy element that threatens the moving element
- Maintain 360-degree security
- Use Javelins to destroy any exposed enemy vehicles
- Employ squads to lay a base of sustained fire to keep the enemy fixed or suppressed in his fighting positions
- Prevent the enemy from employing accurate direct fires against the protected force

IV. Clear

Note: See also pp. 7-3 to 7-7 for TTPs of entering and clearing buildings.

Offensive Operations

Clearing requires the platoon to remove all enemy forces and eliminate organized resistance within an assigned area. The platoon may be tasked with clearing an objective area during an attack to facilitate the movement of the remainder of the company, or may be assigned clearance of a specific part of a larger objective area. Infantry platoons are normally best suited to conduct clearance operations, which in many cases will involve working in restrictive terrain, to include clearing a —

- Defile, including choke points in the defile and high ground surrounding it
- Heavily wooded area
- Built-up or strip area. Refer to FM 3-06, Urban Operations, and FM 3-06.11, Combined Operations in Urban Terrain, for a detailed discussion of urban combat
- Road, trail, or other narrow corridor, which may include obstacles or other obstructions on the actual roadway and in surrounding wooded and built-up areas

General Terrain Considerations

The platoon leader must consider several important terrain factors when planning and executing the clearance task. Observation and fields of fire may favor the enemy. To be successful, the friendly attacking element must neutralize this advantage by identifying dead spaces where the enemy cannot see or engage friendly elements. It should also identify multiple friendly support-by-fire positions that are necessary to support a complex scheme of maneuver which cover the platoon's approach, the actual clearance task, and friendly maneuver beyond the restrictive terrain.

When clearing in support of tactical vehicles, cover and concealment are normally abundant for Infantry elements, but scarce for trail-bound vehicles. Lack of cover leaves vehicles vulnerable to enemy antiarmor fires. While clearing in support of mechanized vehicles, obstacles influence the maneuver of vehicles entering the objective area. The narrow corridors, trails, or roads associated with restrictive terrain can be easily obstructed with wire, mines, and log cribs.

Key terrain may include areas dominating the objective area, approaches, or exits, and any terrain dominating the area inside the defile, wooded area, or built-up area. Avenues of approach will be limited. The platoon must consider the impact of canalization.

Restrictive Terrain Considerations

Conducting clearance in restrictive terrain is both time consuming and resource intensive. During the planning process, the platoon leader evaluates the tactical requirements, resources, and other considerations for each operation.

During the approach, the platoon leader focuses on moving combat power into the restrictive terrain and posturing it to start clearing the terrain. The approach ends when the rifle squads complete their preparations to conduct an attack. The platoon leader—

- Establishes support-by-fire positions
- Destroys or suppresses any known enemy positions to allow elements to approach the restrictive terrain
- Provides more security by incorporating suppressive indirect fires and obscuring or screening smoke

The platoon leader provides support by fire for the rifle squads. He prepares to support the rifle squads where they enter the restrictive terrain by using—

- High ground on either side of a defile
- Wooded areas on either side of a trail or road
- Buildings on either side of a road in a built-up area
- Movement of rifle squads along axes to provide cover and concealment

Clearance begins as the rifle squads begin their attack in and around the restrictive terrain. Examples of where this maneuver may take place include—

- Both sides of a defile, either along the ridgelines or high along the walls of the defile
- Along the wood lines parallel to a road or trail
- Around and between buildings on either side of the roadway in a built-up area

The following apply during clearance:

- The squads provide a base of fire to allow the weapons squad or support-by-fire element to bound to a new support-by-fire position. This cycle continues until the entire area is cleared.
- Direct-fire plans should cover responsibility for horizontal and vertical observation, and direct fire
- Squads should clear a defile from the top down and should be oriented on objectives on the far side of the defile
- Engineers with manual breaching capability should move with the rifle squads. Engineers may also be needed in the overwatching element to reduce obstacles.

The platoon must secure the far side of the defile, built-up area, or wooded area until the company moves forward to pick up the fight beyond the restrictive terrain. If the restrictive area is large, the platoon may be directed to assist the passage of another element forward to continue the clearance operation. The platoon must be prepared to—

- Destroy enemy forces
- Secure the far side of the restrictive terrain
- Maneuver squads to establish support-by-fire positions on the far side of the restrictive terrain
- Support by fire to protect the deployment of the follow-on force assuming the fight
- Suppress any enemy elements that threaten the company while it exits the restrictive terrain
- Disrupt enemy counterattacks
- Protect the obstacle reduction effort
- Maintain observation beyond the restrictive terrain
- Integrate indirect fires as necessary

Enemy Analysis

Careful analysis of the enemy situation is necessary to ensure the success of clearing. The enemy evaluation should include the following:

- Enemy vehicle location, key weapons, and Infantry elements in the area of operations
- Type and locations of enemy reserve forces
- Type and locations of enemy OPs
- The impact of the enemy's CBRN and or artillery capabilities

Belowground Operations

Belowground operations involve clearing enemy trenches, tunnels, caves, basements, and bunker complexes. The platoon's base-of-fire element and maneuvering squads must maintain close coordination. The weapons squad or support-by-fire element focuses on protecting the squads as they clear the trench line, or maneuver to destroy individual or vehicle positions. The base-of-fire element normally concentrates on destroying key surface structures (especially command posts and crew-served weapons bunkers) and the suppression and destruction of enemy vehicles.

V. Attack by Fire

The platoon maneuvers to a position on the battlefield from where it can observe the enemy and engage him with direct and indirect fires at a distance to destroy or weaken his maneuvers. The platoon destroys the enemy or prevents him from repositioning. The platoon employs long-range fires from dominating terrain. It also uses flanking fires or takes advantage of the standoff range of the unit's weapons systems. The company commander may designate an attack-by-fire position from where the platoon will fix the enemy. An attack-by-fire position is most commonly employed when the mission or tactical situation focuses on destruction or prevention of enemy movement. In the offense, it is usually executed by supporting elements. During defensive operations, it is often a counterattack option for the reserve element.

Considerations

When the platoon is assigned an attack-by-fire position, the platoon leader obtains the most current intelligence update on the enemy and applies his analysis to the information. During planning and preparation, the platoon leader should consider—

- Conducting a line-of-sight analysis during terrain analysis to identify the most favorable locations to destroy or fix the enemy
- Conducting direct and indirect fire planning and integration
- Determining control measures (triggers) for lifting, shifting, or ceasing direct fires
- Determining control measures for shifting or ceasing indirect fires
- Planning and rehearsing actions on contact

Several other considerations may affect the successful execution of an attack by fire. The platoon may be required to conduct an attack against enemy security forces to seize the ground from where it will establish the attack-by-fire position. The initial attack-by-fire position may afford inadequate security or may not allow the platoon to achieve its task or purpose. This could force the platoon to reposition to maintain the desired weapons effects on the enemy force. Because an attack by fire may be conducted well beyond the direct fire range of other platoons, it may not allow the platoon to destroy the targeted enemy force from its initial positions. The platoon may begin to fix the enemy at extended ranges. Additional maneuver would then be required to close with the enemy force and complete its destruction. Throughout an attack by fire, the platoon should reposition or maneuver to maintain flexibility, increase survivability, and maintain desired weapons effects on the enemy. Rifle squad support functions may include:

- Seizing the attack-by-fire position before occupation by mounted sections
- Providing local security for the attack-by-fire position
- Executing timely, decisive actions on contact
- Using maneuver to move to and occupy attack-by-fire positions
- Destroying enemy security elements protecting the targeted force
- Employing effective direct and indirect fires to disrupt, fix, or destroy the enemy force

Defensive Operations

FM 3-0 Operations (2008), pp. 3-10 to 3-12 and FM 3-90 Tactics, chap. 8.

Defensive operations are combat operations conducted to defeat an enemy attack, gain time, economize forces, and develop conditions favorable for offensive or stability operations. The defense alone normally cannot achieve a decision. However, it can create conditions for a counteroffensive operation that lets Army forces regain the initiative. Defensive operations can also establish a shield behind which stability operations can progress. Defensive operations counter enemy offensive operations. They defeat attacks, destroying as much of the attacking enemy as possible. They also preserve control over land, resources, and populations. Defensive operations retain terrain, guard populations, and protect critical capabilities against enemy attacks. They can be used to gain time and economize forces so offensive tasks can be executed elsewhere.

While the offense is the most decisive type of combat operation, the defense is the stronger type. The inherent strengths of the defense include the defender's ability to occupy his positions before the attack and use the available time to prepare his defenses. (Photo by Jeong, Hae-jung).

Successful defensive operations share the following characteristics: preparation, security, disruption, massed effects, and flexibility. Successful defenses are aggressive. Commanders use all available means to disrupt enemy forces. They disrupt attackers and isolate them from mutual support to defeat them in detail. Isolation includes extensive use of command and control warfare. Defenders seek to increase their freedom of maneuver while denying it to attackers. Defending commanders use every opportunity to transition to the offense, even if temporarily. As attackers' losses increase, they falter and the initiative shifts to the defenders. These situations are favorable for counterattacks. Counterattack opportunities rarely last long; defenders strike swiftly when the attackers culminate.

Conditions may not support immediate offensive operations during force projection. In those cases, initial-entry forces defend while the joint force builds combat power. Initial-entry forces should include enough combat power to deter, attack, or defend successfully.

I. Primary Defensive Tasks

At the operational level, an enemy offensive may compel joint forces to conduct major defensive operations. Such operations may require defeating or preventing attacks across international borders, defeating conventional attacks, or halting an insurgent movement's mobilization. Operational defenses may be executed anywhere in the operational area.

The following primary tasks are associated with the defense. Defending commanders combine these tasks to fit the situation:

A. Mobile Defense

In a mobile defense, the defender withholds a large portion of available forces for use as a striking force in a counterattack. Mobile defenses require enough depth to let enemy forces advance into a position that exposes them to counterattack. The defense separates attacking forces from their support and disrupts the enemy's command and control. As enemy forces extend themselves in the defended area and lose momentum and organization, the defender surprises and overwhelms them with a powerful counterattack.

Note: See pp. 3-5 to 3-10.

B. Area Defense

In an area defense, the defender concentrates on denying enemy forces access to designated terrain for a specific time, limiting their freedom of maneuver, and channeling them into killing areas. The defender retains terrain that the attacker must control in order to advance. The enemy force is drawn into a series of kill zones where it is attacked from mutually supporting positions and destroyed, largely by fires. The majority of the defending force is committed defending positions while the rest is kept in reserve. The reserve is used to preserve the integrity of the defense through reinforcement or counterattack.

Note: See pp. 3-11 to 3-18.

C. Retrograde

Retrograde involves organized movement away from the enemy. This includes delays, withdrawals, and retirements. Retrograde operations gain time, preserve forces, place the enemy in unfavorable positions, or avoid combat under undesirable conditions.

Note: See pp. 3-19 to 3-22.

Mobile and Static Elements in the Defense

All three primary defensive tasks use mobile and static elements. In mobile defenses, static positions help control the depth and breadth of the enemy penetration and retain ground from which to launch counterattacks. In area defenses, commanders closely integrate mobile patrols, security forces, sensors, and reserves to cover gaps among defensive positions. In retrograde operations, some units conduct area or mobile defenses along with security operations to protect other units executing carefully controlled maneuver or movement rearward. Static elements fix, disrupt, turn, or block the attackers and gain time for other forces to pull back. Mobile elements maneuver constantly to confuse the enemy and prevent enemy exploitation.

II. Purposes of Defensive Operations

Ref: FM 3-0 Operations (2008), pp. 3-11 to 3-12.

Defending forces await the enemy's attack and counter it. Waiting for the attack is not a passive activity. Commanders conduct aggressive ISR and security operations to find enemy forces and deny them information. Defenders engage enemy forces with fires, spoiling attacks, and security operations to weaken them before they reach the main battle area. Commanders use combined arms and joint capabilities to attack enemy vulnerabilities and seize the initiative.

Army forces conduct defensive operations for the following purposes:

Deter or Defeat Enemy Offensive Operations

The primary purpose of the defense is to deter or defeat enemy offensive operations. Successful defenses stall enemy actions and create opportunities to seize the initiative. Defensive operations may deter potential aggressors if they believe that breaking the friendly defense would be too costly.

Gain Time

Commanders may conduct a defense to gain time. Such defensive operations succeed by slowing or halting an attack while allowing friendly reserves enough time to reinforce the defense. Delaying actions trade space for time to improve defenses, expose enemy forces to joint attack, and prepare counterattacks.

Achieve Economy of Force

The defense is also used to achieve economy of force. Astute use of terrain, depth, and security operations allow friendly forces to minimize resources used defensively. This allows commanders to concentrate combat power for offensive operations.

Retain Key Terrain

The mission of many defensive operations is to retain key terrain. Such defenses are necessary to prevent enemy forces from occupying terrain that is so critical that the outcome of the battle or engagement depends on which side controls it. In operations dominated by stability tasks, friendly bases become key terrain.

Protect the Populace, Critical Assets, and Infrastructure

Defense of the local populace and vital assets supports stability operations and allows Army forces to receive greater support from the host nation. Army forces protect military and civilian areas that are important to success and provide indirect support to operations worldwide. Achieving this purpose begins with defenses around lodgments and bases, ensuring freedom of action. It is very important in counterinsurgency operations, where some facilities have significant economic and political value as opposed to tactical military importance.

Develop Intelligence

As with the offense, defensive operations may develop intelligence. The more successful the defense, the more Army forces learn about the enemy. A particular phase or task within a defense (for example, a covering force mission) may be conducted to satisfy commander's critical information requirements about the enemy's direction of attack and main effort.

III. Characteristics of the Defense

While the offense is the most decisive type of combat operation, the defense is the stronger type. The inherent strengths of the defense include the defender's ability to occupy his positions before the attack and use the available time to prepare his defenses. (Photo by Jeong, Hae-jung).

A. Preparation

The defense has inherent strengths. The defender arrives in the area of operations (AO) before the attacker and uses the available time to prepare. Defenders study the ground and select positions that allow massing fires on likely approaches. They combine natural and manmade obstacles to canalize attacking forces into engagement areas. Defending forces coordinate and rehearse actions on the ground, gaining intimate familiarity with the terrain. They place security and reconnaissance forces throughout the AO. These preparations multiply the effectiveness of the defense. Preparation ends only when defenders retrograde or begin to fight. Until then, preparations are continuous. Preparations in depth continue, even as the close fight begins.

B. Security

Commanders secure their forces principally through security operations, force protection, and IO. Security operations help deceive the enemy as to friendly locations, strengths, and weaknesses. They also inhibit or defeat enemy reconnaissance operations. These measures provide early warning and disrupt enemy attacks early and continuously. Force protection efforts preserve combat power. Offensive IO inaccurately portray friendly forces and mislead enemy commanders through military deception, operations security, and electronic warfare. These measures contribute to the defender's security.

C. Disruption

Defenders disrupt attackers' tempo and synchronization with actions designed to prevent them from massing combat power. Disruptive actions attempt to unhinge the enemy's preparations and, ultimately, his attacks. Methods include defeating or misdirecting enemy reconnaissance forces, breaking up his formations, isolating his units, and attacking or disrupting his systems. Defenders never allow attackers to fully prepare. They use spoiling attacks before enemies can focus combat power, and counterattack before they can consolidate any gains. Defenders target offensive IO against enemy C2 systems and constantly disrupt the enemy.

D. Massing Effects

Defenders seek to mass the effects of overwhelming combat power where they choose and shift it to support the decisive operation. To obtain an advantage at decisive points, defenders economize and accept risk in some areas; retain and, when necessary, reconstitute a reserve; and maneuver to gain local superiority at the point of decision. Defenders may surrender some ground to gain time to concentrate forces.

Commanders accept risk in some areas to mass effects elsewhere. Obstacles, security forces, and fires can assist in reducing risk. Since concentrating forces increases the threat of large losses from weapons of mass destruction (WMD), commanders use deception and concealment to hide force concentrations. They also protect their forces with ADA.

F. Flexibility

Defensive operations require flexible plans. Planning focuses on preparations in depth, use of reserves, and the ability to shift the main effort. Commanders add flexibility by designating supplementary positions, designing counterattack plans, and preparing to counterattack.

Defensive Operations

I. Mobile Defense

Ref: FM 3-90 Tactics, chap 10; and FM 3-21.10 (FM 7-10) The Infantry Rifle Company, chap 5.

The mobile defense is a type of defensive operation that concentrates on the destruction or defeat of the enemy through a decisive attack by a striking force. It focuses on destroying the attacking force by permitting the enemy to advance into a position that exposes him to counterattack and envelopment. The commander holds the majority of his available combat power in a striking force for his decisive operation, a major counterattack. He commits the minimum possible combat power to his fixing force that conducts shaping operations to control the depth and breadth of the enemy's advance. The fixing force also retains the terrain required to conduct the striking force's decisive counterattack. The area defense, on the other hand, focuses on retaining terrain by absorbing the enemy into an interlocked series of positions, where he can be destroyed largely by fires.

The mobile defense focuses on defeating or destroying the enemy by allowing him to advance to a point where he is exposed to a decisive counterattack by the striking force. The decisive operation is a counterattack conducted by the striking force. (Photo by Jeong, Hae-jung).

Small units do not normally conduct a mobile defense because of their inability to fight multiple engagements throughout the width, depth, and height of the AO, while simultaneously resourcing striking, fixing, and reserve forces. Typically, the striking force in a mobile defense may consist of one-half to two-thirds of the defender's combat power. Smaller units generally conduct an area defense or a delay as part of the fixing force as the commander shapes the enemy's penetration or they attack as part of the striking force. Alternatively, they can constitute a portion of the reserve.

The factors of METT-TC may dictate that a unit conducts a mobile defense when defending against an enemy force with greater combat power but less mobility. A commander may also employ a mobile defense when defending a large area of operations (AO) without well-defined avenues of approach, such as flat, open terrain. The mobile defense is preferred in an environment where the enemy may employ weapons of mass destruction because this type of defense reduces the vulnerability of the force to attack and preserves its freedom of action.

I. Organization

The commander organizes his main body into two principal groups—the fixing force and the striking force. In the mobile defense, reconnaissance and security, reserve, and sustaining forces accomplish the same tasks as in an area defense. The commander completes any required adjustments in task organization before he commits his units to the fight.

A. The Fixing Force

Organized by the commander with the minimum combat power needed to accomplish its mission, the fixing force turns, blocks, and delays the attacking enemy force. It tries to shape the enemy penetration or contain his advance. Typically, it has most of the countermobility assets of the defending unit. The fixing force may conduct defensive actions over considerable depth within the main battle area (MBA). However, it must be prepared to stop and hold terrain on short notice to assist the striking force on its commitment. The operations of the fixing force establish the conditions for a decisive attack by the striking force at a favorable tactical location. The fixing force executes its portion of the battle essentially as a combination of an area defense and a delaying action. The actions of the fixing force are shaping operations.

B. The Striking Force

The striking force decisively engages the enemy as he becomes exposed in his attempts to overcome the fixing force. The term “striking force” is used rather than reserve because the term “reserve” indicates an uncommitted force. The striking force is a committed force and has the resources to conduct a decisive counterattack as part of the mobile defense. It is the commander’s decisive operation.

The striking force contains the maximum combat power available to the commander at the time of its counterattack. The striking force is a combined arms force that has greater combat power and mobility than the force it seeks to defeat or destroy. The commander considers the effects of surprise when determining the relative combat power of the striking force and its targeted enemy unit. The striking force is normally fully task organized with all combat support (CS) and combat service support (CSS) assets before its actual commitment. The commander positions engineer mobility-enhancing assets with the lead elements of the striking force.

The striking force is the key to a successful mobile defense. All of its contingencies relate to its attack. If the opportunity does not exist to decisively commit the striking for ce, the defender repositions his forces to establish the conditions for success. The striking force must have mobility equal to or greater than that of its targeted enemy unit. It can obtain this mobility through proper task organization, countermobility operations to slow and disrupt enemy movements, and mobility operations to facilitate the rapid shifting of friendly formations. The striking force requires access to multiple routes because an attacking enemy normally goes to great length to deny the defending force freedom of action.

The mobile defense is dynamic in its approach. Standoff weaponry such as mines, IED, mortars, and rockets are used to disrupt enemy activity. (Dept. of Army photo by Yu, Hu Son).

II. Planning & Preparation

The key to successful mobile defensive operations is the integration and synchronization of all available assets to maximize the combat power of the defending unit, particularly the striking force. The commander achieves integration and synchronization when he can employ their combined effects at decisive times and places.

Preparations for conducting a mobile defense include developing the fixing force's defensive positions and Engagement Areas (EAs). The commander aggressively uses his reconnaissance assets to track enemy units as they approach. Engineers participate in conducting route and area reconnaissance to find and classify existing routes. They improve existing routes and open new routes for use during the battle

III. Conducting the Mobile Defense - A Small Unit Perspective

FM 3-90 Tactics divides the execution of a mobile defense into five phases for discussion purposes. The length and nature of each phase, if it occurs at all, varies from situation to situation according to the factors of METT-TC. The phases of defensive operations are gain and maintain enemy contact, disrupt the enemy, fix the enemy, maneuver, and follow through.

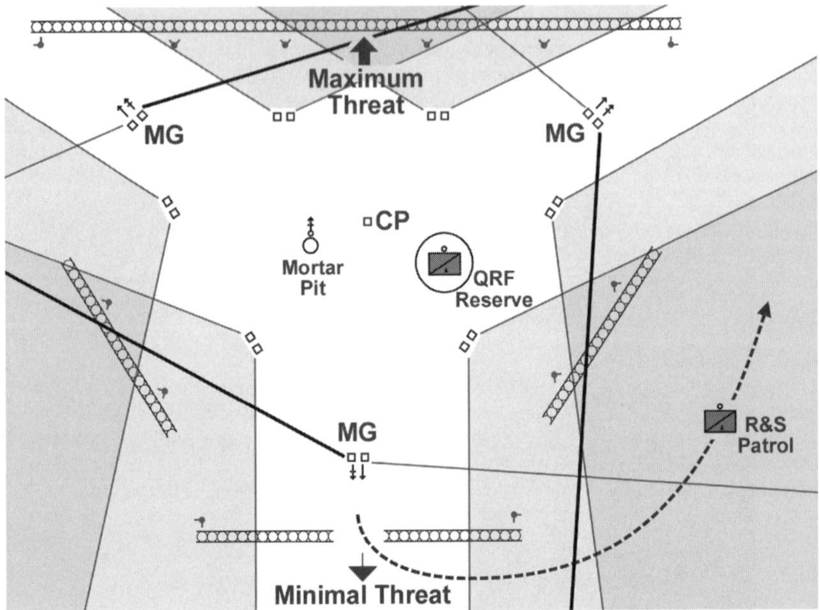

The mobile defense makes use of multiple defensive perimeters that are networked together for mutual support. All the principles of the defense are employed—obstacles, coordinated fires, R&S patrols, and a reserve force. (Ref: FM 7-10, chap 5, fig. 5-19).

1. Gain and Maintain Enemy Contact

The commander conducting a mobile defense focuses on discovering the exact location of the enemy and his strength to facilitate the effectiveness of the striking force. The security force (guard or cover) or the fixing force confirms the enemy's COA and main avenues of approach. The commander normally tasks other ISR assets to determine the location of enemy reserves and follow-on forces. Early detection of the enemy's decisive operation provides the commander with reaction time to adjust the fixing force's positions and shape the enemy penetration, which, in turn, provides the time necessary to commit the striking force. The striking force commander requires as close to real-time updates of the enemy situation as are possible to ensure that the striking force engages the enemy at the right location and time.

2. Disrupt the Enemy

In a mobile defense, the commander conducts shaping operations designed to shape the enemy's penetration into the MBA and disrupt the enemy's introduction of fresh forces into the fight. These shaping operations help establish the preconditions for committing the striking force by isolating the object of the striking force and destroying the enemy's key C2 nodes, logistics resupply units, and reserves. Whenever possible the commander sequences these shaping operations, to include offensive information operations, so that the impact of their effects coincides with the commitment of the striking force. To generate a tempo that temporarily paralyzes enemy C2, the intensity of these shaping operations may increase dramatically on the commitment of the striking force. The commander continues to conduct shaping operations once the striking force commits to prevent enemy forces from outside the objective area from interfering with executing the decisive counterattack.

3. Fix the Enemy

Fixing the enemy is the second half of shaping operations and results in establishing the conditions necessary for decisive operations by the striking force. Typically, the commander of the defending force allows the enemy force to penetrate into the defensive AO before the striking force attacks. The fixing force may employ a combination of area defense, delay, and strong point defensive techniques to shape the enemy penetration. The intent of the fixing force is not necessarily to defeat the enemy but to shape the penetration to facilitate a decisive counterattack by the striking force. The commander ensures that the missions and task organization of subordinate units within the fixing force are consistent with his concept for shaping the enemy penetration. Defensive positions within the fixing force may not be contiguous since the fixing force contains only the minimum-essential combat power to accomplish its mission.

4. Maneuver

The commander's situational understanding is critical in establishing the conditions that initiate the striking force's movement and in determining the general area that serves as a focus for the counterattack. Situational understanding includes identifying those points in time and space where the counterattack proves decisive. A force-oriented objective or an EA usually indicates the decisive point. The staff synchronizes the unit's activities in time and space to sufficiently mass the effects of the striking force at the right time and place.

The actions of the striking force are the echelon's decisive operation on its commitment. The commander's ISR systems focus entirely on tracking the enemy's advance. The striking force commander continuously receives intelligence and combat information updates that allow him to adjust his counterattack as necessary to defeat the targeted enemy. Once the enemy starts his attack, any forward-deployed elements of the striking force withdraw to AAs or attack positions and prepare for their commitment in counterattack.

The enemy attempts to discover the strength, composition, and location of the units that constitute the fixing force and the striking force. The commander uses security forces and information operations to deny the enemy this information and degrade the collection capabilities of enemy ISR assets. The commander routinely repositions to mislead the enemy and to protect his force. In addition, his plans and preparations incorporate defensive information operations. The commander normally tries to portray an area defense while hiding the existence and location of the striking force.

5. Follow Through

All defensive operations intend to create the opportunity to transition to the offense. In a mobile defense, that transitional opportunity generally results from the success of the striking force's attack. The commander exploits his success and attempts to establish conditions for a pursuit if his assessment of the striking force's attack is that there are opportunities for future offensive operations.

The striking force assembles in one or more areas depending on the width of the AO, the terrain, enemy capabilities, and the planned manner of employment. Before the enemy attack begins, the striking force may deploy all or some of its elements forward in the MBA to—

- Deceive the enemy regarding the purpose of the force
- Occupy dummy battle positions.
- Create a false impression of unit boundaries, which is important when operating with a mix of heavy and light forces or multinational forces.
- Conduct reconnaissance of routes between the striking force's AAs and potential EAs

On Point

At the small unit level, the mobile defensive perimeter is established much in the same way as a patrol base—using the triangle method. The difference between a mobile defense and a patrol base is that the mobile defensive perimeter will be used for a long period of time. While it will likely remain intentionally hidden from enemy detection, the development of advanced fighting positions and obstacles resembles more an area defense than the temporary a patrol base. However, unlike the area defense, the mobile defensive perimeter is formed in 360-degrees to fight from all angles.

1. **Obstacles**—preferably wire obstacles—are placed completely around the perimeter, in front of each of the lines of the triangle. Anti-personnel mines are carefully emplaced and marked on each squad's sector sketch.

2. **Communication**—preferably field phones—are established at each of the apexes and back to the CP in the center. The wire is appropriately hung and camouflaged in the trees or buried underground. Additionally, communication is established with adjacent defensive perimeters. These measures are essential in requesting or rendering aid in the event of an enemy offensive.

3. **Crew served weapons** such as mortars or recoilless rifles are located near the CP, while machine gun crews are located at each of the three apexes. Here the reserve force rests, eats and carries out other duties.

4. **OP/LP or R&S patrols** are sent out in irregular patterns to obtain intelligence on enemy movement in the immediate area. Additionally, these patrols are intended to thwart the enemy's effort to gain information regarding the size, activity, and location of the defensive perimeter.

5. Coordinated **secondary sectors of fire** are designated so that each of the fighting positions can also *fire in toward the center* of the defensive perimeter! This drastic measure will only take place if one of the defensive lines of the triangle is breeched and the CP is abandoned. A designated signal indicates that the CP has withdrawn, issuing the order to "commence fire" for the other two lengths of the defensive perimeter. The advantage of such a drastic measure is that it adds depth to the defense because the remaining two lines can fire upon the enemy attack force as they attempt to clear and reorganize on their objective. This measure allows the other two lines of the defensive triangle to take the enemy under fire from two directions.

6. In the event one line of the triangle is overrun, the **reserve force** also withdraws with the command team. This frees the reserve force to conduct counterattacks against the enemy's flank or rear—from directions the enemy is ill prepared to fight.

Defensive Operations

II. Area Defense

Ref: FM 3-90 Tactics, chap 8 and 9; FM 3-21.10 (FM 7-10) The Infantry Rifle Company, chap 5; and FM 3-21.8 (FM 7-8) Infantry Rifle Platoon and Squad, chap 8.

The area defense is a type of defensive operation that concentrates on denying enemy forces access to designated terrain for a specific time rather than destroying the enemy outright. An area defense capitalizes on the strength inherent in closely integrated defensive organization on the ground.

A commander should conduct an area defense when the following conditions occur:

- When directed to defend or retain specified terrain
- When he cannot resource a striking force
- The forces available have less mobility than the enemy
- The terrain affords natural lines of resistance and limits the enemy to a few well-defined avenues of approach, thereby restricting the enemy's maneuver
- There is enough time to organize the position
- Terrain constraints and lack of friendly air superiority limit the striking force's options in a mobile defense to a few probable employment options

The area defense retains dominance over a given geographical location. It does this by employing a fortified defensive line, a screening force, and a reserve force. Particular care is taken in coordinating and synchronizing fire control measures in order to repel any enemy attack.

The reserve force is perhaps the single most decisive element of the defense. The reserve may reinforce a failing line, occupy a secondary defensive position, or counterattack. (Photo by Jeong, Hae-jung).

I. Area Defense - Organization

The platoon will normally defend in accordance with command orders using one of these basic techniques *(see pp. 3-23 to 3-28)*:

- Defend an area
- Defend a battle position
- Defend a strongpoint
- Defend a perimeter
- Defend a reverse slope

The commander conducting an area defense combines static and mobile actions to accomplish his assigned mission. Static actions usually consist of fires from prepared positions. Mobile actions include using the fires provided by units in prepared positions as a base for counterattacks and repositioning units between defensive positions. The commander can use his reserve and uncommitted forces to conduct counterattacks and spoiling attacks to desynchronize the enemy or prevent him from massing.

A well-conducted area defense is anything but static. It's actually quite active in that it continues to advance its own fighting position while it patrols forward to gather intelligence on the enemy. The area defense has great depth and will track and channel the enemy from considerable distances beyond the defense.

Primary Positions

In addition to establishing the platoon's primary positions, the platoon leader and subordinate leaders normally plan for preparation and occupation of alternate, supplementary, and subsequent positions. This is done IAW the company order. The platoon and/or company reserve need to know the location of these positions. The following are tactical considerations for these positions.

Alternate Positions

The following characteristics and considerations apply to an alternate position:

- Covers the same avenue of approach or sector of fire as the primary position
- Located slightly to the front, flank, or rear of the primary position
- Positioned forward of the primary defensive positions during limited visibility operations
- Normally employed to supplement or support positions with weapons of limited range, such as Infantry squad positions. They are also used as an alternate position to fall back to if the original position is rendered ineffective or as a position for Soldiers to rest or perform maintenance

Supplementary Positions

The following characteristics and considerations apply to a supplementary position:

- Covers an avenue of approach or sector of fire different from those covered by the primary position
- Occupied based on specific enemy actions

Subsequent Positions

The following characteristics and considerations apply to a subsequent position:

- Covers the same avenue of approach and or sector of fire as the primary position
- Located in depth through the defensive area
- Occupied based on specific enemy actions or conducted as part of the higher headquarters' scheme of maneuver

As part of a larger element, the platoon conducts defensive operations in a sequence of integrated and overlapping phases:

- Reconnaissance, security operations, and enemy preparatory fires
- Occupation
- Approach of the enemy main attack
- Enemy assault
- Counterattack
- Consolidation and reorganization

The defense makes use of obstacles to expose and/or slow the enemy advance in our prepared engagement areas. Troops use of wire obstacles and mines in defilades that cannot be covered by fire. (Photo by Jeong, Hae-jung).

At the small unit level, the area defense typically employs three teams and rotates those teams through the three tasked responsibilities—manning the line, manning the reserve, and patrolling forward. Each team takes its turn in conducting the three tasked responsibilities.

The line includes 2-man fighting positions and crew served weapon positions. It also includes the observation post/listening post (OP/LP) that is positioned just forward of our defensive line. Finally, while the command post (CP) is located behind our line near the reserve force, it is also part of the line force. The command team, however, does not rotate to the other assigned tasks, but rotates a rest plan amongst the command team.

This organization permits:

- About 50 percent of the force on the defensive line at all times
- A reserve force of 25 percent to add depth to our position
- A patrolling force of 25 percent forward to monitor enemy activity

The reserve and screening forces make up half of the total force for the area defense. The line force utilizes the other half of our troops. The troops are typically rotated in 2-hour intervals. That's two hours on the line, two hours patrolling, two hours on the line again, and two hours in reserve (where troops can implement a sleep plan).

II. Planning & Preparation

Platoons establish defensive positions IAW the platoon leader and commander's plan. They mark engagement areas using marking techniques prescribed by unit SOP. The platoon physically marks obstacles, TRPs, targets, and trigger lines in the engagement area. During limited visibility, the platoon can use infrared light sources to mark TRPs for the rifle squads. When possible, platoons should mark TRPs with both a thermal and an infrared source so the rifle squads can use the TRP.

Fire control measures are critical for the success of the area defense. These control measures help the defense to engage the attacking enemy at greater distances, synchronize the final defensive fires of the line, and minimize the possibility of fratricide. (Photo by Jeong, Hae-jung).

A. Range Card

A range card is a sketch of a sector that a direct fire weapons system is assigned to cover. Range cards aid in planning and controlling fires. They also assist crews in acquiring targets during limited visibility, and orient replacement personnel, platoons, or squads that are moving into position. During good visibility, the gunner should have no problems maintaining orientation in his sector. During poor visibility, he may not be able to detect lateral limits. If the gunner becomes disoriented and cannot find or locate reference points or sector limit markers, he can use the range card to locate the limits. The gunner should make the range card so he becomes more familiar with the terrain in his sector. He should continually assess the sector and, if necessary, update his range card.

B. Sector Sketch

The sector sketch illustrates how each fighting position is interlocked and how the left and right flanks of the defensive line are secured. The flanks are tied in with adjacent friendly units or with naturally occurring or man-made obstacles to stop the enemy approach. Additionally, the sector sketch identifies engagement areas, final protective fires, locations of our wire and landmine obstacles, the OP/LP, the CP, and assigned alternate fighting positions.

C. Sectors of Fire

Each fighting position must be placed so that it has an interlocking sector of fire. This means that every fighting position has supporting fire to its immediate front from the fighting positions to its left and right. This also ensures that no matter which section of the line the enemy attacks, the enemy will be engaged by a minimum of three fighting positions simultaneously.

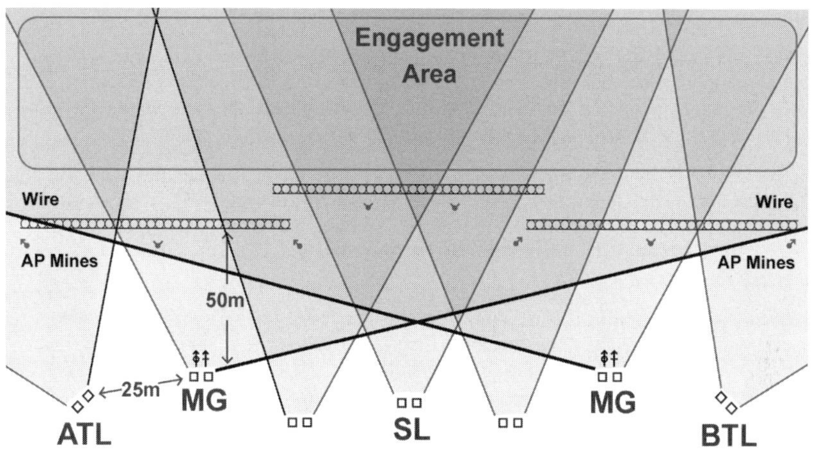

The effort is to use obstacles and terrain to slow or stop the enemy in the engagement area. Weapons are coordinated with interlocking fires to cover the obstacles and destroy the enemy. (Ref: FM 7-8, chap 2, section VI, fig. 2-42).

D. Engagement Areas

Engagement areas indicate the location the commander intends to defeat the enemy. The success of any engagement depends on how effectively the platoon leader can integrate the obstacle and indirect fire plans with his direct fire plan in the engagement area to achieve the platoon's purpose. At the platoon level, engagement area development remains a complex function that requires parallel planning and preparation if the platoon is to accomplish its assigned tasks. Despite this complexity, engagement area development resembles a drill. The platoon leader and his subordinate leaders use a standardized set of procedures. Beginning with an evaluation of the factors of METT-TC, the development process covers these steps:

- Identify likely enemy avenues of approach
- Identify the enemy scheme of maneuver
- Determine where to kill the enemy
- Plan and integrate obstacles
- Emplace weapons systems
- Plan and integrate indirect fires
- Conduct an engagement area rehearsal

III. Conducting the Area Defense - A Small Unit Perspective

The area defense forms the forward line of troops (FLOT). Typically, the FLOT defends against one direction in approximately a 120° frontal-fan that overlooks the designated engagement areas within the forward edge of battle area (FEBA). The defensive line interlocks with friendly units or impassable terrain to the left and right of the position.

1. Prior to moving up to the FEBA, the patrol leader (PL) moves the patrol into security halt at an appropriate distance. The PL conducts a leader's recon of the FEBA and selects the best location to establish a defensive line. The PL issues a five-point contingency plan with the assistant patrol leader (APL) before leaving on the recon.

2. The PL moves up to the FEBA with at least a security team. The security team is placed in over-watch at the designated release point. This allows the PL to move more freely about the terrain and determine how best to place the defensive line. The leader's recon may require moving the entire recon team across the FEBA to consider possible avenues for an enemy attack.

3. Once the PL confirms or adjusts the plan, the security team is given a five-point contingency plan and left at the release point to monitor the FEBA. The PL returns to the patrol to disseminate any changes to the original plan.

4. Upon returning, the rest of the patrol forms into the line team, the reserve force, and the screening force. The order of march depends on the OPORD, but typically the screening force is first in formation so that it may move forward for security as the line team establishes the FLOT. The PL leads the patrol and links up with the security team at the release point.

Mortars serve as combat force multipliers. They add significant punch against targets within the engagement area and break up the enemy's attack formations. Their placement and fires are carefully considered. (Dept. of Army photo by Gary L. Kieffer).

5. After linking up with the security team, the PL designates the location of fighting positions for crew-served weapons and indicates their primary direction of fire. The PL then designates a CP at an appropriate distance behind the line, typically towards the center of the entire line. The PL designates an OP/LP location just forward of any wire obstacles. The PL designates a 'fall back' position—an alternate position that can still cover the same engagement area within the FEBA.

6. The PL coordinates with units to his left and right to be certain he has adequately linked in with friendly defenses. Meanwhile the team leaders disseminate to every member of the patrol the location of the CP, the OP/LP, and the alternate position.

7. At this point, the line team leader assigns each member a fighting position and a sector of fire to fill in the lazy "W". He ensures that all positions interlock with at least the position to their left and right. Fighting positions are 2-man positions and are placed only close enough that they mutually support each other's immediate front. This distance varies according to different types of terrain. But at a minimum, the positions must be able to cover forward obstacles with fire. Landmine and concertina wire obstacles are placed out of hand grenade range (40 meters or more) and are in full view of friendly troops.

8. The reserve force locates behind the CP, out of sight from the line and out of the way of assigned indirect fire crews. The reserve force familiarizes with the defensive line and the alternative position.

Communication devices are established at key locations—the CP, flanks, and OP/LP. Field telephones are faster than runners, and more secure than radios. (Photo by Jeong, Hae-jung).

9. Communication is established between key positions. This typically involves the use of field phones and landlines wire. Field phones are more secure than radios and are not concerned with high traffic and frequency availability. Most field phones transmit a distance of several kilometers—ample distance for a defensive position.

10. At this point in the defense, the PL assumes the role of the forward unit commander. He collects the sector sketches from the team leaders to create his own master sketch and reports progress to higher command.

IV. Priorities of Work in the Defense

Occupation and preparation of the defense site is conducted concurrently with the TLP and the development of the engagement area (if required). The platoon occupies defensive positions IAW the company commander's plan and the results of the platoon's reconnaissance. To ensure an effective and efficient occupation, the reconnaissance element marks the friendly positions. These tentative positions are then entered on the operational graphics. Each squad moves in or is led in by a guide to its marker. Once in position, each squad leader checks his position location. As the platoon occupies its positions, the platoon leader manages the positioning of each squad to ensure they locate IAW the tentative plan. If the platoon leader notes discrepancies between actual positioning of the squads and his plan, he makes the corrections. Security is placed out in front of the platoon. The platoon leader must personally walk the fighting positions to ensure that everyone understands the plan and that the following are IAW the plan:

- Weapons orientation and general sectors of fire
- Crew served weapons positions
- Rifle squads' positions in relation to each other

Unit priorities of work are normally found in SOPs. However, the commander will dictate the priorities of work for the company based on the factors of METT-TC. Several actions may be accomplished at the same time. Leaders must constantly supervise the preparation of fighting positions, both for tactical usefulness and proper construction.

Leaders must ensure that Soldiers prepare for the defense quickly and efficiently. Work must be done in order of priority to accomplish the most in the least amount of time while maintaining security and the ability to respond to enemy action. Below are basic considerations for priorities of work.

- Emplace local security (all leaders)
- Position and assign sectors of fire for each squad (platoon leader)
- Position and assign sectors of fire for the CCMS and medium machine gun teams (platoon leader)
- Position and assign sectors of fire for M249 MG, grenadiers, and riflemen (squad leaders)
- Establish command post and wire communications
- Designate FPLs and FPFs
- Clear fields of fire and prepare range cards
- Prepare sector sketches (leaders)
- Dig fighting positions
- Establish communication and coordination with the company and adjacent units
- Coordinate with adjacent units
- Review sector sketches
- Emplace antitank and Claymore mines, then wire and other obstacles
- Mark or improve marking for TRPs and other fire control measures
- Improve primary fighting positions and add overhead cover
- Prepare supplementary and then alternate positions (same procedure as the primary position)
- Establish sleep and rest plans
- Distribute and stockpile ammunition, food, and water
- Dig trenches to connect positions
- Continue to improve positions—construct revetments, replace camouflage, and add to overhead cover

Defensive Operations

III. Retrograde

Ref: FM 3-90 Tactics, chap 11 and FM 3-21.10 (FM 7-10) The Infantry Rifle Company, pp. 5-43 to 5-50.

The retrograde is a type of defensive operation that involves organized movement away from the enemy. The enemy may force these operations or a commander may execute them voluntarily. In either case, the higher commander of the force executing the operation must approve the retrograde. Retrograde operations are transitional operations; they are not considered in isolation. The commander executes retrogrades to—

- Disengage from operations
- Gain time without fighting a decisive engagement
- Resist, exhaust, and damage an enemy in situations that do not favor a defense
- Draw the enemy into an unfavorable situation or extend his lines of communication (LOCs)
- Preserve the force or avoid combat under undesirable conditions, such as continuing an operation that no longer promises success
- Reposition forces to more favorable locations or conform to movements of other friendly troops
- Position the force for use elsewhere in other missions
- Simplify the logistic sustainment of the force by shortening LOCs
- Position the force where it can safely conduct reconstitution
- Adjust the defensive scheme, such as secure more favorable terrain

The retrograde is a maneuver that places time and space between friendly forces and an attacking enemy in order to reconsolidate and coordinate an effective defense or counterattack. (Photo by Jeong, Hae-jung).

Conducting the Retrograde - A Small Unit Perspective

There are three forms of retrograde—delay, withdraw, and retirement. In all cases of retrograde, combat leaders must be very careful to maintain unit integrity and discipline.

I. Delay

This operation allows the unit to trade space for time, avoiding decisive engagement and safeguarding its elements. A delay is a series of defensive and offensive actions over subsequent positions in depth. It is an economy of force operation that trades space for time. While the enemy gains access to the vacated area (space), friendly elements have time to conduct necessary operations, while retaining freedom of action and maneuver. This allows friendly forces to influence the action; they can prevent decisive engagement or postpone action to occur at a more critical time or place on the battlefield. For either type of delay mission, the flow of the operation can be summarized as "hit hard, then move." A successful delay has three key components.

- The ability to stop or slow the enemy's momentum while avoiding decisive engagement
- The ability to degrade the enemy's combat power
- The ability to maintain a mobility advantage

There are two types of delaying operations at the small unit level:

A. Delay Within a Sector

The company might be assigned a mission to delay within a sector AO. The higher commander normally provides guidance regarding intent and desired effect on the enemy, but he minimizes restrictions regarding terrain, time, and coordination with adjacent forces. This form of a delay is normally assigned when force preservation is the highest priority and there is considerable depth to the AO.

B. Delay Forward of a Specified Line for a Specified Time

The company might be assigned a mission to delay forward of a specific control measure for a specific period. This mission is assigned when the battalion must control the enemy's attack and retain specified terrain to achieve some purpose relative to another element, such as setting the conditions for a counterattack, for completion of defensive preparations, or for the movement of other forces or civilians. The focus of this delay mission is clearly on time, terrain, and enemy destruction. It carries a much higher risk for the battalion, with the likelihood of all or part of the unit becoming decisively engaged. The timing of the operation is controlled graphically by a series of phase lines with associated dates and times to define the desired delay-until period.

Delay missions usually conclude in one of three ways: a defense, a withdrawal, or a counterattack. Planning options should address all three possibilities.

The delaying force always takes advantage of terrain where friendly forces can direct effective and high volume fires at the enemy as they advance. The more challenging the terrain is to maneuver across, the more likely that terrain offers appropriate avenues of escape with which the delaying force can displace. Open terrain also has advantages, namely that the enemy can be engaged at farther distances.

When displacing from one defensive position, the next delaying position must be able to take the enemy under fire. This action not only protects the forward-most friendly delaying force as it displaces, but also serves to distract the enemy force with violent fires. The enemy will soon find that their initial objective (the forward friendly delaying force) has withdrawn, and they must now deal with yet another threat. In this manner, the delaying force is split into multiple teams in order to complicate the situation for the attacking enemy.

II. Withdrawal

A withdrawal is a planned operation in which a force in contact disengages from an The commander uses this operation to break enemy contact, especially when he needs to free the unit for a new mission. Withdrawal is a planned operation in which a force in contact disengages from an enemy force. Withdrawals may or may not be conducted under enemy pressure. The two types of withdrawals are assisted and unassisted.

A. Assisted

The assisting force occupies positions to the rear of the withdrawing unit and prepares to accept control of the situation. It can also assist the withdrawing unit with route reconnaissance, route maintenance, fire support, and sustainment. Both forces closely coordinate the withdrawal. After coordination, the withdrawing unit delays to a battle handover line, conducts a passage of lines, and moves to its final destination.

B. Unassisted

The withdrawing unit establishes routes and develops plans for the withdrawal and then establishes a security force as the rear guard while the main body withdraws. Sustainment and CS elements normally withdraw first followed by combat forces. To deceive the enemy as to the friendly movement, battalion may establish a detachment left in contact (DLIC) if withdrawing under enemy pressure. As the unit withdraws, the DLIC disengages from the enemy and follows the main body to its final destination.

Phases

Withdrawals are accomplished in three overlapping phases, as follows.

- **Preparation**. The commander dispatches quartering parties, issues WARNOs, and initiates planning. Nonessential vehicles are moved to the rear.
- **Disengagement**. Designated elements begin movement to the rear. They break contact and conduct tactical movement to a designated assembly area or position.
- **Security**. In this phase, a security force protects and helps the other elements as they disengage or move to their new positions. This is done either by a DLIC, which the unit itself designates in an unassisted withdrawal, or by a security force provided by the higher headquarters in an assisted withdrawal. As necessary, the security force assumes responsibility for the sector, deceives the enemy, and protects the movement of disengaged elements by providing overwatch and suppressive fires. In an assisted withdrawal, the security phase ends when the security force has assumed responsibility for the fight and the withdrawing element has completed its movement. In an unassisted withdrawal, this phase ends when the DLIC completes its disengagement and movement to the rear.

III. Retirement

A retirement is conducted to move a force that is not in contact away from the enemy. Typically, the company conducts a retirement as part of a larger force while another unit's security force protects their movement. A retiring unit organizes for combat but does not anticipate interference by enemy ground forces. Triggers for a retirement may include the requirement to reposition forces for future operations or to accommodate other changes to the current CONOP. The retiring unit should move sustainment elements and supplies first, and then should move toward an assembly area that supports preparations for the next mission. Where speed and security are the most important considerations, units conduct retirements as tactical road marches.

The retiring unit generally moves toward an assembly area, which should support the preparations for the unit's next mission. When determining the routes the retiring force takes to the assembly area, the commander considers the unit's capability to support defensive actions if combat occurs during the retirement.

On Point

Retrogrades conducted under pressure of enemy contact are extremely dangerous combat operations. This is partly due to the fact that the enemy is almost always much larger than friendly forces, and almost always is on the offensive. But retrogrades are also dangerous because they often require friendly forces to break up into multiple elements, synchronize the fight, and then coordinate a link-up under austere conditions.

Retrograde operations are conducted to improve a tactical situation or to prevent a worse situation from developing. Companies normally conduct retrogrades as part of a larger force but may conduct independent retrogrades (withdrawal) as required such as on a raid. Retrograde operations accomplish the following:

- Resist, exhaust, and defeat enemy forces
- Draw the enemy into an unfavorable situation
- Avoid contact in undesirable conditions
- Gain time
- Disengage a force from battle for use elsewhere in other missions
- Reposition forces, shorten lines of communication, or conform to movements of other friendly units
- Secure more favorable terrain

The delay and withdraw retrograde operations require an enormous amount of coordinated fires. In turn this means that communication between maneuvering and displacing friendly elements becomes paramount. Without it, fratricide becomes certain.

Reconstitution

Combat leaders must recognize that troops do not like to retrograde. Retrogrades can negatively affect the participating soldiers' attitude more than any other type of operation because they may view the retrograde as a defeat. A commander must not allow retrograde operations to reduce or destroy unit morale. Leaders must maintain unit aggressiveness. By planning and efficiently executing the retrograde and ensuring that soldiers understand the purpose and duration of the operation, the commander can counter any negative effects of the operation on unit morale. After completing a retrograde operation, the commander may reconstitute the force.

Note: FM 4-100.9 establishes the basic principles of reconstitution.

IV. Small Unit Defensive Techniques

Ref: FM 3-21.8 (FM 7-8) The Infantry Rifle Platoon and Squad, pp. 8-23 to 8-33.

Though the outcome of decisive combat derives from offensive actions, leaders often find it is necessary, even advisable, to defend. The general task and purpose of all defensive operations is to defeat an enemy attack and gain the initiative for offensive operations. It is important to set conditions of the defense so friendly forces can destroy or fix the enemy while preparing to seize the initiative and return to the offense. The platoon may conduct the defense to gain time, retain key terrain, facilitate other operations, preoccupy the enemy in one area while friendly forces attack him in another, or erode enemy forces. A well coordinated defense can also set the conditions for follow-on forces and follow-on operations.

Platoon Defensive Techniques

A platoon will normally defend IAW using one of these basic techniques:

Defend an Area

Defend a Battle Position

Defend a Strongpoint

Defend a Perimeter

Defend a Reverse Slope

Ref: FM 3-21.8 (FM 7-10), p. 8-23.

I. Defend An Area

Defending an area sector allows a unit to maintain flank contact and security while ensuring unity of effort in the scheme of maneuver. Areas afford depth in the platoon defense. They allow the platoon to achieve the platoon leader's desired end state while facilitating clearance of fires at the appropriate level of responsibility. The company commander normally orders a platoon to defend an area when flexibility is desired, when retention of specific terrain features is not necessary, or when the unit cannot concentrate fires because of any of the following factors:

- Extended frontages
- Intervening, or cross-compartmented, terrain features
- Multiple avenues of approach

The platoon is assigned an area defense mission to prevent a specific amount of enemy forces from penetrating the area of operations. To maintain the integrity of the area defense, the platoon must remain tied to adjacent units on the flanks. The platoon may be directed to conduct the defense in one of two ways.

He may specify a series of subsequent defensive positions within the area from where the platoon will defend to ensure that the fires of two platoons can be massed.

He may assign an area to the platoon. The platoon leader assumes responsibility for most tactical decisions and controlling maneuvers of his subordinate squads by assigning them a series of subsequent defensive positions. This is done IAW guidance from the company commander in the form of intent, specified tasks, and the concept of the operation. The company commander normally assigns an area to a platoon only when it is fighting in isolation.

II. Defend a Battle Position

The company commander assigns the defensive technique of defending a battle position to his platoons when he wants to mass the fires of two or more platoons in a company engagement area, or to position a platoon to execute a counterattack. A unit defends from a battle position to—

- Destroy an enemy force in the engagement area
- Block an enemy avenue of approach
- Control key or decisive terrain
- Fix the enemy force to allow another friendly unit to maneuver

The company commander designates engagement areas to allow each platoon to concentrate its fires or to place it in an advantageous position for the counterattack. Battle positions are developed in such a manner to provide the platoon the ability to place direct fire throughout the engagement area. The size of the platoon battle position can vary, but it should provide enough depth and maneuver space for subordinate squads to maneuver into alternate or supplementary positions and to counterattack. The battle position is a general position on the ground. The platoon leader places his squads on the most favorable terrain in the battle position based on the higher unit mission and commander's intent. The platoon then fights to retain the position unless ordered by the company commander to counterattack or displace. The following are basic methods of employing a platoon in a battle position:

1. Same battle position, same avenue of approach

Rifle squads are on the same battle position covering the same avenue of approach. The platoon can defend against mounted and dismounted attacks and move rapidly to another position.

All squads are in the same battle position when the terrain provides good observation, fields of fire, and cover and concealment.

Employing all the squads of the platoon on the same battle position covering the same avenue of approach is the most conservative use of the platoon. Its primary advantages are that it facilitates command and control functions because of the proximity of squad elements on the same approach and it provides increased security.

2. Same battle position, multiple avenues of approach

Rifle squads occupy the same battle position but cover multiple enemy avenues of approach.

3. Different battle positions, same avenue of approach

Rifle squads are on different battle positions covering the same avenue of approach. If positioned on separate battle positions, rifle squads must fight in relation to each other when covering the same avenues of approach. A weapons squad can provide supporting fires for the rifle squads from their primary, alternate, or supplementary positions. All squads are positioned to engage enemy forces on the same avenue of approach, but at different ranges.

4. Different battle positions, multiple avenues of approach

Squads may be employed on different battle positions and multiple avenues of approach to ensure that the squad battle positions cannot be fixed, isolated, or defeated by the enemy.

III. Defend a Strongpoint

Defending a strongpoint is not a common mission for an Infantry platoon. A strong-point defense requires extensive engineer support (expertise, materials, and equipment), and takes a long time to complete. When the platoon is directed to defend a strongpoint, it must retain the position until ordered to withdraw. The success of the strong-point defense depends on how well the position is tied into the existing terrain. This defense is most effective when it is employed in terrain that provides cover and concealment to both the strongpoint and its supporting obstacles. Mountainous, forested, or urban terrain can be adapted easily to a strongpoint defense. Strongpoints placed in more open terrain require the use of reverse slopes or of extensive camouflage and deception efforts. This defensive mission may require the platoon to—

- Hold key or decisive terrain critical to the company or battalion scheme of maneuver
- Provide a pivot to maneuver friendly forces
- Block an avenue of approach
- Canalize the enemy into one or more engagement areas

A. Characteristics of the Strongpoint Defense

The prime characteristic of an effective strongpoint is that it cannot be easily overrun or bypassed. It must be positioned and constructed so the enemy knows he can reduce it only at the risk of heavy casualties and significant loss of materiel. He must be forced to employ massive artillery concentrations and dismounted Infantry assaults in his attack, so the strongpoint must be tied in with existing obstacles and positioned to afford 360-degree security in observation and fighting positions.

B. Techniques and Considerations

A variety of techniques and considerations are involved in establishing and executing the strongpoint defense, including considerations for displacement and withdrawal from the strongpoint.

The platoon leader begins by determining the projected size of the strongpoint. He does this through assessing the number of weapons systems and individual Soldiers available to conduct the assigned mission, and by assessing the terrain on which the platoon will fight. He must remember that although a strongpoint is usually tied into a company defense and flanked by other defensive positions, it must afford 360-degree observation and firing capability.

The platoon leader must ensure that the layout and organization of the strongpoint maximizes the capabilities of the platoon's personnel strength and weapons systems without sacrificing the security of the position. Platoon options range from positioning CCMS outside the strongpoint (with the rifle squads occupying fighting positions inside it), to placing all assets within the position. From the standpoint of planning and terrain management, placing everything in the strongpoint is the most difficult option and potentially the most dangerous because of the danger of enemy encirclement.

Weapons Positions

In laying out the strongpoint, the platoon leader designates weapon positions that support the company defensive plan. Once these primary positions have been identified, he continues around the strongpoint, siting weapons on other possible enemy avenues of approach and engagement areas until he has the ability to orient effectively in any direction. The fighting positions facing the company engagement area may be along one line of defense or staggered in depth along multiple lines of defense (if the terrain supports positions in depth).

Reserve Force

The platoon's reserve may be comprised of a fire team, squad, or combination of the two. The platoon leader must know how to influence the strongpoint battle by employing his reserve. He has several employment options including reinforcing a portion of the defensive line or counterattacking along a portion of the perimeter against an identified enemy main effort.

Routes or Axes

The platoon leader should identify routes or axes that will allow the reserve to move to any area of the strongpoint. He should then designate positions the reserve can occupy once they arrive. These routes and positions should afford sufficient cover to allow the reserve to reach its destination without enemy interdiction. The platoon leader should give special consideration to developing a direct fire plan for each contingency involving the reserve. The key area of focus may be a plan for isolating an enemy penetration of the perimeter. Rehearsals cover actions the platoon takes if it has to fall back to a second defensive perimeter, including direct fire control measures necessary to accomplish the maneuver. FPF may be employed to assist in the displacement.

Obstacles

Engineers support strongpoint defense by reinforcing the existing obstacles. Priorities of work will vary depending on the factors of METT-TC, especially the enemy situation and time available. For example, the first 12 hours of the strongpoint construction effort may be critical for emplacing countermobility obstacles and survivability positions, and command and control bunkers. If the focus of engineer support is to make the terrain approaching the strongpoint impassable, the battalion engineer effort must be adjusted accordingly.

The battalion obstacle plan provides the foundation for the company strongpoint obstacle plan. The commander or platoon leader determines how he can integrate protective obstacles (designed to defeat dismounted enemy Infantry assaults) into the overall countermobility plan. If adequate time and resources are available, he should plan to reinforce existing obstacles using field-expedient demolitions.

Once the enemy has identified the strongpoint, he will mass all the fires he can spare against the position. To safeguard his rifle squads, the platoon leader must arrange for construction of overhead cover for individual fighting positions. If the strongpoint is in a more open position (such as on a reverse slope), he may also plan for interconnecting trenchlines. This will allow Soldiers to move between positions without exposure to direct and indirect fires. If time permits, these crawl trenches can be improved to fighting trenches or standard trenches.

IV. Defend a Perimeter

A perimeter defense allows the defending force to orient in all directions. In terms of weapons emplacement, direct and indirect fire integration, and reserve employment, a platoon leader conducting a perimeter defense should consider the same factors as for a strongpoint operation.

The perimeter defense allows only limited maneuver and limited depth. Therefore, the platoon may be called on to execute a perimeter defense under the following conditions:

- Holding critical terrain in areas where the defense is not tied in with adjacent units
- Defending in place when it has been bypassed and isolated by the enemy
- Conducting occupation of an independent assembly area or reserve position
- Preparing a strongpoint
- Concentrating fires in two or more adjacent avenues of approach
- Defending fire support or engineer assets
- Occupying a patrol base

The major advantage of the perimeter defense is the platoon's ability to defend against an enemy avenue of approach. A perimeter defense differs from other defenses in that—

- The trace of the platoon is circular or triangular rather than linear
- Unoccupied areas between squads are smaller
- Flanks of squads are bent back to conform to the plan
- The bulk of combat power is on the perimeter
- The reserve is centrally located

V. Defend a Reverse Slope

The platoon leader's analysis of the factors of METT-TC often leads him to employ his forces on the reverse slope. If the rifle squads are on a mounted avenue of approach, they must be concealed from enemy direct fire systems. This means rifle squads should be protected from enemy tanks and observed artillery fire.

The majority of a rifle squad's weapons are not effective beyond 600 meters. To reduce or prevent destruction from enemy direct and indirect fires beyond that range, a reverse-slope defense should be considered. Using this defense conflicts to some extent with the need for maximum observation forward to adjust fire on the enemy, and the need for long-range fields of fire for CCMS. In some cases it may be necessary for these weapons systems to be deployed forward while the rifle squads remain on the reverse slope. CCMS gunners withdraw from their forward positions as the battle closes. Their new positions should be selected to take advantage of their long-range fires, and to get enfilade shots from the depth and flanks of the reverse slope.

The nature of the enemy may change at night, and the rifle squads may occupy the forward slope or crest to deny it to the enemy. In these circumstances, it is feasible for a rifle squad to have an alternate night position forward. The area forward of the topographical crest must be controlled by friendly forces through aggressive patrolling and both active and passive reconnaissance measures. The platoon should use all of its night vision devices to deny the enemy undetected entry into the platoon's defensive area. CCMS are key parts of the platoon's surveillance plan and should be positioned to take advantage of their thermal sights. The enemy must not be allowed to take advantage of reduced visibility to advance to a position of advantage without being taken under fire.

The company commander normally makes the decision to position platoons on a reverse slope. He does so when—

- He wishes to surprise or deceive the enemy about the location of his defensive position
- Forward slope positions might be made weak by direct enemy fire
- Occupation of the forward slope is not essential to achieve depth and mutual support
- Fields of fire on the reverse slope are better or at least sufficient to accomplish the mission
- Forward slope positions are likely to be the target of concentrated enemy artillery fires

Advantages

The following are advantages of a reverse-slope defense:

- Enemy observation of the position, including the use of surveillance devices and radar, is masked
- Enemy cannot engage the position with direct fire without coming within range of the defender's weapons
- Enemy indirect fire will be less effective because of the lack of observation
- Enemy may be deceived about the strength and location of positions
- Defenders have more freedom of movement out of sight of the enemy

Disadvantages

Disadvantages of a reverse-slope defense include the following:

- Observation to the front is limited
- Fields of fire to the front are reduced
- Enemy can begin his assault from a closer range

Obstacles

Obstacles are necessary in a reverse-slope defense. Because the enemy will be engaged at close range, obstacles should prevent the enemy from closing too quickly and overrunning the positions. Obstacles on the reverse slope can halt, disrupt, and expose enemy vehicles to flank antitank fires. Obstacles should also block the enemy to facilitate the platoon's disengagement.

Chap 4

I. Stability Operations

Ref: FM 3-0 Operations (2008), chap. 3 and FM 3-21.10 (FM 7-10) The Infantry Rifle Company, chap. 6. When revised, FM 3-07 will discuss stability operations in detail.

Stability operations encompass various military missions, tasks, and activities conducted outside the United States in coordination with other instruments of national power to maintain or reestablish a safe and secure environment, provide essential governmental services, emergency infrastructure reconstruction, and humanitarian relief (JP 3-0). Stability operations can be conducted in support of a host-nation or interim government or as part of an occupation when no government exists.

Stability operations involve both coercive and constructive military actions. They help to establish a safe and secure environment and facilitate reconciliation among local or regional adversaries. Stability operations can also help establish political, legal, social, and economic institutions and support the transition to legitimate local governance. It is essential that stability operations maintain the initiative by pursing objectives that resolve the causes of instability. Stability operations cannot succeed if they only react to enemy initiatives. (Dept. of Army photo by Sgt. Robert Yde).

Coordination, integration, and synchronization between host-nation elements, other government agencies, and Army forces are enhanced by transparency and credibility. The degree to which the host nation cooperates is fundamental. Commanders publicize their mandate and intentions. Within the limits of operations security, they make the populace aware of the techniques used to provide security and control. Actions on the ground reinforced by a clear and consistent message produce transparency. This transparency reinforces credibility. Credibility reflects the populace's assessment of whether the force can accomplish the mission. Army forces require the structure, resources, and rules of engagement appropriate to accomplishing the mission and discharging their duties swiftly and firmly. They must leave no doubt as to their capability and intentions.

Stability Operations (Tasks & Purposes)

Ref: FM 3-0 Operations (2008), pp. 3-13 to 3-15. When revised, FM 3-07 will discuss stability operations in detail.

I. Primary Stability Tasks

The combination of tasks conducted during stability operations depends on the situation. In some operations, the host nation can meet most or all of the population's requirements. In those cases, Army forces work with and through host-nation authorities. Commanders use civil affairs operations to mitigate the impact of the military presence on the populace and vice versa. Conversely, Army forces operating in a failed state may be required to support the well-being of the local populace. That situation requires Army forces to work with civilian agencies to restore basic capabilities. Again, civil affairs operations are important in establishing the trust between Army forces and civilian organizations required for effective, working relationships.

Stability operations may be necessary to develop host-nation capacities for security and the capacity to employ security forces, a viable market economy, the rule of law, and an effective government. Army forces with the host nation develop these capacities. The goal is a stable civil situation that is sustainable by host-nation assets and without Army forces. Security, the health of the local economy, and the capacity for self-government are related. Without security, the local economy falters. A functioning economy provides employment and reduces the dependence of the population on the military for necessities. Security and economic stability are precursors to an effective and stable government.

Army forces perform five primary stability tasks:

1. Civil Security

Civil security involves protecting the populace from external and internal threats. Ideally, Army forces defeat external threats posed by enemy forces that can attack population centers. Simultaneously, they assist host-nation police and security elements as the host nation maintains internal security against terrorists, criminals, and small, hostile groups. In some situations, there is no adequate host-nation capability for civil security and Army forces provide most of it while simultaneously developing host nation capabilities. Civil security is required for the other stability tasks to be effective. As soon the host nation security apparatus can safely conduct this task, Army forces turn security over to them.

2. Civil Control

Civil control regulates selected behavior and activities of individuals and groups. This control reduces risk to individuals or groups and promotes security. Civil control channels the populace's activities to allow provision of security and essential services while coexisting with a military force conducting operations. A curfew is an example of civil control.

3. Restore Essential Services

Army forces establish or restore the most basic services and protect them until a civil authority or the host nation can provide them. Normally, Army forces support civilian and host-nation agencies. When the host-nation cannot perform its role, Army forces may provide the basics directly. Essential services include the following:

- Emergency medical care and rescue
- Preventing epidemic disease
- Providing food and water
- Providing emergency shelter
- Providing basic sanitation (sewage and garbage disposal)

Stability & COIN Opns

4. Support to Governance

Stability operations establish conditions that enable actions by civilian and host-nation agencies to succeed. By establishing security and control, stability operations provide a foundation for transitioning authority to civilian agencies and eventually to the host nation. Once this transition is complete, commanders focus on transferring control to a legitimate civil authority according to the desired end state. Support to governance includes the following:

- Developing and supporting host-nation control of public activities, the rule of law, and civil administration
- Maintaining security, control, and essential services through host-nation agencies. This includes training and equipping host-nation security forces and police.
- Supporting host nation efforts to normalize the succession of power (elections and appointment of officials)

5. Support to Economic and Infrastructure Development

Support to economic and infrastructure development helps a host nation develop capability and capacity in these areas. It may involve direct and indirect military assistance to local, regional, and national entities.

II. Purposes of Stability Operations

Although Army forces focus on achieving the military end state, they ultimately need to create conditions where the other instruments of national power are predominant. Stability operations focus on creating those conditions. The following paragraphs discuss the purposes of stability operations.

1. Provide a Secure Environment

A key stability task is providing a safe, secure environment. This involves isolating enemy fighters from the local populace and protecting the population. By providing security and helping host-nation authorities control civilians, Army forces begin the process of separating the enemy from the general population. Information engagement complements physical isolation by persuading the populace to support an acceptable, legitimate host-nation government. This isolates the enemy politically and economically.

2. Secure Land Areas

Effective stability operations help to secure land areas in conjunction with host-nation capabilities. Areas of population unrest often divert forces that may be urgently needed elsewhere. In contrast, stable areas may support bases and infrastructure for friendly forces, allowing commitment of forces somewhere else.

3. Meet the Critical Needs of the Populace

Often, stability operations are required to meet the critical needs of the populace. Army forces can provide essential services until the host-nation government or other agencies can do so.

4. Gain Support for Host-Nation Government

Successful stability operations ultimately depend on the legitimacy of the host nation government—its acceptance by the populace as the governing body. All stability operations are conducted with that aim.

5. Shape Environment for Interagency/Host-Nation Success

Stability operations shape the environment for interagency and host-nation success. They do this by providing the security and control necessary for host-nation and interagency elements to function, and supporting them in other key functions.

III. Types of Stability Operations

Ref: FM 3-21.10 (FM 7-10) The Infantry Company, pp. 6-6 to 6-8.

Stability operations typically fall into ten broad types that are neither discrete nor mutually exclusive. For example, a force engaged in a peace operation may also find itself conducting arms control or a show of force to set the conditions for achieving an end state. Stability operations normally occur in conjunction with either offensive, defensive, or support operations.

Peace Operations

Peace operations encompass three general areas: operations in support of diplomatic efforts, peacekeeping, and peace enforcement.

- **Peacekeeping Operations**. A peacekeeping force monitors and facilitates the implementation of cease-fires, truce negotiations, and other such agreements. In doing so, it must assure all sides in the dispute that the other involved parties are not taking advantage of settlement terms to their own benefit. The Infantry company most often observes, monitors, or supervises and aids the parties involved in the dispute. The peacekeeping force must remain entirely neutral. If it loses a reputation for impartiality, its usefulness within the peacekeeping mission is compromised.
- **Peace Enforcement Operations**. What characteristics distinguish peace enforcement activities from wartime operations and from other stability operations? The difference is that PEO compel compliance with international resolutions or sanctions, and they restore or maintain peace and order. They might entail combat, armed intervention, or the physical threat of armed intervention. Under the provisions of an international agreement, the battalion and its subordinate companies might have to use coercive military power to compel compliance with the applicable international sanctions or resolutions.

Foreign Internal Defense

Foreign internal defense means the participation, by the civilian and military agencies of a government, in any action programs taken by another government to free and protect its society from subversion, lawlessness, and insurgency (JP 1-02). The objective is to promote stability by helping the host nation establish and maintain institutions and facilities that can fill its people's needs. Army forces in foreign internal defense normally advise and assist host-nation forces conducting operations to increase their capabilities.

Security Assistance

Army forces assist in providing HN security by training, advising, and assisting allied and friendly armed forces. Security assistance includes the participation of Army forces in any program through which the US provides defense articles, military training, and other defense-related services to support national policies and objectives. Security assistance can take the form of grants, loans, credit, or cash sales (JP 3-07).

Humanitarian Assistance

Humanitarian and civic assistance (HCA) programs help the HN populace in conjunction with military operations and exercises. Foreign humanitarian assistance (FHA) operations are also limited in scope and duration. They focus only on providing prompt aid to resolve an immediate crisis. In contrast to foreign humanitarian (only) assistance operations, HCA is planned, and provides only--

- Medical, dental, and veterinary care in rural areas of a country.
- Construction of rudimentary surface transportation systems.

- Well-drilling and construction of basic sanitation facilities.
- Basic construction and repair of public facilities.

US forces conduct FHA operations outside the borders of the US or its territories. The purpose is to relieve or reduce the results of natural or manmade disasters or other endemic conditions that pose a serious threat to life (disease, starvation) or property. The US military typically supplements the HN authorities along with other governmental agencies, nongovernmental organizations, private voluntary organizations, and unaffiliated individuals. Most FHA operations resemble civil support operations. The distinction between the two is that, inside the US and its territories, The Posse Comitatus Act (PCA) prevents the use of the military from becoming a civil police force, or guardia civil. The PCA does not apply to US forces overseas. In vague or hostile situations, FHA activities are handled as a subset of a larger stability, offensive, or defensive operation.

Support to Insurgency

This type of support includes assistance provided by US forces to help a friendly nation or group that is trying to combat insurgent elements or to stage an insurgency itself. This type of stability activity is normally conducted by special operating forces.

Support to Counterdrug Operations

US military forces might be tasked for a variety of counter-drug activities, which are always conducted in conjunction with another government agency. These activities include destroying illicit drugs and disrupting or interdicting drug manufacturing, growing, processing, and smuggling operations. Counter-drug support may take the form of advisory personnel, mobile training teams, offshore training activities, and assistance in logistics, communications, and intelligence.

Combatting of Terrorism

In all types of stability operations, antiterrorism and counterterrorism activities are a continuous requirement in protecting installations, units, and individuals from the threat of terrorism. Antiterrorism focuses on defensive measures used to reduce the vulnerability of individuals and property to terrorist attacks. Counterterrorism encompasses a full range of offensive measures to prevent, deter, and respond to terrorism. (For more information on these activities, see JP 3-07.2.)

Noncombatant Evacuation (NEO)

A noncombatant evacuation operation (NEO) is conducted primarily to evacuate US citizens whose lives are in danger. It can also evacuate natives and third-country nationals. An NEO involves swift insertions and temporary occupation of an objective followed by a planned withdrawal. The company uses only the force needed to protect evacuees and defend itself.

Arms Control

To prevent a conflict from escalating, an Infantry company can conduct arms-control inspections and disarm belligerents. Collecting, storing, and destroying conventional munitions and weapons systems can deter belligerents from resuming hostilities.

Show of Force

Deploying forces abroad lends credibility to a nation's promises and commitments. Credible show-of-force operations bolster and reassure allies. Infantry companies participating in a show-of-force mission focus all preparations on the assumption that combat is probable. A show of force can quickly and unexpectedly escalate into conflict, although the intent is to avoid this.

Civil affairs operations are activities that enhance the relationship between military forces and civil authorities in areas where military forces are present. They involve application of civil affairs functional specialty skills, in areas that are normally the responsibility of civil government. These operations involve establishing, maintaining, influencing, or exploiting relations between military forces and all levels of host-nation government agencies. These activities are fundamental to executing stability tasks. Civil affairs personnel, other Army forces, other government agencies, or a combination of all three perform these tasks.

Note: JPs 3-57 and 3-57.1 and FMs 3-05.40 and 3-05.401 contain civil affairs doctrine.

IV. Use of Force in Stability Operations

The presence of armed Soldiers operating among the local populace causes tension. Discipline and strict adherence to the rules of engagement are essential but not sufficient to reassure the population. In addressing the populace's apprehension, commanders balance protecting the force, defeating enemy forces, and taking constructive action throughout the area of operations. They also stress cultural awareness in training and preparing for operations. Cultural awareness makes Soldiers more effective when operating in a foreign population and allows them to leverage local culture to enhance the effectiveness of their operations.

While speed, surprise, and shock are vital considerations in lethal actions; perseverance, legitimacy, and restraint are vital considerations in stability and civil support operations.

When using force, precision is as important in stability missions as applying massed, overwhelming force is in offensive and defensive operations. Commanders at every level emphasize that in stability operations violence not precisely applied is counterproductive. (Dept. of Army photo).

In peace operations, commanders emphasize impartiality in the use of force in addition to credibility and transparency. Impartiality is not neutrality. Impartiality does not imply that Army forces treat all sides equally. Force is used against threats in accordance with the rules of engagement. Fair treatment of the local populace improves the prospects for lasting peace, stability, and security.

V. Small Unit Stability Tasks

Stability operations are complex and demanding. A small unit in a stability operation -- an Infantry company in this example -- must master skills from negotiating to establishing OPs and checkpoints to escorting a convoy. The tasks and techniques in this section come from FM 3-21.10 (FM 7-10) The Infantry Rifle Company, and include lessons learned and should help the Infantry company commander implement these and other tasks.

A. Establish and Occupy a Lodgement Area or a Forward Operating Base (FOB)

A lodgment area (base camp) or forward operating base (FOB) is a well-prepared position used as a base of operations and staging area for the occupying unit. Like an assembly area or defensive strongpoint, the lodgment area also provides some force protection because it requires all-round security. However, several other factors distinguish a lodgment area from a less permanent position.

Due to the probability of long-term occupation, the lodgment requires a lot of preparation and logistical support. It needs shelters and facilities that can support the force and its attachments the whole time. Also, the area must be positioned and developed so the unit can effectively conduct its primary missions, such as PEO and counterterrorism, throughout its area of responsibility.

In establishing a lodgment, the Infantry company can either use existing facilities or request construction of new ones. Existing structures are immediately available, and require little or no construction support from engineers and members of the company. However, they might fall short of meeting the company's operational needs, and their proximity to other structures can pose security problems.

The company can establish and occupy a lodgment area as part of a battalion or, given enough support from battalion, as a separate element.

B. Monitor Compliance with an Agreement

Compliance monitoring involves observing belligerents and working with them to ensure they meet the conditions of one or more applicable agreements. Examples of the process include overseeing the separation of opposing combat elements, the withdrawal of heavy weapons from a sector, or the clearance of a minefield. Planning for compliance monitoring should cover, but is not limited to, the following considerations.

- Liaison teams, with suitable communications and transportation assets, are assigned to the headquarters of the opposing sides. Liaison personnel maintain communications with the leaders of their assigned element and talk directly to each other and to their mutual commander (the Infantry company or battalion commander).
- The commander positions himself at the point where violations are most likely to occur
- He positions platoons and squads where they can observe the opposing parties, instructing them to assess compliance and report any violations
- As directed, the commander keeps higher headquarters informed of all developments, including his assessment of compliance and noncompliance

C. Negotiations (Small Unit)

Ref: FM 3-21.10 (FM 7-10) The Infantry Rifle Company, pp. 6-11 to 6-12.

Infantry company leaders might have to conduct negotiations. The two main types of negotiations follow.

A. Situational Negotiations

Situational negotiations allow immediate discussion and resolution of an issue or problem. For example, members of an advance guard might have to negotiate the passage of a convoy through a checkpoint.

At the company level, situational negotiations are far more common than preplanned ones. In stability operations, the commander, his subordinate leaders, and other Soldiers conduct some form of negotiations almost daily. To do this, they must thoroughly understand the ROE and ROI.

Members of the company apply this working knowledge to the process of discussing, and whenever possible, resolving issues and problems between opposing parties, which might include the company itself. The negotiator must know when he has exhausted his options under the ROE and ROI, and turn over the discussion to a higher authority. Negotiations move up through the levels of authority until the issue is resolved.

To prepare, leaders rehearse the ROE and ROI. One good way is to rehearse how to apply ROE and ROI in an example stability situation such as operating a checkpoint.

B. Preplanned Negotiations

Preplanned negotiations allow discussion and resolution of an upcoming, specific issue or problem. For example, the Infantry company commander conducts a work coordination meeting between leaders of the belligerents to determine mine-clearing responsibilities. As with situational negotiations, preplanned negotiations require leaders to know and understand the ROE and ROI. However, before a preplanned negotiation, leaders must also know every aspect of the dispute or issue. The negotiator's goal is to reach an agreement that is acceptable to both sides, and that reduces antagonism and the threat of renewed hostilities.

Negotiation Steps

1. Identify Purpose of Negotiations

Before contacting leaders of the belligerent parties to initiate the negotiation process, the commander must familiarize himself with both the situation and the area in which his unit will operate. This includes identifying and evaluating AAs that connect the opposing forces. Results of the negotiation process, which might be lengthy and complicated, must be based on national or international agreements or accords. Negotiation topics include--

- When the sides will withdraw
- Positions to which they will withdraw (these should preclude observation and direct fire by the opposing parties)
- What forces or elements will move during each phase of the operation
- Pre-positioning of peace forces that can intervene in case of renewed hostilities
- Control of heavy weapons
- Mine clearance
- Formal protest procedures for the belligerent parties

2. Establish Proper Context

The commander must earn the trust and confidence of each opposing party. This includes establishing an atmosphere (and a physical setting) that participants will judge to be both fair and safe. The commander must--

- Always conduct joint negotiations on matters that affect both parties
- When serving as a mediator, remain neutral at all times
- Learn as much as possible about the belligerents, the details of the dispute or issue under negotiation, and other factors such as the geography of the area and specific limitations or restrictions, including the ROE and ROI
- Gain and keep the trust of the opposing parties by being firm, fair, and polite
- Use tact, and remain patient and objective
- Follow applicable local and national laws and international agreements exactly

3. Prepare

Thorough, exacting preparation is another important factor in ensuring the success of the negotiation process. Company personnel--

- Negotiate sequentially, from subordinate level to senior level
- Select and prepare a meeting place that is acceptable to all parties
- Arrange for interpreters and adequate communications facilities, as necessary
- Ensure that all opposing parties, as well as the negotiating company, use a common map (edition and scale)
- Coordinate all necessary movement
- Establish local security
- Keep higher headquarters informed throughout preparation and during the negotiations
- Arrange to record the negotiations (use audio or video recording equipment, if available)

4. Negotiate

Negotiators must always strive to maintain control of the session. They must be firm, yet even-handed, in leading the discussion. At the same time, they must be flexible, with a willingness to accept recommendations from the opposing parties and from their own assistants and advisors, who--

- Exchange greetings
- Introduce all participants by name, including negotiators and any advisors
- Consider the use of small talk at the beginning of the session to put the participants at ease
- Allow each side to state its case without interruptions and prejudgments
- Record issues presented by both sides
- If one side makes a statement that is incorrect, be prepared to produce evidence or proof to establish the facts
- If the negotiating team or peacekeeping force has a preferred solution, present it and encourage both sides to accept it
- Close the meeting by explaining to both sides what they have agreed to and what actions they must take. If necessary, be prepared to present this information in writing for their signatures.
- Do not negotiate or make deals in the presence of the media
- Maintain the highest standards of conduct at all times

D. Establishing Observation Posts and Checkpoints

Ref: FM 3-21.10 (FM 7-10) The Infantry Company, pp. 6-13 to 6-19

Observation Posts

Constructing and operating OPs is a high-frequency task for Infantry companies and subordinate elements whenever they must establish area security. Each OP is established for a specified time and purpose. Some OPs are overt (clearly visible) and deliberately constructed. Others are covert and designed to observe an area or target without the knowledge of the local population. Each type of OP must be integrated into supporting direct and indirect fire plans and into the overall observation plan.

An OP is similar in construction to a bunker and it is supported by fighting positions, barriers, and patrols. Covert operations may include sniper or designated marksmen positions over-watching TAIs. The Infantry company or a subordinate element might be directed to establish a checkpoint to achieve one or more of the following purposes:

- Obtain intelligence
- Identify enemy combatants or seize illegal weapons
- Disrupt enemy movement or actions
- Deter illegal movement
- Create an instant or temporary roadblock
- Control movement into the area of operations or onto a specific route
- Demonstrate the presence of US or peace forces
- Prevent smuggling of contraband
- Enforce the terms of peace agreements
- Serve as an OP, patrol base, or both

Checkpoints

One of the main missions conducted during OIF was the vehicle or traffic checkpoint. Units considered these standard steady-state operations and through repetitive execution could perform them virtually like battle drills; clearly beneficial given the often constrained planning and preparation time at company and platoon level. Checkpoint layout, construction, and operating should reflect METT-TC factors, including the amount of time available for emplacing it.

The Infantry company or a subordinate element might be directed to establish a checkpoint to achieve one or more of the following purposes.

- Obtain intelligence
- Identify enemy combatants or seize illegal weapons
- Disrupt enemy movement or actions
- Deter illegal movement
- Create an instant or temporary roadblock
- Control movement into the area of operations or onto a specific route
- Demonstrate the presence of US or peace forces
- Prevent smuggling of contraband
- Enforce the terms of peace agreements
- Serve as an OP, patrol base, or both

Some common types of checkpoints are discussed below.

1. Deliberate Checkpoints

These might be permanent or semi-permanent. They are typically constructed and employed to protect an operating base or well-established MSRs. Deliberate checkpoints are often used to secure the entrances to lodgment areas or base camps. They may also be used at critical intersections or along heavily traveled routes to monitor traffic and pedestrian flow. Deliberate checkpoints can be constructed so that all vehicles and personnel are checked or where only random searches occur (ROE and METT-TC dependent).

- They are useful deterrents and send a strong law and order or US presence message
- Deliberate checkpoints and their locations are known to terrorists and insurgents. Commanders must weigh the costs to the benefits of operating deliberate checkpoints.
- Commanders must consider that deliberate checkpoints may quickly become enemy targets and US Soldiers operating deliberate checkpoints are highly visible and viable targets for enemy attack

2. Hasty Checkpoints

Such checkpoints are planned and used only for a short, set period. Hasty checkpoints are normally employed during the conduct of a vehicle or foot patrol. The hasty checkpoint is similar in nature to the deliberate checkpoint but only uses transportable materials.

- The hasty checkpoint is mobile and can be quickly positioned
- While more adaptable, the hasty checkpoint does not send the constant visual reminder of US presence to the local population that the deliberate checkpoint does
- Because they can be quickly established and removed, hasty checkpoints are likely to be more effective in disrupting enemy actions. They are also less likely to be deliberately targeted by enemy forces.

3. Snap Checkpoints

Such checkpoints are conducted when specific intelligence indicates that a checkpoint hinders the enemy's freedom of movement at a specific time and place. Snap checkpoints are very similar to hasty checkpoints. The major difference is that hasty checkpoints are often random actions conducted as part of a patrol, whereas snap checkpoints are deliberate and based on either enemy analysis or quickly developed actionable intelligence. Snap checkpoints are normally conducted immediately and often with little to no deliberate planning.

4. Vehicular Traffic Stop Checkpoints

Such checkpoints are conducted by multiple sections of vehicle-equipped Infantrymen. This type of operation involves two or three sections of vehicles that patrol an area looking for a specific type of vehicle or specific personnel such as a particular model and color of car. Once this vehicle or person is identified, the vehicle or person is forced to stop and then searched. Normally the vehicle sections move single file with enough distance between the first two sections to allow civilian traffic to move between the sections (50 to 500 meters based on visibility, road conditions, and METT-TC.) If either section spots a targeted vehicle or person in a static or parked position, then the patrol cordons and searches the area, again based on METT-TC, or requests additional assistance. The patrol should move slightly slower than normal civilian traffic so that civilian traffic will pass the rear section. As civilian traffic passes the rear section, the patrol radio to the lead section if it spots a targeted vehicle. Once a targeted vehicle has moved between the two sections, both sections move abreast to effectively block the road and close the distance between themselves. They block in the targeted vehicle. The sections slowly force the targeted vehicle to pull to the side of the road and stop, and then they use normal vehicle search techniques. A third section can be employed as a reserve, as additional security, or simply as additional Soldiers.

E. Search

Searches are an important aspect of populace and resource control. The need to conduct search operations or to employ search procedures is a continuous requirement. A search can orient on people, materiel, buildings, or terrain. A search usually involves both civil police and Soldiers but may involve only Soldiers. Misuse of search authority can adversely affect the outcome of operations. Soldiers must conduct and lawfully record the seizure of contraband, evidence, intelligence material, supplies, or other minor items for their seizure to be of future legal value. Proper use of authority during searches gains the respect and support of the people.

F. Patrol

Note: See chap. 8 for information on patrols and patrolling.

Patrolling is also a high-frequency task during stability operations. The primary advantage of the dismounted patrol is that they provide a strong presence and enable regular interface with the local population. This procedure greatly helps in gathering vital information as well as in developing the base of knowledge of the unit's AO. Planning and execution of an area security patrol and presence patrol are similar to procedures for other tactical patrols except that the patrol usually occurs in urban areas and patrol leaders must consider political implications and ROE.

- **Presence Patrols**. US forces are deployed increasingly in combat operations in urban areas and in support of stability operations missions all around the world. The Infantry company and platoons conduct a presence patrol much the same as a combat patrol, and the planning considerations are similar. The main difference is that the patrol wants to both show force and lend confidence and stability to the local population of the host nation (HN).
- **Vehicle-Supported Patrols**. Infantry units might find themselves conducting frequent vehicle-assisted or vehicle-mounted patrols. The same considerations that apply to any dismounted patrol apply to vehicle-mounted patrols.

G. Escort a Convoy

This mission requires the Infantry company to provide a convoy with security and close-in protection from direct fire while on the move. Infantry forces must be augmented with additional transportation assets to carry out this mission.

H. Open and Secure Routes

This task is a mobility operation normally conducted by the engineers. The Infantry company might be tasked to assist in route clearance and to provide overwatch support. Route clearance may achieve one of several tactical purposes.

I. Conduct Reserve Operations

Reserve operations in the stability environment are similar to those in other tactical operations. They too allow the Infantry company commander to plan for a variety of contingencies based on the higher unit's mission.

J. Control Crowds

Large crowds or unlawful civil gatherings or disturbances pose a serious threat to US troops. Commanders must consider the effects of mob mentality, the willingness of enemies to manipulate media, and the ease with which a small, isolated group of Soldiers can be overwhelmed by masses of people. The police forces of each state and territory are normally responsible for controlling crowds involved in mass demonstrations, industrial, political and social disturbances, riots, and other civil disturbances. The prime role of US troops in the control of unlawful assemblies or demonstrations is to support and protect the police, innocent bystanders, and property.

II. Counterinsurgency (COIN) Operations

Ref: FM 3-24 Counterinsurgency, chap. 1 and chap. 5.

Insurgency and counterinsurgency (COIN) are complex subsets of warfare. Globalization, technological advancement, urbanization, and extremists who conduct suicide attacks for their cause have certainly influenced contemporary conflict; however, warfare in the 21st century retains many of the characteristics it has exhibited since ancient times. Warfare remains a violent clash of interests between organized groups characterized by the use of force. Achieving victory still depends on a group's ability to mobilize support for its political interests (often religiously or ethnically based) and to generate enough violence to achieve political consequences. Means to achieve these goals are not limited to conventional forces employed by nation-states.

Offensive and defensive operations are integral to COIN. COIN differs from peacekeeping operations in this regard. In peacekeeping operations, combat is not expected and the goal is an absence of violence. In COIN, such an absence may actually mask insurgent preparations for combat. (Dept. of Army photo by Staff Sgt. Jason T. Bailey).

Insurgency and its tactics are as old as warfare itself. Joint doctrine defines an insurgency as an organized movement aimed at the overthrow of a constituted government through the use of subversion and armed conflict (JP 1-02). Stated another way, an insurgency is an organized, protracted politico-military struggle designed to weaken the control and legitimacy of an established government, occupying power, or other political authority while increasing insurgent control. Counterinsurgency is military, paramilitary, political, economic, psychological, and civic actions taken by a government to defeat insurgency (JP 1-02). These definitions are a good starting point, but they do not properly highlight a key paradox: though insurgency and COIN are two sides of a phenomenon that has been called revolutionary war or internal war, they are distinctly different types of operations. In addition, insurgency and COIN are included within a broad category of conflict known as irregular warfare.

I. Aspects of Counterinsurgency

The purpose of America's ground forces is to fight and win the Nation's wars. Throughout history, however, the Army and Marine Corps have been called on to perform many tasks beyond pure combat; this has been particularly true during the conduct of COIN operations. COIN requires Soldiers and Marines to be ready both to fight and to build—depending on the security situation and a variety of other factors. The full spectrum operations doctrine (described in FM 3-0) captures this reality.

All full spectrum operations executed overseas—including COIN operations—include offensive, defensive, and stability operations that commanders combine to achieve the desired end state. The exact mix varies depending on the situation and the mission. Commanders weight each operation based on their assessment of the campaign's phase and the situation in their AO. They shift the weight among these operations as necessary to address situations in different parts of the AO while continuing to pursue their overall objectives.

Aspects of Counterinsurgency Opns

COIN is a combination of offensive, defensive, and stability operations.

STABILITY
- **Civil Security**
- **Civil Control**
- **Essential Services**
- **Governance**
- **Economic and Infrastructure Development**

OFFENSE

DEFENSE

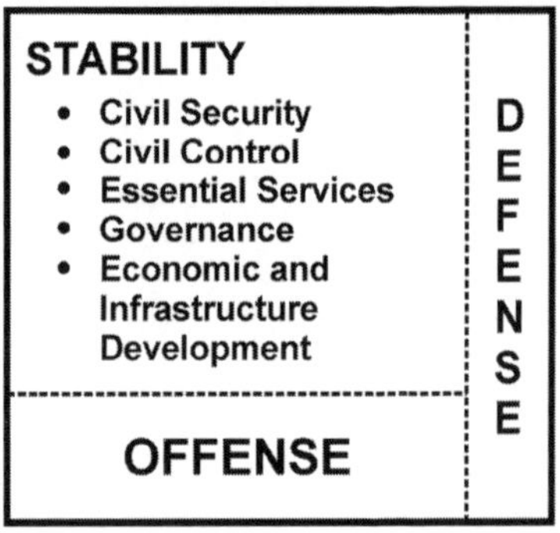

The proportion of effort devoted to offensive, defensive, and stability operations within COIN is changed over time in response to the situation and can vary geographically and by echelon.

Ref: FM 3-24, fig. 1-1, p. 1-19.

In almost every case, counterinsurgents face a populace containing an active minority supporting the government and an equally small militant faction opposing it. Success requires the government to be accepted as legitimate by most of that uncommitted middle, which also includes passive supporters of both sides. Because of the ease of sowing disorder, it is usually not enough for counterinsurgents to get 51 percent of popular support; a solid majority is often essential. However, a passive populace may be all that is necessary for a well-supported insurgency to seize political power.

II. The Nature of Counterinsurgency Operations

Ref: FM 3-24 Counterinsurgency, pp. 5-1 to 5-2.

Counterinsurgency (COIN) operations require synchronized application of military, paramilitary, political, economic, psychological, and civic actions. Successful counterinsurgents support or develop local institutions with legitimacy and the ability to provide basic services, economic opportunity, public order, and security. Successful COIN efforts include civilian agencies, U.S. military forces, and multinational forces. COIN operations combine offensive, defensive, and stability operations to achieve the stable and secure environment needed for effective governance, essential services, and economic development.

The focus of COIN operations generally progresses through three indistinct stages that can be envisioned with a medical analogy:

Initial Stage: "Stop the Bleeding"

Initially, COIN operations are similar to emergency first aid for the patient. The goal is to protect the population, break the insurgents' initiative and momentum, and set the conditions for further engagement. Limited offensive operations may be undertaken, but are complemented by stability operations focused on civil security. During this stage, friendly and enemy information needed to complete the common operational picture is collected and initial running estimates are developed. Counterinsurgents also begin shaping the information environment, including the expectations of the local populace.

Middle Stage: "Inpatient Care—Recovery"

The middle stage is characterized by efforts aimed at assisting the patient through long-term recovery or restoration of health—which in this case means achieving stability. Counterinsurgents are most active here, working aggressively along all logical lines of operations (LLOs). The desire in this stage is to develop and build resident capability and capacity in the HN government and security forces. As civil security is assured, focus expands to include governance, provision of essential services, and stimulation of economic development. Relationships with HN counterparts in the government and security forces and with the local populace are developed and strengthened. These relationships increase the flow of human and other types of intelligence. This intelligence facilitates measured offensive operations in conjunction with the HN security forces. The host nation increases its legitimacy through providing security, expanding effective governance, providing essential services, and achieving incremental success in meeting public expectations.

Late Stage: "Outpatient Care—Self-Sufficiency"

Stage three is characterized by the expansion of stability operations across contested regions, ideally using HN forces. The main goal for this stage is to transition responsibility for COIN operations to HN leadership. In this stage, the multinational force works with the host nation in an increasingly supporting role, turning over responsibility wherever and whenever appropriate. Quick reaction forces and fire support capabilities may still be needed in some areas, but more functions along all LLOs are performed by HN forces with the low-key assistance of multinational advisors. As the security, governing, and economic capacity of the host nation increases, the need for foreign assistance is reduced. At this stage, the host nation has established or reestablished the systems needed to provide effective and stable government that sustains the rule of law. The government secures its citizens continuously, sustains and builds legitimacy through effective governance, has effectively isolated the insurgency, and can manage and meet the expectations of the nation's entire population.

III. Historical Principles for Counterinsurgency

Ref: FM 3-24 Counterinsurgency, pp. 1-20 to 1-24.

The historical principles and contemporary imperatives derived from the historical record and detailed below provide some guideposts for forces engaged in COIN operations. The following principles are derived from past insurgencies.

Legitimacy Is the Main Objective

The primary objective of any COIN operation is to foster development of effective governance by a legitimate government. Counterinsurgents achieve this objective by the balanced application of both military and nonmilitary means. All governments rule through a combination of consent and coercion. Governments described as "legitimate" rule primarily with the consent of the governed; those described as "illegitimate" tend to rely mainly or entirely on coercion. Citizens of the latter obey the state for fear of the consequences of doing otherwise, rather than because they voluntarily accept its rule. A government that derives its powers from the governed tends to be accepted by its citizens as legitimate. It still uses coercion—for example, against criminals—but most of its citizens voluntarily accept its governance.

Unity of Effort Is Essential

Unity of effort must be present at every echelon of a COIN operation. Otherwise, well-intentioned but uncoordinated actions can cancel each other or provide vulnerabilities for insurgents to exploit. Ideally, a single counterinsurgent leader has authority over all government agencies involved in COIN operations. Usually, however, military commanders work to achieve unity of effort through liaison with leaders of a wide variety of nonmilitary agencies. The U.S. Ambassador and country team, along with senior HN representatives, must be key players in higher level planning; similar connections are needed throughout the chain of command. NGOs often play an important role at the local level. Many such agencies resist being overtly involved with military forces; however, efforts to establish some kind of liaison are needed. The most important connections are those with joint, interagency, multinational, and HN organizations.

Political Factors Are Primary

At the beginning of a COIN operation, military actions may appear predominant as security forces conduct operations to secure the populace and kill or capture insurgents; however, political objectives must guide the military's approach. Commanders must, for example, consider how operations contribute to strengthening the HN government's legitimacy and achieving U.S. political goals. This means that political and diplomatic leaders must actively participate throughout the conduct (planning, preparation, execution, and assessment) of COIN operations. The political and military aspects of insurgencies are so bound together as to be inseparable. Most insurgent approaches recognize that fact. Military actions executed without properly assessing their political effects at best result in reduced effectiveness and at worst are counterproductive.

Counterinsurgents Must Understand the Environment

Successful conduct of COIN operations depends on thoroughly understanding the society and culture within which they are being conducted. In most COIN operations in which U.S. forces participate, insurgents hold a distinct advantage in their level of local knowledge. Effective COIN operations require a greater emphasis on certain skills, such as language and cultural understanding, than does conventional warfare. The interconnected, politico-military nature of insurgency and COIN requires immersion in the people and their lives to achieve victory.

Intelligence Drives Operations

Without good intelligence, counterinsurgents are like blind boxers wasting energy flailing at unseen opponents and perhaps causing unintended harm. With good intelligence, counterinsurgents are like surgeons cutting out cancerous tissue while keeping other vital organs intact. Effective operations are shaped by timely, specific, and reliable intelligence, gathered and analyzed at the lowest possible level and disseminated throughout the force. Because of the dispersed nature of COIN operations, counterinsurgents' own actions are a key generator of intelligence. A cycle develops where operations produce intelligence that drives subsequent operations. Reporting by units, members of the country team, and associated civilian agencies is often of greater importance than reporting by specialized intelligence assets.

Insurgents Must be Isolated from Their Cause and Support

It is easier to separate an insurgency from its resources and let it die than to kill every insurgent. Clearly, killing or capturing insurgents will be necessary, especially when an insurgency is based in religious or ideological extremism. However, killing every insurgent is normally impossible. Attempting to do so can also be counterproductive in some cases; it risks generating popular resentment, creating martyrs that motivate new recruits, and producing cycles of revenge.

Dynamic insurgencies can replace losses quickly. Skillful counterinsurgents must thus cut off the sources of that recuperative power. Some sources can be reduced by redressing the social, political, and economic grievances that fuel the insurgency. Physical support can be cut off by population control or border security. International or local legal action might be required to limit financial support. Urban insurgents, however, are especially difficult to isolate from their cause and sources of support.

Security Under the Rule of Law is Essential

The cornerstone of any COIN effort is establishing security for the civilian populace. Without a secure environment, no permanent reforms can be implemented and disorder spreads. To establish legitimacy, commanders transition security activities from combat operations to law enforcement as quickly as in line with local culture and practices to deal with such criminals enhances the HN government's legitimacy. Soldiers and Marines help establish HN institutions that sustain that legal regime, including police forces, court systems, and penal facilities. It is important to remember that the violence level must be reduced enough for police forces to maintain order prior to any transition; otherwise, COIN forces will be unable to secure the populace and may lose the legitimacy gained by the transition.

Counterinsurgents Should Prepare for a Long-Term Commitment

Insurgencies are protracted by nature. Thus, COIN operations always demand considerable expenditures of time and resources. The populace may prefer the HN government to the insurgents; however, people do not actively support a government unless they are convinced that the counterinsurgents have the means, ability, stamina, and will to win. The insurgents' primary battle is against the HN government, not the United States; however, U.S. support can be crucial to building public faith in that government's viability. The populace must have confidence in the staying power of both the counterinsurgents and the HN government. Insurgents and local populations often believe that a few casualties or a few years will cause the United States to abandon a COIN effort. Constant reaffirmations of commitment, backed by deeds, can overcome that perception and bolster faith in the steadfastness of U.S. support.

Preparing for a protracted COIN effort requires establishing headquarters and support structures designed for long-term operations. Planning and commitments should be based on sustainable operating tempo and personnel tempo limits for the various components of the force.

IV. Contemporary Imperatives of Counterinsurgency

Ref: FM 3-24 Counterinsurgency, pp. 1-24 to 1-26.

Recent COIN experiences have identified an important set of additional imperatives to keep in mind for success.

Manage Information and Expectations

Information and expectations are related; skillful counterinsurgents manage both. To limit discontent and build support, the HN government and any counterinsurgents assisting it create and maintain a realistic set of expectations among the populace, friendly military forces, and the international community. IO (including psychological operations and the related activities of public affairs and civil-military operations) are key tools to accomplish this. Achieving steady progress toward a set of reasonable expectations can increase the populace's tolerance for the inevitable inconveniences entailed by ongoing COIN operations. Where a large U.S. force is present to help establish a regime, such progress can extend the period before an army of liberation becomes perceived as an army of occupation.

U.S. forces start with a built-in challenge because of their reputation for accomplishment, what some call the "man on the moon syndrome." This refers to the expressed disbelief that a nation able to put a man on the moon cannot quickly restore basic services. U.S. agencies trying to fan enthusiasm for their efforts should avoid making unrealistic promises. In some cultures, failure to deliver promised results is automatically interpreted as deliberate deception, rather than good intentions gone awry. In other cultures, exorbitant promises are normal and people do not expect them to be kept. Effective counterinsurgents understand local norms; they use locally tailored approaches to control expectations. Managing expectations also involves demonstrating economic and political progress to show the populace how life is improving. Increasing the number of people who feel they have a stake in the success of the state and its government is a key to successful COIN operations. In the end, victory comes, in large measure, by convincing the populace that their life will be better under the HN government than under an insurgent regime.

Use the Appropriate Level of Force

Any use of force generates a series of reactions. There may be times when an overwhelming effort is necessary to destroy or intimidate an opponent and reassure the populace. Extremist insurgent combatants often have to be killed. In any case, however, counterinsurgents should calculate carefully the type and amount of force to be applied and who wields it for any operation. An operation that kills five insurgents is counterproductive if collateral damage leads to the recruitment of fifty more insurgents.

In a COIN environment, it is vital for commanders to adopt appropriate and measured levels of force and apply that force precisely so that it accomplishes the mission without causing unnecessary loss of life or suffering. Normally, counterinsurgents can use escalation of force/force continuum procedures to minimize potential loss of life. These procedures are especially appropriate during convoy operations and at checkpoints and roadblocks. Escalation of force (Army)/force continuum (Marine Corps) refers to using lesser means of force when such use is likely to achieve the desired effects and Soldiers and Marines can do so without endangering themselves, others, or mission accomplishment. Escalation of force/force continuum procedures do not limit the right of self-defense, including the use of deadly force when such force is necessary to defend against a hostile act or demonstrated hostile intent. Commanders ensure that their Soldiers and Marines are properly trained in such procedures and, more importantly, in methods of shaping situations so that small-unit leaders have to make fewer split-second, life-or-death decisions.

Who wields force is also important. If the HN police have a reasonable reputation for competence and impartiality, it is better for them to execute urban raids; the populace is likely to view that application of force as more legitimate. This is true even if the police are not as well armed or as capable as military units. However, local circumstances affect this decision. If the police are seen as part of an ethnic or sectarian group oppressing the general population, their use may be counterproductive. Effective counterinsurgents thus understand the character of the local police and popular perceptions of both police and military units. This understanding helps ensure that the application of force is appropriate and reinforces the rule of law.

Learn and Adapt

An effective counterinsurgent force is a learning organization. Insurgents constantly shift between military and political phases and tactics. In addition, networked insurgents constantly exchange information about their enemy's vulnerabilities—even with insurgents in distant theaters. However, skillful counterinsurgents can adapt at least as fast as insurgents. Every unit needs to be able to make observations, draw and apply lessons, and assess results. Commanders must develop an effective system to circulate best practices throughout their command. Combatant commanders might also need to seek new laws or policies that authorize or resource necessary changes. Insurgents shift their AOs looking for weak links, so widespread competence is required throughout the counterinsurgent force.

Empower the Lowest Levels

Mission command is the conduct of military operations through decentralized execution based upon mission orders for effective mission accomplishment. Successful mission command results from subordinate leaders at all echelons exercising disciplined initiative within the commander's intent to accomplish missions. It requires an environment of trust and mutual understanding (FM 6-0). It is the Army's and Marine Corps' preferred method for commanding and controlling forces during all types of operations. Under mission command, commanders provide subordinates with a mission, their commander's intent, a concept of operations, and resources adequate to accomplish the mission. Higher commanders empower subordinates to make decisions within the commander's intent. They leave details of execution to their subordinates and expect them to use initiative and judgment to accomplish the mission.

Mission command is ideally suited to the mosaic nature of COIN operations. Local commanders have the best grasp of their situations. Under mission command, they are given access to or control of the resources needed to produce timely intelligence, conduct effective tactical operations, and manage IO and civil-military operations. Thus, effective COIN operations are decentralized, and higher commanders owe it to their subordinates to push as many capabilities as possible down to their level. Mission command encourages the initiative of subordinates and facilitates the learning that must occur at every level. It is a major characteristic of a COIN force that can adapt and react at least as quickly as the insurgents.

Support the Host Nation

U.S. forces committed to a COIN effort are there to assist a HN government. The long-term goal is to leave a government able to stand by itself. In the end, the host nation has to win on its own. Achieving this requires development of viable local leaders and institutions. U.S. forces and agencies can help, but HN elements must accept responsibilities to achieve real victory. While it may be easier for U.S. military units to conduct operations themselves, it is better to work to strengthen local forces and institutions and then assist them. HN governments have the final responsibility to solve their own problems. Eventually all foreign armies are seen as interlopers or occupiers; the sooner the main effort can transition to HN institutions, without unacceptable degradation, the better.

V. Paradoxes of COIN Operations

Ref: FM 3-24 Counterinsurgency, pp. 1-26 to 1-28.

The principles and imperatives discussed above reveal that COIN presents a complex and often unfamiliar set of missions and considerations. In many ways, the conduct of COIN is counter intuitive to the traditional U.S. view of war—although COIN operations have actually formed a substantial part of the U.S. military experience. Some representative paradoxes of COIN are presented here as examples of the different mindset required. These paradoxes are offered to stimulate thinking, not to limit it. The applicability of the thoughts behind the paradoxes depends on a sense of the local situation and, in particular, the state of the insurgency. For example, the admonition "Sometimes, the More Force Used, the Less Effective It Is" does not apply when the enemy is "coming over the barricades"; however, that thought is applicable when increased security is achieved in an area. In short, these paradoxes should not be reduced to a checklist; rather, they should be used with considerable thought.

Sometimes, the More You Protect Your Force, the Less Secure You May Be

Ultimate success in COIN is gained by protecting the populace, not the COIN force. If military forces remain in their compounds, they lose touch with the people, appear to be running scared, and cede the initiative to the insurgents. Aggressive saturation patrolling, ambushes, and listening post operations must be conducted, risk shared with the populace, and contact maintained. The effectiveness of establishing patrol bases and operational support bases should be weighed against the effectiveness of using larger unit bases. (FM 90-8 discusses saturation patrolling and operational support bases.) These practices ensure access to the intelligence needed to drive operations. Following them reinforces the connections with the populace that help establish real legitimacy.

Sometimes, the More Force Is Used, the Less Effective It Is

Any use of force produces many effects, not all of which can be foreseen. The more force applied, the greater the chance of collateral damage and mistakes. Using substantial force also increases the opportunity for insurgent propaganda to portray lethal military activities as brutal. In contrast, using force precisely and discriminately strengthens the rule of law that needs to be established. As noted above, the key for counterinsurgents is knowing when more force is needed—and when it might be counterproductive. This judgment involves constant assessment of the security situation and a sense of timing regarding insurgents' actions.

The More Successful the Counterinsurgency Is, the Less Force Can Be Used and the More Risk Must Be Accepted

This paradox is really a corollary to the previous one. As the level of insurgent violence drops, the requirements of international law and the expectations of the populace lead to a reduction in direct military actions by counterinsurgents. More reliance is placed on police work, rules of engagement may be tightened, and troops may have to exercise increased restraint. Soldiers and Marines may also have to accept more risk to maintain involvement with the people.

Sometimes Doing Nothing Is the Best Reaction

Often insurgents carry out a terrorist act or guerrilla raid with the primary purpose of enticing counterinsurgents to overreact, or at least to react in a way that insurgents can exploit—for example, opening fire on a crowd or executing a clearing operation that creates more enemies than it takes off the streets. If an assessment of the effects of a course of action determines that more negative than positive effects may result, an alternative should be considered—potentially including not acting.

Some of the Best Weapons for Counterinsurgents Do Not Shoot

Counterinsurgents often achieve the most meaningful success in garnering public support and legitimacy for the HN government with activities that do not involve killing insurgents (though, again, killing clearly will often be necessary). Arguably, the decisive battle is for the people's minds; hence synchronizing IO with efforts along the other LLOs is critical. Every action, including uses of force, must be "wrapped in a bodyguard of information." While security is essential to setting the stage for overall progress, lasting victory comes from a vibrant economy, political participation, and restored hope. Particularly after security has been achieved, dollars and ballots will have more important effects than bombs and bullets. This is a time when "money is ammunition." Depending on the state of the insurgency, therefore, Soldiers and Marines should prepare to execute many nonmilitary missions to support COIN efforts.

The Host Nation Doing Something Tolerably Is Normally Better Than Us Doing It Well

It is just as important to consider who performs an operation as to assess how well it is done. Where the United States is supporting a host nation, long-term success requires establishing viable HN leaders and institutions that can carry on without significant U.S. support. General Creighton Abrams, the U.S. commander in Vietnam in 1971, recognized this fact when he said, "There's very clear evidence,...in some things, that we helped too much. And we retarded the Vietnamese by doing it....We can't run this thing....They've got to run it. The nearer we get to that the better off they are and the better off we are." T.E. Lawrence made a similar observation while leading the Arab Revolt against the Ottoman Empire in 1917: "Do not try to do too much with your own hands. Better the Arabs do it tolerably than that you do it perfectly. It is their war, and you are to help them, not to win it for them."

If a Tactic Works this Week, It Might Not Work Next Week; If It Works in this Province, It Might Not Work in the Next

Competent insurgents are adaptive. They are often part of a widespread network that communicates constantly and instantly. Insurgents quickly adjust to successful COIN practices and rapidly disseminate information throughout the insurgency. Indeed, the more effective a COIN tactic is, the faster it may become out of date because insurgents have a greater need to counter it. Effective leaders at all levels avoid complacency and are at least as adaptive as their enemies. There is no "silver bullet" set of COIN procedures. Constantly developing new practices is essential.

Tactical Success Guarantees Nothing

As important as they are in achieving security, military actions by themselves cannot achieve success in COIN. Insurgents that never defeat counterinsurgents in combat still may achieve their strategic objectives. Tactical actions thus must be linked not only to strategic and operational military objectives but also to the host nation's essential political goals. Without those connections, lives and resources may be wasted for no real gain.

Many Important Decisions Are Not Made by Generals

Successful COIN operations require competence and judgment by Soldiers and Marines at all levels. Indeed, young leaders—so-called "strategic corporals"—often make decisions at the tactical level that have strategic consequences. Senior leaders set the proper direction and climate with thorough training and clear guidance; then they trust their subordinates to do the right thing. Preparation for tactical-level leaders requires more than just mastering Service doctrine; they must also be trained and educated to adapt to their local situations, understand the legal and ethical implications of their actions, and exercise initiative and sound judgment in accordance with their senior commanders' intent.

V. Successful and Unsuccessful Counterinsurgeny Practices

Ref: FM 3-24 Counterinsurgency, table 1-1, p. 1-29.

The following table lists some practices that have contributed significantly to success or failure in past counterinsurgencies.

Successful Practices

- Emphasize intelligence
- Focus on the population, its need, and its security
- Establish and expand secure areas
- Isolate insurgents from the population (population control)
- Conduct effective, pervasive, and continuous information operations
- Provide amnesty and rehabilitation for those willing to support the new government
- Place host-nation police in the lead with military support as soon as the security situation permits
- Expand and diversify the host-nation police force
- Train military forces to conduct counterinsurgency operations
- Embed quality advisors and special forces with host-nation forces
- Deny sanctuary to insurgents
- Encourage strong political and military cooperation and information sharing
- Secure host-nation borders
- Protect key infrastructure

Unsuccessful Practices

- Overemphasize killing and capturing the enemy rather than securing and engaging the populace
- Conduct large-scale operations as the norm
- Concentrate military forces in large bases for protection
- Focus special forces primarily on raiding
- Place low priority on assigning quality advisors to host-nation forces
- Build and train host-nation security forces in the U.S. military's image
- Ignore peacetime government processes, including legal procedures
- Allow open borders, airspace and coastlines

Tactical Enabling Operations

I. Security Operations

Ref: FM 3-90 Tactics, chap 12.

Security operations are those operations undertaken by a commander to provide early and accurate warning of enemy operations, to provide the force being protected with time and maneuver space within which to react to the enemy, and to develop the situation to allow the commander to effectively use the protected force.

Security operations must provide information regarding enemy movement and capacity while giving the commander enough time and space with which to form an effective response. (Photo by Jeong, Hae-jung).

I. Forms of Security Operations

There are five forms of security operations -- screen, guard, cover, area security and local security.

A. Screen

Screen is a form of security operations that primarily provides early warning to the protected force. A unit performing a screen observes, identifies, and reports enemy actions. Generally, a screening force engages and destroys enemy reconnaissance elements within its capabilities—augmented by indirect fires—but otherwise fights only in self-defense. The screen has the minimum combat power necessary to provide the desired early warning, which allows the commander to retain the bulk of his combat power for commitment at the decisive place and time. A screen provides the least amount of protection of any security mission; it does not have the combat power to develop the situation.

A screen is appropriate to cover gaps between forces, exposed flanks, or the rear of stationary and moving forces. The commander can place a screen in front of a stationary formation when the likelihood of enemy action is small, the expected enemy force is small, or the main body needs only limited time, once it is warned, to react effectively. Designed to provide minimum security with minimum forces, a screen is usually an economy-of-force operation based on calculated risk. If a significant enemy force is expected or a significant amount of time and space is needed to provide the required degree of protection, the commander should assign and resource a guard or cover mission instead of a screen. The security element forward of a moving force must conduct a guard or cover because a screen lacks the combat power to defeat or contain the lead elements of an enemy force.

Security Fundamentals

Principles of Security Operations	Techniques Used to Perform Security Operations	Information Required from Controlling Headquarters
• Three General Orders • Provide early and accurate warning • Provide reaction time and maneuver space • Orient on the force / facility being secured • Perform continuous reconnaissance • Maintain enemy contact	• Observation post • Combat outpost • Battle position • Patrols • Combat formations • Movement techniques • Infiltration • Movement to contact • Dismounted, mounted, and air insertion • Roadblocks • Checkpoints • Convoy and route security • Searches	• Trace of the security area (front, sides, and rear boundaries), and initial position within the area • Time security is to be established • Main body size and location • Mission, purpose and commander's intent of the controlling headquarters • Counterreconnaissance and engagement criteria • Method of movement to occupy the area (zone reconnaissance, infiltration, tactical road march, movement to contact; mounted, dismounted, or air insertion) • Trigger for displacement and method of control when displacing. • Possible follow-on missions

Ref: FM 3-21.8 (FM 7-8), table H-1, p. H-2.

Critical Tasks for a Screen

Unless the commander orders otherwise, a security force conducting a screen performs certain tasks within the limits of its capabilities. A unit can normally screen an avenue of approach two echelons larger than itself. If a security force does not have the time or other resources to complete all of these tasks, the security force commander must inform the commander assigning the mission of the shortfall and request guidance on which tasks must be completed and their priority. After starting the screen, if the security unit commander determines that he cannot complete an assigned task, such as maintain continuous surveillance on all avenues of approach into an AO, he reports and awaits further instructions. Normally, the main force commander does not place a time limit on the duration of the screen, as doing so may force the screening force to accept decisive engagement. Screen tasks are to:

- Allow no enemy ground element to pass through the screen undetected and unreported
- Maintain continuous surveillance of all avenues of approach larger than a designated size into the area under all visibility conditions
- Destroy or repel all enemy reconnaissance patrols within its capabilities.
- Locate the lead elements of each enemy advance guard and determine its direction of movement in a defensive screen
- Maintain contact with enemy forces and report any activity in the AO
- Maintain contact with the main body and any security forces operating on its flanks
- Impede and harass the enemy within its capabilities while displacing

II. Fundamentals of Security Ops

Ref: FM 3-90 Tactics, pp. 12-2 to 12-3.

1. Provide Early and Accurate Warning

The security force provides early warning by detecting the enemy force quickly and reporting information accurately to the main body commander. The security force operates at varying distances from the main body based on the factors of METT-TC. As a minimum, it should operate far enough from the main body to prevent enemy ground forces from observing or engaging the main body with direct fires. The earlier the security force detects the enemy, the more time the main body has to assess the changing situation and react. The commander positions ground security and aeroscouts to provide long-range observation of expected enemy avenues of approach, and he reinforces and integrates them with available intelligence collection systems to maximize warning time.

2. Provide Reaction Time and Maneuver Space

The security force provides the main body with enough reaction time and maneuver space to effectively respond to likely enemy actions by operating at a distance from the main body and by offering resistance to enemy forces. The commander determines the amount of time and space required to effectively respond from information provided by the intelligence preparation of the battlefield (IPB) process and the main body commander's guidance regarding time to react to enemy courses of action (COA) based on the factors of METT-TC. The security force that operates farthest from the main body and offers more resistance provides more time and space to the main body. It attempts to hinder the enemy's advance by acting within its capabilities and mission constraints.

3. Orient on the Force or Facility to Be Secured

The security force focuses all its actions on protecting and providing early warning to the secured force or facility. It operates between the main body and known or suspected enemy units. The security force must move as the main body moves and orient on its movement. The security force commander must know the main body's scheme of maneuver to maneuver his force to remain between the main body and the enemy. The value of terrain occupied by the security force hinges on the protection it provides to the main body commander.

4. Perform Continuous Reconnaissance

The security force aggressively and continuously seeks the enemy and reconnoiters key terrain. It conducts active area or zone reconnaissance to detect enemy movement or enemy preparations for action and to learn as much as possible about the terrain. The ultimate goal is to determine the enemy's COA and assist the main body in countering it. Terrain information focuses on its possible use by the enemy or the friendly force, either for offensive or defensive operations. Stationary security forces use combinations of OPs, aviation, patrols, intelligence collection assets, and battle positions (BPs) to perform reconnaissance. Moving security forces perform zone, area, or route reconnaissance along with using OPs and BPs, to accomplish this fundamental.

5. Maintain Enemy Contact

Once the security force makes enemy contact, it does not break contact unless specifically directed by the main force commander. The security asset that first makes contact does not have to maintain that contact if the entire security force maintains contact with the enemy. The security force commander ensures that his subordinate security assets hand off contact with the enemy from one security asset to another in this case. The security force must continuously collect information on the enemy's activities to assist the main body in determining potential and actual enemy COAs and to prevent the enemy from surprising the main body. This requires continuous visual contact, the ability to use direct and indirect fires, freedom to maneuver, and depth in space and time.

Screen Movement Methods

Method	Characteristics	Advantages	Disadvantages
Alternate Bounds by OPs	■ Main body moves faster ■ Conducted by platoon or company/troop ■ Contact is possible ■ Conducted rear to front	■ Very secure method ■ Maintains maximum surveillance over the security area	■ Execution takes time ■ Disrupts unit integrity
Alternate Bounds by Units	■ Main body moves faster ■ Conducted by platoon or company/troop ■ Contact is possible ■ Conducted rear to front	■ Execution does not take a great deal of time ■ Maintains good surveillance over the security area ■ Maintains unit integrity	■ May leave temporary gaps in coverage
Successive Bounds	■ Main body moving slowly ■ Conducted by platoon or company/troop ■ Contact is possible ■ Conducted simultaneous-ly or in succession ■ Units should maintain an air screen during ground movement	■ Most secure method ■ Maintains maximum surveillance ■ Maintains unit integrity	■ Execution takes the most time ■ Unit is less secure when all elements are moving simultaneously ■ Simultaneous movement may leave temporary gaps
Continuous Marching	■ Main body is moving relatively quickly ■ Performed as a route reconnaissance ■ Enemy contact not likely ■ Unit should maintain an air screen on the flank	■ OPs displace quickly ■ Maintains unit integrity	■ Least secure method

Ref: FM 3-90, table 12-1, p. 12-6.

B. Guard

Guard is a form of security operations whose primary task is to protect the main body by fighting to gain time while also observing and reporting information and preventing enemy ground observation of and direct fire against the main body. Units conducting a guard mission cannot operate independently because they rely upon fires and combat support assets of the main body.

A guard differs from a screen in that a guard force contains sufficient combat power to defeat, cause the withdrawal of, or fix the lead elements of an enemy ground force before it can engage the main body with direct fire. A guard force routinely engages enemy forces with direct and indirect fires. A screening force, however, primarily uses indirect fires or close air support to destroy enemy reconnaissance elements and slow the movement of other enemy forces. A guard force uses all means at its disposal, including decisive engagement, to prevent the enemy from penetrating to a position were it could observe and engage the main body. It operates within the range of the main body's fire support weapons, deploying over a narrower front than a comparable-size screening force to permit concentrating combat power.

Types of Guard Operations

1. **Advance guard**
2. **Flank guard**
3. **Rear guard**

Ref: FM 3-90, pp. 12-21 to 12-25.

The three types of guard operations are advance, flank, and rear guard. A commander can assign a guard mission to protect either a stationary or a moving force.

Guard tasks:

- Destroy the enemy advance guard
- Maintain contact with enemy forces and report activity in the AO
- Maintain continuous surveillance of avenues of approach into the AO under all visibility conditions
- Impede and harass the enemy within its capabilities while displacing
- Cause the enemy main body to deploy, and then report its direction of travel
- Allow no enemy ground element to pass through the security area undetected and unreported
- Destroy or cause the withdrawal of all enemy reconnaissance patrols
- Maintain contact with its main body and any other security forces operating on its flanks

C. Cover

Cover is a form of security operations whose primary task is to protect the main body by fighting to gain time while also observing and reporting information and preventing enemy ground observation of and direct fire against the main body.

The covering force's distance forward of the main body depends on the intentions and instructions of the main body commander, the terrain, the location and strength of the enemy, and the rates of march of both the main body and the covering force. The width of the covering force area is the same as the AO of the main body.

A *covering force* is a self-contained force capable of operating independently of the main body, unlike a screening or guard force. A covering force, or portions of it, often becomes decisively engaged with enemy forces. Therefore, the covering force must have substantial combat power to engage the enemy and accomplish its mission. A covering force develops the situation earlier than a screen or a guard force. It fights longer and more often and defeats larger enemy forces.

While a covering force provides more security than a screen or guard force, it also requires more resources. Before assigning a cover mission, the main body commander must ensure that he has sufficient combat power to resource a covering force and the decisive operation. When the commander lacks the resources to support both, he must assign his security force a less resource-intensive security mission, either a screen or a guard.

A covering force accomplishes all the tasks of screening and guard forces. A covering force for a stationary force performs a defensive mission, while a covering force for a moving force generally conducts offensive actions. A covering force normally operates forward of the main body in the offense or defense, or to the rear for a retrograde operation. Unusual circumstances could dictate a flank covering force, but this is normally a screen or guard mission.

1. Offensive Cover

An offensive covering force seizes the initiative early for the main body commander, allowing him to attack decisively. Some critical tasks include

- Performing zone reconnaissance along the main body's axis of advance or within the AO

- Clearing or bypassing enemy forces within the AO in accordance with bypass criteria
- Denying the enemy information about the strength, composition, and objective of the main body
- Penetrating the enemy's security area to locate enemy main defensive positions
- Determining enemy strengths and dispositions
- Locating gaps or weaknesses in the enemy's defensive scheme
- Defeating or repelling enemy forces as directed by the higher commander
- Deceiving the enemy into thinking the main body has been committed and causing him to launch counterattacks prematurely
- Fixing enemy forces to allow the main body to maneuver around enemy strengths or through weaknesses
- Destroying enemy reconnaissance, the advance guard, and the lead elements of the main body
- Determining the location of enemy assailable flanks
- Fixing enemy forces to allow the main body to maneuver around enemy strengths or through weaknesses

2. Defensive Cover

A defensive covering force prevents the enemy from attacking at the time, place, and combat strength of his choosing. Defensive cover gains time for the main body, enabling it to deploy, move, or prepare defenses in the MBA. It accomplishes this by disrupting the enemy's attack, destroying his initiative, and establishing the conditions for decisive operations. A defensive covering force emphasizes the following tasks:

- Prevent the main body from being surprised and becoming engaged by direct-fire weapons
- Defeat enemy advance guard formations
- Maintain continuous surveillance of high-speed avenues of approach into the security area
- Defeat all enemy reconnaissance formations before they can observe the main body
- Cause the deployment of the enemy main body
- Determine the size, strength, composition, and direction of the enemy's main effort
- Destroy, defeat, or attrit enemy forces within its capacity
- Deprive the enemy of his fire support and air defense umbrellas, or require him to displace them before he attacks the MBA
- Deceive the enemy regarding the location of main body and main defensive positions
- Avoid being bypassed

D. Area Security

Area security is a form of security operations conducted to protect friendly forces, installations, routes, and actions within a specific area.

Area security operations may be offensive or defensive in nature. They focus on the protected force, installation, route, or area. Forces to protect range from echelon headquarters through artillery and echelon reserves to the sustaining base. Protected installations can also be part of the sustaining base or they can constitute part of the area's infrastructure. Areas to secure range from specific points (bridges and defiles) and terrain features (ridge lines and hills) to large population centers and their adjacent areas.

Operations in noncontiguous AOs require commanders to emphasize area security. During offensive and retrograde operations, the speed at which the main body moves provides some measure of security. Rapidly moving units in open terrain can rely on technical assets to provide advance warning of enemy forces. In restrictive terrain, security forces focus on key terrain such as potential choke points.

E. Local Security

Local security consists of low-level security operations conducted near a unit to prevent surprise by the enemy.

Local security includes any local measure taken by units against enemy actions. It involves avoiding detection by the enemy or deceiving the enemy about friendly positions and intentions. It also includes finding any enemy forces in the immediate vicinity and knowing as much about their positions and intentions as possible. Local security prevents a unit from being surprised and is an important part of maintaining the initiative. The requirement for maintaining local security is an inherent part of all operations. Units perform local security when conducting full spectrum operations, including tactical enabling operations.

Units use both active and passive measures to provide local security.

1. Active Measures

- Using OPs and patrols
- Establishing specific levels of alert within the unit. The commander adjusts those levels based on the factors of METT-TC
- Establishing stand-to times. The unit SOP should detail the unit's activities during the conduct of stand-to

2. Passive Measures

Passive local security measures include using camouflage, movement control, noise and light discipline, and proper communications procedures. It also includes employing available ground sensors, night-vision devices, and daylight sights to maintain surveillance over the area immediately around the unit.

* Combat Outposts

A combat outpost is a reinforced OP capable of conducting limited combat operations. Using combat outposts is a technique for employing security forces in restrictive terrain that precludes mounted security forces from covering the area. They are also used when smaller OPs are in danger of being overrun by enemy forces infiltrating into and through the security area. The commander uses a combat outpost when he wants to extend the depth of his security area, when he wants his forward OPs to remain in place until they can observe the enemy's main body, or when he anticipates that his forward OPs will be encircled by enemy forces. Both mounted and dismounted forces can employ combat outposts.

On Point

Combat leaders require advanced warning of an enemy attack. Not every troop can remain at the ready 100 percent of the time. To protect the friendly force, security operations project patrols and targeting systems that can detect enemy activity.

Security operations conduct many of the same activities and use the same technologies as reconnaissance operations. The principal difference between the two is that while reconnaissance operations are dedicated to the enemy force and resources, security operations are dedicated to the friendly force and resources.

It may help to think of these two operations in simplistic terms. Reconnaissance operations tend to be offensive in nature, whereas security operations are more defensive in nature.

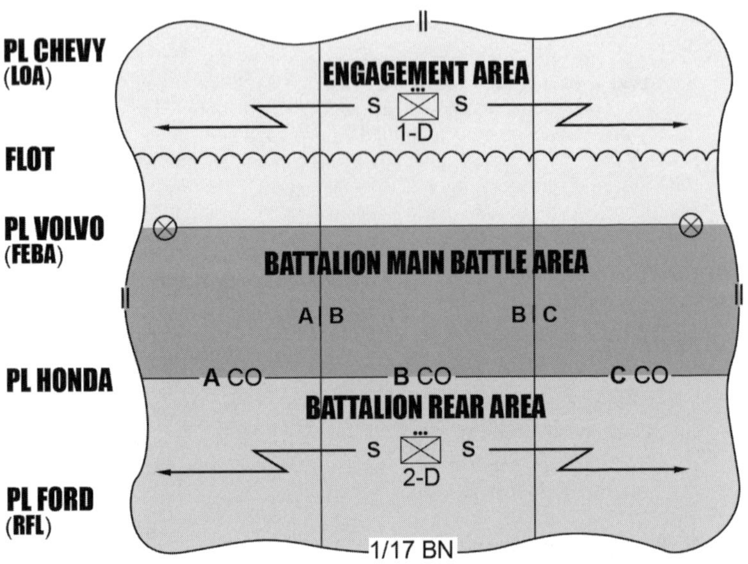

Security operations include activities throughout the area of operations. They are denoted by lightning bolts from the unit to the boundaries. In this case, the 'S' indicates screening operations in the engagement area forward of the FLOT, and in the battalion's rear area. (Ref: FM 3-90, chap 12, fig. 12-1).

The main body commander must designate the exact force to secure. This designation determines the limits of the security force's responsibilities. The security force must orient on the force it is securing. If the main body moves, the security force also moves to maintain its position in relation to the main body. The limited capabilities of most maneuver platoons prohibit them from having a mission separate from their parent company. Scout platoons are the exception to this rule.

The main body commander must determine when to establish the security force. He decides this based on the activity of the main body and expected enemy activity. He must allow enough time for the security force to move into and occupy the security area to prevent enemy forces from penetrating the security area undetected. The factors of METT-TC influence how the security force deploys to and occupies the screen line. If the security mission is the result of a current reconnaissance mission, the security force is already positioned to begin its mission. This occurs frequently when a reconnaissance mission halts at a designated PL. Analyzing the factors of METT-TC determines which deployment technique meets mission requirements.

Tactical Enabling Operations

II. Reconnaissance Ops

Ref: FM 3-90 Tactics, chap 13; and FM 7-92 Infantry Reconnaissance Platoon and Squad (Airborne, Air Assault, Light Infantry), chap 1 and 4; FM 3-21.10 (FM 7-10) The Infantry Rifle Company, pp. 8-1 to 8-4.

Reconnaissance operations are those operations undertaken to obtain, by visual observation or other detection methods, information about the activities and resources of an enemy or potential enemy, or to secure data concerning the meteorological, hydrographical or geographical characteristics and the indigenous population of a particular area. Reconnaissance primarily relies on the human dynamic rather than technical means. Reconnaissance is performed before, during, and after other operations to provide information used in the intelligence preparation of the battlefield (IPB) process, as well as by the commander in order to formulate, confirm, or modify his course of action (COA).

Reconnaissance is a process of gathering information to help the commander shape his understanding of the battlespace. Reconnaissance uses many techniques and technologies to collect this information, but it is still largely a human endeavor. (Photo by Jeong, Hae-jung).

Reconnaissance Objective

The commander orients his reconnaissance assets by identifying a reconnaissance objective within the area of operations (AO). The reconnaissance objective is a terrain feature, geographic area, or an enemy force about which the commander wants to obtain additional information. The reconnaissance objective clarifies the intent of the reconnaissance effort by specifying the most important result to obtain from the reconnaissance effort. The commander assigns a reconnaissance objective based on his priority information requirements (PIR) resulting from the IPB process and the reconnaissance asset's capabilities and limitations. The reconnaissance objective can be information about a specific geographical location, such as the cross-country trafficability, a specific enemy activity to be confirmed or denied, or a specific enemy unit to be located and tracked.

I. Reconnaissance Fundamentals

At this point the PL should know the specific recon mission and have received and developed the maneuver control measures. Before delving into the execution of each type of reconnaissance, it's important to delineate the fundamentals of recon patrols. There are seven rules to remember.

1. Ensure continuous recon

Reconnaissance happens before, during, and after an engagement. Before the engagement, the recon team develops the commander's picture of the battlefield. During the engagement, the recon team lets the commander know if the plan is having its intended effect upon the enemy force. After the engagement, the recon team helps the commander to determine the enemy's next move.

2. Don't keep recon assets in reserve

Of course, the recon team should not be run until it is exhausted. However, the recon team acts as the commander's eyes and ears forward. There is no reason to keep one ear or one eye in reserve! Recon assets must be managed to allow continuous reconnaissance. That includes a rest plan.

3. Orient on the objective

Don't just throw the recon team forward without a specified objective! Name the type of recon mission and name the objective within the AO. This helps the commander prioritize the recon assets and objectives, plus gives focus to the recon team for the most economical use of time.

4. Report information rapidly and accurately

Over time, information loses value because more often than not, the battlefield is rapidly changing. Recon teams give timely reports on exactly what they see (without exaggeration) and exactly what they do not see. A common mistake in reconnaissance is the failure to report when no enemy force or presence is detected. Failing to report does nothing for the commander. A report of negative activity gives the commander a better understanding of where the enemy *isn't* located, at least.

5. Retain freedom of maneuver

As stated earlier, a recon team that becomes engaged in a firefight with the enemy is fixed to a given location. Without the ability to maneuver, that recon team can only report what is to its immediate front. In short, it has become no more useful in developing the battlefield picture than any other line unit.

6. Gain and maintain contact

Recon teams seek to gain contact with the enemy. More often than not, the recon team uses a combination of stealth and surveillance to maintain contact with the enemy. The recon team maintains contact with the enemy until the commander orders them to withdraw. The recon patrol leader may also break contact if the recon team is decisively engaged, but then seeks to regain contact immediately.

7. Develop the situation rapidly

Once contact is gained, the recon team must quickly discern the threat. For an enemy force, that means identifying the approximate size of the enemy force, the activity and direction of movement, and possibly the enemy's disposition and capabilities. When evaluating an enemy obstacle, the recon team must discern the type of obstacle, the extent of the obstacle, and whether or not it is covered by enemy fire. Often, enemy obstacles tell the commander a fair amount of information regarding the capabilities and even the location of the enemy force.

II. Organization

The responsibility for conducting reconnaissance does not reside solely with specifically organized units. Every unit has an implied mission to report information about the terrain, civilian activities, and friendly and enemy dispositions, regardless of its battlefield location and primary function. Frontline troops and reconnaissance patrols of maneuver units at all echelons collect information on enemy units with which they are in contact. In rear areas, reserve maneuver forces, fire support assets, air defense, military police, host nation agencies, combat support, and combat service support elements observe and report civilian and enemy activity.

The small unit commander develops the enemy situation through active and passive reconnaissance. Passive reconnaissance includes techniques such as map, photographic and small, unmanned aerial systems (SUAS) reconnaissance and surveillance. Active methods include ground reconnaissance and reconnaissance by fire. Active reconnaissance operations are also classified as stealthy or aggressive:

- **Stealthy Reconnaissance**. Stealthy reconnaissance emphasizes procedures and techniques that allow the unit to avoid detection and engagement by the enemy. It is more time-consuming than aggressive reconnaissance. To be effective, stealthy reconnaissance must rely primarily on elements that make maximum use of covered and concealed terrain. The company's primary assets for stealthy reconnaissance are its Infantry squads or SUASs.
- **Aggressive Reconnaissance**. Aggressive reconnaissance is characterized by the speed and manner in which the reconnaissance element develops the situation once contact is made with an enemy force. A unit conducting aggressive reconnaissance uses both direct and indirect fires and movement to develop the situation. In conducting a patrol, the unit employs the principles of tactical movement to maintain security. The patrolling element maximizes the use of cover and concealment and conducts bounding overwatch as necessary to avoid detection.

III. Planning & Preparation

Reconnaissance planning starts with the company commander's identification of critical information requirements. The company commander then compares his CCIR list to that of the battalion commander. If the company commander identifies CCIR not covered on the battalion list, he shares them with the battalion commander and staff. The company commander requests that battalion or higher headquarter commit assets to confirm his CCIR. Based on the results of that request, the company commander can commit his forces to gather the information needed. This process begins while the unit is planning or preparing for an operation. It often continues during the conduct of the operation. Once the operation is under way, the commander continues to identify information requirements.

In planning for route, zone, or area reconnaissance, the company commander determines the objective of the mission, and identifies whether the reconnaissance will orient on the terrain or on the enemy force. He provides the company with clear guidance on the objective of the reconnaissance. The patrol leader (PL) typically identifies any additional maneuver control measures. This might include a direction of advance, anticipated listening halts, en route rally points (ERP), objective rally points (ORP) and target reference points (TRP).

III. Forms of the Reconnaissance

The four forms of reconnaissance operations—

- Route reconnaissance
- Zone reconnaissance
- Area reconnaissance
- Reconnaissance in force (RIF)

A. The Route Reconnaissance

Route reconnaissance is a form of reconnaissance that focuses along a specific line of communication, such as a road, railway, or cross-country mobility corridor. It provides new or updated information on route conditions, such as obstacles and bridge classifications, and enemy and civilian activity along the route. A route reconnaissance includes not only the route itself, but also all terrain along the route from which the enemy could influence the friendly force's movement.

The commander may assign a route reconnaissance as a separate mission or as a specified task for a unit conducting a zone or area reconnaissance. A scout platoon can conduct a route reconnaissance over only one route at a time. For larger organizations, the number of scout platoons available directly influences the number of routes that can be covered at one time. Integrating ground, air, and technical assets assures a faster and more complete route reconnaissance.

Depending on the length of route to be reconnoitered, the route recon may be conducted with great stealth, or it may be conducted with great mobility. The effort is to gather intelligence on the route and its conditions. (Dept. of Army photo by Arthur McQueen).

Route Reconnaissance Tasks

- Find, report, and clear within capabilities all enemy forces that can influence movement along the route
- Determine the trafficability of the route; can it support the friendly force?
- Reconnoiter all terrain that the enemy can use to dominate movement along the route, such as choke points, ambush sites, and pickup zones, landing zones, and drop zones
- Reconnoiter all built-up areas, contaminated areas, and lateral routes along the route
- Evaluate and classify all bridges, defiles, overpasses and underpasses, and culverts along the route

- Locate any fords, crossing sites, or bypasses for existing and reinforcing obstacles (including built-up areas) along the route
- Locate all obstacles and create lanes as specified in execution orders
- Report the above route information to the headquarters initiating the route reconnaissance mission, to include providing a sketch map or a route overlay

Note: See FM 3-34.212 and FM 3-20.95 for additional information concerning route reconnaissance.

Conducting the Route Reconnaissance - A Small Unit Perspective

Reconnaissance teams develop the picture of the battlefield for the commander. Reconnaissance provides information that is critical to the process of intelligence preparation of the battlespace (IPB). The commander employs his intelligence, surveillance, and reconnaissance (ISR) assets as either a "recon push" or "recon pull".

Recon push

Recon push means that prior to a battle, the commander identifies one or more named area of interest (NAI) for a recon mission. In this manner, the recon team is pushed toward an objective within the area of operation (AO) and will develop the situation for the commander.

Recon Pull

Recon pull means that during a battle, the commander identifies an enemy or geographical objective for one or more recon teams. In this manner, each recon team has significant latitude of movement throughout the AO in order to gain contact with the enemy objective, develop the situation, and pull the main force, altering the direction of advance in order to engage the enemy.

Steps

1. In the case of route recon, the patrol typically begins from the assembly area (AA) and the start point serves in the same manner as a release point. During a route recon, a highly mobile reserve force may follow a safe distance behind the recon team. In such cases, the PL issues a contingency plan for both the recon team and the reserve force.

2. The patrol moves along a designated direction of advance or LOC. At each phase line and NAI, the recon team conducts a security halt for the entire patrol—including the reserve force. This security halt becomes an ERP. From the ERP, the recon team gathers information using the butterfly technique.

3. The distance each recon team will travel out from the route depends greatly on the visibility of the terrain and/or the size of the obstacle. The recon team gathers all information regarding road conditions, obstacles, bridges, enemy activity, civilian traffic, and natural choke points along parallel terrain where the enemy might impose a threat along the route.

4. Upon returning to the security halt, each recon team disseminates information among the patrol members. A written record is kept to log all information and the PL will report to higher command after each rendezvous back at the ERP.

5. The recon patrol continues on route to the next phase line or NAI and the entire process repeats itself until the patrol has adequately navigated the entire route. At that time, the PL may be required to move the recon patrol back to the FLOT or the patrol may be tasked to another mission. In either case, the PL must make a full report to higher command.

B. The Zone Reconnaissance

Zone reconnaissance is a form of reconnaissance that involves a directed effort to obtain detailed information on all routes, obstacles, terrain, and enemy forces within a zone defined by boundaries. It is appropriate when the enemy situation is vague, existing knowledge of the terrain is limited, or combat operations have altered the terrain. A zone reconnaissance may include several route or area reconnaissance missions assigned to subordinate units.

A zone reconnaissance is normally a deliberate, time-consuming process. It takes more time than any other reconnaissance mission, so the commander must allow adequate time to conduct it. A zone reconnaissance is normally conducted over an extended distance. It requires all ground elements executing the zone reconnaissance to be employed abreast of each other. However, when the reconnaissance objective is the enemy force, a commander may forgo a detailed reconnaissance of the zone and focus his assets on those named areas of interest (NAI) that would reveal enemy dispositions and intentions.

Zone Reconnaissance Tasks

Unless the commander orders otherwise, a unit conducting a zone reconnaissance performs the following tasks within the limits of its capabilities. A commander issue guidance on which tasks the unit must complete or the priority of tasks, which is usually clear from the reconnaissance objective. Tasks include:

- Find and report all enemy forces within the zone
- Clear all enemy forces in the designated AO within the capability of the unit conducting reconnaissance
- Determine the trafficability of all terrain within the zone, including built-up areas
- Locate and determine the extent of all contaminated areas in the zone
- Evaluate and classify all bridges, defiles, overpasses, underpasses, and culverts in the zone
- Locate any fords, crossing sites, or bypasses for existing and reinforcing obstacles (including built-up areas) in the zone
- Locate all obstacles and create lanes as specified in execution orders
- Report the above information to the commander directing the zone reconnaissance, to include providing a sketch map or overlay

Conducting the Zone Reconnaissance - A Small Unit Perspective

A zone recon collects detailed information of the terrain, obstacles, routes, and enemy forces within a specified zone that has been designated by boundaries on a map.

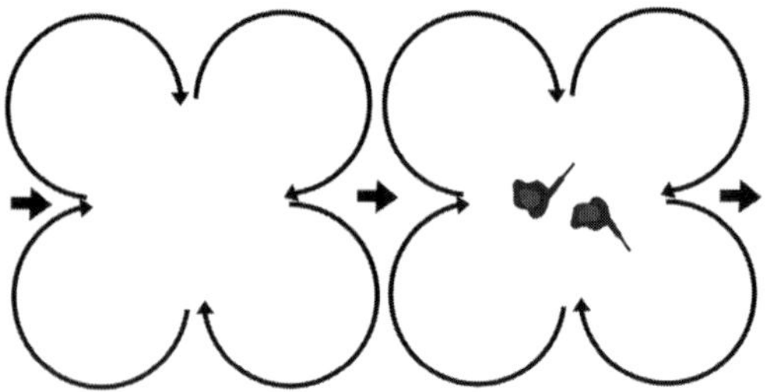

This method of conducting a zone reconnaissance uses a series of rally points to stop and then dispatch the recon teams. The patrol then moves to the next rally point. Zone recon tends to be a time consuming mission. (Ref: FM 7-92, chap 4, fig. 4-6)

Tactical Enabling Ops

1. Upon occupying the ORP, the PL confirms the location of the recon objective. All special equipment is prepared for use and plans are finalized. In this case, the ORP acts more like an assault position in that the patrol will not defend the ORP, nor will they return to the ORP.

The converging route method uses multiple recon teams—and therefore requires larger numbers of troops. Rally points are established and the multiple recon teams move along a designated lane or terrain feature. (Ref: FM 7-92, chap 4, fig. 4-7)

2. **Converging Route Method:** This method uses multiple recon teams that do NOT meet again until they rendezvous at the far side of the zone! This means that a rally point is clearly established on an easily recognized terrain feature or landmark at the far side of the recon objective. Additionally, a near recognition signal is established to ensure that the fireteams do not mistakenly fire upon each other!

3. At the release point, the PL divides the patrol into the assigned recon teams. The PL must travel with one of these teams. The PL issues each recon team a contingency plan.

4. The recon teams depart the release point and move along parallel directions of advance through the specified zone. The recon teams stop at each phase line and NAI to conduct recons using the butterfly technique—which makes use of a series of designated, en route rally points. The recon team pays particular attention to signs of enemy activity:

- Fresh trash and cigarette butts indicate recent enemy activity
- Boot prints and bent vegetation indicate the direction of enemy travel
- The number of pressed vegetation spots at rest stops indicate the size of enemy patrols

Ultimately, the recon teams look for enemy movement, the size of their patrols, and established routes of movement. Also of great importance is the type of activity. For example, is the enemy running re-supply routes or ambush patrols? All enemy resources—outposts, water points, and obstacles such as a minefield—are thoroughly investigated.

5. Each time the recon teams reassemble in a rally point, information is disseminated and reported back to the PL, if possible. The PL in turn makes reports back to higher command.

6. The recon teams rendezvous at the far end of the objective and the PL takes charge of all collected information, disseminating the information to the patrol members and issuing another report to higher command.

7. The patrol moves back to the FLOT via an alternative route. It is generally not a good idea to return using the same route as the reconnaissance. To do so would invite the possibility of an enemy ambush, if in fact the enemy observed your movement. Upon arrival, the PL reports directly to the commander.

C. The Area Reconnaissance

Area reconnaissance is a form of reconnaissance that focuses on obtaining detailed information about the terrain or enemy activity within a prescribed area. This area may include a town, a ridgeline, woods, an airhead, or any other feature critical to operations. The area may consist of a single point, such as a bridge or an installation. Areas are normally smaller than zones and are not usually contiguous to other friendly areas targeted for reconnaissance.

Area Reconnaissance Tasks

The tasks for an area reconnaissance are the same as for a zone reconnaissance, to include:

- Find and report all enemy forces within the zone
- Clear all enemy forces in the designated AO within the capability of the unit conducting reconnaissance
- Determine the trafficability of all terrain within the zone, including built-up areas
- Locate and determine the extent of all contaminated areas in the zone
- Evaluate and classify all bridges, defiles, overpasses, underpasses, and culverts in the zone
- Locate any fords, crossing sites, or bypasses for existing and reinforcing obstacles (including built-up areas) in the zone
- Locate all obstacles and create lanes as specified in execution orders
- Report the above information to the commander directing the zone reconnaissance, to include providing a sketch map or overlay

Conducting the Area Reconnaissance - A Small Unit Perspective

The area recon has the objective of obtaining detailed information on an identified terrain feature, man-made feature, or enemy force within a specified area. This area is much smaller in terms of space than the objectives for the other forms of recon and thereby allows for a much smaller recon team.

1. Upon occupying the ORP, the PL confirms the location of the recon objective. All special equipment is prepared for use and plans are finalized. The PL issues contingency plans to the recon team(s) and to the security team left to defend the ORP.

2. The PL moves to the release point and dispatches the recon team(s) to approach the objective. Typically, the PL moves back to the ORP or may opt to accompany one of the recon teams if there are limited troops available. This decision is made in the planning phase of the mission.

Single-Team Method

3. Using the clock method, the recon team approaches the recon objective from its closest point. This point now becomes the six o'clock position of the objective. The recon team will observe the enemy force, the enemy activity, and obstacles using stealth.

4. The recon team records all pertinent information:

- A sketch of their vantage point, including terrain and enemy structures
- An exact number of enemy personnel sighted
- A descriptive list of all equipment, uniforms and markings
- The time of guard shift, eating, and sleeping shift rotations
- The direction, time, and size of any patrols coming or going from the area

5. The recon team then withdraws and maneuvers to the approximate nine o'clock position. The recon team repeats their observation and recording activities. The recon team continues on to the twelve o'clock position and then the three o'clock position, obtaining information from all four vantage points—if such a maneuver is possible. At a bare minimum, the recon team must observe the targeted area from two vantage points.

Double-Team Method

3. When the troops are available, the PL may choose to dispatch two recon teams to the objective. This speeds the gathering of information, but also creates a very real danger of fratricide. To coordinate this so that there is little chance of the two recon teams actually making contact, the teams are assigned opposite vantage points.

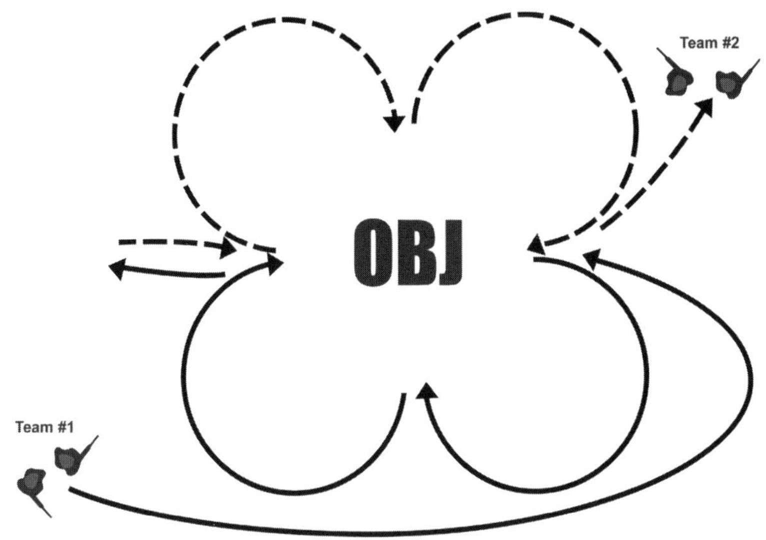

The double team method of the area recon uses multiple, small teams to capitalize on time and place the "smallest footprint" forward. This is important when stealth is a factor. (Ref: FM 7-92, chap 4, fig. 4-5)

4. Both teams are dispatched together and proceed toward the closest point of the targeted area. Upon locating this six o'clock position, a designated recon team would then withdraw slightly and proceed to the approximate twelve o'clock position.

5. Both recon teams record the same pertinent information as list for the single-team method. However, the recon team at the six o'clock position will proceed only to the vantage point of the nine o'clock position and then return to the ORP. Likewise, the recon team at the twelve o'clock position will proceed only to the three o'clock vantage point, and then return to the ORP.

Dissemination of Information

6. Once the recon team(s) returns to the ORP, all information is immediately disseminated among every member of the recon patrol. If there is time, additional copies of the sketches and record lists should be made. This will increase the likelihood of the gathered information making it back to the commander if the patrol is ambushed in route.

7. The recon team returns to the forward line of troops (FLOT) via a pre-designated route. Upon arrival, the PL reports directly to the commander.

D. Reconnaissance in Force (RIF)

A reconnaissance in force is a deliberate combat operation designed to discover or test the enemy's strength, dispositions, and reactions or to obtain other information. Battalion-size task forces or larger organizations usually conduct a reconnaissance in force (RIF) mission. A commander assigns a RIF mission when the enemy is known to be operating within an area and the commander cannot obtain adequate intelligence by any other means. A unit may also conduct a RIF in restrictive-type terrain where the enemy is likely to ambush smaller reconnaissance forces. A RIF is an aggressive reconnaissance, conducted as an offensive operation with clearly stated reconnaissance objectives. The overall goal of a RIF is to determine enemy weaknesses that can be exploited.

Reconnaissance in Force Tasks

A unit conducting a RIF performs the following tasks within the limits of its capabilities. If a unit does not have the time or resources to complete all of these tasks, it must inform the commander assigning the mission. He must then issue further guidance on which tasks the unit must complete or the priority of tasks, which is usually clear from the reconnaissance objective. Tasks include:

- Penetrating the enemy's security area and determining its size and depth
- Determining the location and disposition of enemy main positions
- Attacking enemy main positions and attempting to cause the enemy to react by using local reserves or major counterattack forces, employing fire support assets, adjusting positions, and employing specific weapon systems
- Determining weaknesses in the enemy's dispositions to exploit

On Point

A commander needs to know what lies ahead of the friendly force before an engagement, during an engagement, and after an engagement. The reconnaissance team acts as the eyes and ears for the commander. This is absolutely essential for situational awareness.

Reconnaissance is the means by which a commander "sees" the battlefield. In spite of all the wonderful tools available for conducting surveillance, the task of recon is by and large a human endeavor. That means boots on the ground.

Contact with the enemy does not necessarily mean to engage the enemy in a firefight. For the sake of reconnaissance, contact means to observe the enemy, develop the situation, and pass back the pertinent information that the commander needs in order to make a sound tactical decision.

The principles of Mission, Enemy, Terrain and weather, Time available, Troops available, Civilians on the battlefield (METT-TC) dictate the reconnaissance effort. Though each principle consideration is important, the consideration of time is critical in establishing how much stealth is required.

- Unlimited time + great detail needed means that considerable stealth is required
- Limited time + little detail needed means that considerable speed is required

Tactical Enabling Operations

III. Relief in Place

Ref: FM 3-90 Tactics, chap 15 and FM 3-21.10 (FM 7-10) The Infantry Rifle Company, pp. 8-8 to 8-12.

A relief in place is a tactical enabling operation in which, by the direction of higher authority, all or part of a unit is replaced in an area by the incoming unit. A commander conducts a relief in place as part of a larger operation, primarily to maintain the combat effectiveness of committed units. A relief in place may also be conducted--

- To reorganize, reconstitute, or re-equip a unit that has sustained heavy losses
- To rest units that have conducted sustained operations
- To establish the security force or the detachment left in contact (DLIC) during a withdrawal operation
- To allow the relieved unit to conduct another operation

A unit may relieve another unit by assuming their same defensive position, or the new unit may opt to develop new defensive positions that afford it a better means to coordinate fires against the enemy within the engagement area. (Photo by Jeong, Hae-jung).

The higher headquarters directs when and where to conduct the relief and establishes the appropriate control measures. Normally, the unit relieved is defending. However, a relief may set the stage for resuming offensive operations. A relief may also serve to free the relieved unit for other tasks, such as decontamination, reconstitution, routine rest, resupply, maintenance, or specialized training. Sometimes, as part of a larger operation, a commander wants the enemy force to discover the relief, because that discovery might cause it to do something in response that is prejudicial to its interest, such as move reserves from an area where the friendly commander wants to conduct a penetration.

Conducting the Relief in Place - A Small Unit Perspective

I. Organization

Both units involved in a relief in place should be of similar type—such as mounted or dismounted—and task organized to help maintain operations security (OPSEC). The relieving unit usually assumes as closely as possible the same task organization as the unit being relieved. It assigns responsibilities and deploys in a configuration similar to the relieved unit.

The relieving unit establishes advance parties to conduct detailed coordination and preparations for the operation, down to the company level and possibly to the platoon level. These advance parties infiltrate forward to avoid detection. They normally include the echelon's tactical command post, which co-locates with the main headquarters of the unit being relieved. The commander may also attach additional liaison personnel to subordinate units to ensure a smooth changeover between subordinate units.

II. Planning & Preparation

Once ordered to conduct a relief in place, the commander of the relieving unit contacts the commander of the unit to be relieved. The co-location of unit command posts also helps achieve the level of coordination required. If the relieved unit's forward elements can defend the AO, the relieving unit executes the relief in place from the rear to the front. This facilitates movement and terrain management.

Hasty or Deliberate

A relief is either deliberate or hasty, depending on the amount of planning and preparations. The major differences are the depth and detail of planning and, potentially, the execution time. Detailed planning generally facilitates shorter execution time by determining exactly what the commander believes he needs to do and the resources needed to accomplish the mission. Deliberate planning allows the commander and his staff to identify, develop, and coordinate solutions to most potential problems before they occur and to ensure the availability of resources when and where they are needed.

In a deliberate relief, units exchange plans and liaison personnel, conduct briefings, perform detailed reconnaissance, and publish orders with detailed instructions. In a hasty relief, the commander abbreviates the planning process and controls the execution using oral and fragmentary orders.

Preparations begin with an exchange of liaison officers and NCOs from both the forward unit and the relieving unit. The effort is to identify maneuver control measures. At a minimum this means identifying the AO boundaries, assembly area (AA), routes, release points, and battle positions. Furthermore, each battle position must identify the engagement area, target reference points (TRP), defensive fires measures, and fire support measures to the incoming friendly forces.

The final preparation focuses on whether there will be new positions created, or old positions simply occupied by the incoming friendly force. Obviously, the activity and noise inherent in the construction of new fighting positions is a dead giveaway that a relief in place is underway. If stealth is an important factor, then simply assuming the older battle positions would be best. However, often enough the relief in place also has the intention of developing a more advantageous battle position. This must also be planned and coordinated.

III. Execution

Techniques: Sequential, Simultaneous or Staggered

There are three techniques for conducting a relief: sequentially, simultaneously, or staggered. A sequential relief occurs when each element within the relieved unit is relieved in succession, from right to left or left to right, depending on how it is deployed. A simultaneous relief occurs when all elements are relieved at the same time. A staggered relief occurs when the commander relieves each element in a sequence determined by the tactical situation, not its geographical orientation. Simultaneous relief takes the least time to execute, but is more easily detected by the enemy. Sequential or staggered reliefs can take place over a significant amount of time.

In practice, small units almost always conduct the relief simultaneously. While it is true at higher echelons, larger units may phase the relief in place sequentially or staggered, small units such as companies and platoons almost always assume their position en mass in a simultaneous manner.

1. Upon receiving the warning order (WARNO), the fresh unit will exchange of liaison officers and/or NCOs with the forward unit. This is done to achieve three effects:

- To identify the forward unit's battle positions as well as friendly and enemy situations
- To form the relieving unit into a similar task organization as the forward unit
- To coordinate link up operations

2. The plan is developed and rehearsed. This plan will balance the need for speed with the need for stealth. Similarly, the plan will dictate whether new battle positions will be created, or the forward unit's battle positions will be assumed instead. There is considerable coordination that must take place at headquarters-level to ensure that the relief takes place smoothly; that security is maintained for force protection; and that any chance of fratricide is mitigated—particularly if the relief will take place in hours of limited visibility.

3. An advanced guard of the fresh unit conducts the relief first. They will move forward of the forward line of troops (FLOT) to conduct screening operations. This activity is intended to deny observation to enemy reconnaissance teams and provide early warning of an enemy attack.

4. The fresh unit moves into the AO and halts in the AA. The liaison coordinates for a guide, and the fresh unit moves along its assigned route to a release point immediately behind the battle position. At the release point, the two leaders meet (from the incoming fresh unit and the forward unit) to conduct final coordination.

5. At a previously designated time, signal, or condition, the subordinate platoons, squad, and fireteams guide into and assume the fighting positions of the forward unit—with the forward unit troops still in place!

6. Once the fresh unit has assumed all of the fighting positions within the sector, the Forward unit commander passes command of the battle position to the new unit commander. The passage of command is communicated by radio, field phone, or a predesignated signal.

7. On order, the relieved unit now begins to egress back through the release point and follows the same route back to their assigned AA. Typically the last fighting positions to withdraw are the crew-served weapon positions. Once all other relieved troops have fallen back, these crews will follow suit.

8. A variation on the relief in place operation may take place if the intent of the fresh unit is to immediately transition into offensive action. In this case, the forward unit does not relinquish command, and at a minimum, the crew-served weapons are maintained in place to provide cover fire for the fresh unit's advance into the engagement area.

On Point

Units cannot remain on the front line indefinitely. Troops become exhausted and complacent, and the decision-making process is degraded. For this reason, a scheduled relief of the forward unit may take place. There are additional reasons a unit may require relief. In the event the forward unit has come under chemical attack, or experienced unusually high casualties the forward unit may also be relieved.

The relief in place operation is directed by a higher authority for a fresh unit to assume the duties and geographic area of operations (AO) of the forward unit. This may be conducted deliberately or hastily depending on the amount of time available for planning. As a general rule of thumb, the more planning, the quicker and smoother the relief in place goes.

The enemy in front of the unit to be relieved almost always detects the relief in place. This is due to the increased activity and noise, as well as the appearance of new or different equipment. The hastier the relief in place is conducted, the quicker the enemy is to recognize the relief.

The relief in place should be a routine operation. However, anecdotal evidence indicates a disproportional amount of incidents of fratricide occur during relief in place and passage of lines operations. The relief in place leaves the forces massed to the point of having little to no room for maneuver and vulnerable to enemy attack.

To complicate things further, the relief in place is often conducted during conditions of limited visibility, and when relieving the FLOT there is always the possibility of a firefight. That does not present such a significant threat to the forward unit, per se. After all, they have a better grasp of situational awareness—the direction and capability of the enemy, assigned sectors of fire, and an understanding of where the other friendly fighting positions are located. Furthermore, the forward unit troops are relatively secure within their fighting positions for most of the relief in place.

This is not true for the relieving unit coming in fresh. They are not familiar to the enemy positions, directions, or even capabilities. The relieving unit is not fully aware of the location of every forward unit's position. And the relieving unit is moving forward—outside the protection of the fighting positions.

Both units should make every effort to keep the enemy from knowing about the relief. Try to conduct the relief during limited visibility to reduce the risk of discovery by a capable threat.

The dispositions, activities, and radio traffic of the relieved unit must be maintained throughout the relief. Both companies should be on the relieved company's net. The relieved company continues routine traffic, which the relieving company monitors. Once the relief is complete and on a prearranged signal, the relieving company changes to their assigned frequency. Security activities, such as OPs and patrols, must maintain the established schedule. This might require some personnel from the relieving unit being placed under operational control (OPCON) of the relieved unit before the relief.

Tactical Enabling Operations

IV. Passage of Lines

Ref: FM 3-90 Tactics, chap 16; FM 7-85 Ranger Unit Operations, chap 6; and FM 3-21.10 (FM 7-10) The Infantry Rifle Company, pp. 8-13 to 8-17.

Passage of lines is a tactical enabling operation in which one unit moves through another unit's positions with the intent of moving into or out of enemy contact. A commander conducts a passage of lines to continue an attack or conduct a counterattack, retrograde security or main battle forces, and anytime one unit cannot bypass another unit's position. The conduct of a passage of lines potentially involves close combat. It involves transferring the responsibility for an area of operations (AO) between two commanders. That transfer of responsibility usually occurs when roughly two-thirds of the passing force has moved through the passage point. If not directed by higher authority, the unit commanders determine—by mutual agreement—the time to pass command.

The patrol forms into a tight 360-degree assembly area just behind the forward line of troops. The patrol leader coordinates with the forward unit commander. (Photo by Jeong, Hae-jung).

A passage of lines occurs under two basic conditions. A forward passage of lines occurs when a unit passes through another unit's positions while moving toward the enemy. A rearward passage of lines occurs when a unit passes through another unit's positions while moving away from the enemy. Reasons for conducting a passage of lines are to—

- Sustain the tempo of an offensive operation
- Maintain the viability of the defense by transferring responsibility from one unit to another
- Transition from a delay or security operation by one force to a defense
- Free a unit for another mission or task

I. Conducting a Passage of Lines - A Small Unit Perspective

Passage of lines consists of essentially two tasks, (1) coordinating the time and place of the *departure*, and (2) coordinating the time, place and signals of the *reentry* through the FLOT. This means we identify a time and a passage point for both phases. The forward unit commander identifies the passage lane, which is the precise route our patrol takes through his defensive position. Use the following for planning a passage of lines:

1. Contact and coordinate with the forward unit commander
2. Move to an assembly area (AA) behind the passage point
3. Link up with the guide to depart the FLOT
4. Conduct a security halt past the forward edge of battle area (FEBA)
5. Complete the mission
6. Return to the passage point
7. Render the far & near recognition signal to the forward unit commander
8. Link up with the guide to reenter the FLOT
9. Move into the AA to debrief the patrol

Let's break it down into two parts, departing the FLOT and reentering the FLOT. The process is more detailed; however the list will make sense as the mission planning is conceptualized.

Departing the Forward Line of Own Troops (FLOT)

1. Communicate and coordinate with the forward unit commander. The PL coordinates the time and place of the patrol's departure and reentry with the forward unit commander. The PL chooses an appropriate time. The forward unit commander _chooses the appropriate passage lane through his defense. The forward unit commander also assigns a guide to lead the patrol through the wire and mine obstacles forward of the FLOT.

2. Move to the AA behind the passage point. Here the final planning, rehearsals, and coordination with the forward unit commander takes place. For this coordination, the forward unit commander supplies the following information to the patrol:

- An orientation on terrain
- Known or suspected enemy positions
- Recent enemy activity
- The location of friendly OP/LP and obstacles—wire and minefields
- Available combat support—guides, fire support, medevac and reaction forces

The PL provides the following information to the forward unit commander:

- The patrol's unit designation
- The size of the patrol
- The departure and reentry times
- All coordinating signals—near and far recognition

3. Link up with the guide to depart the FLOT through the passage lane. Once the patrol has occupied the AA, the forward unit commander links the PL with a guide. The PL restates the patrol's departure and reentry times, and near and far recognition signals for the guide. The guide is then introduced to the patrol's pointman and dragman. This allows the guide to recognize the beginning and ending of the patrol as he counts each member through the passage lane.

Tactical Enabling Ops

The PL also establishes a time limit for which the guide will wait on the far side of the passage lane. This measure allows the guide to lead the patrol back through the passage lane if the patrol is attacked in the FEBA and needs to reenter the FLOT quickly!

4. Conduct a security halt past the FEBA. As soon as the patrol passes through the passage lane of the FLOT, the patrol enters the FEBA. The patrol moves to the far side of the FEBA, seeks adequate concealment, and conducts a security halt. This first security halt is called the "listening halt." Every member of the patrol sits comfortably and then removes their headgear. Making no noise, the patrol must listen to the indigenous sounds for about five minutes. This lets the patrol member's eyes and ears adjust to the new environment.

5. Complete the Mission. When the PL is comfortable that the patrol is safe and has adjusted to the noise, sights, and smells, the patrol continues towards the objective. When the mission is complete, the patrol will return to the FLOT. Under normal circumstances the patrol returns using a different route than the patrol's advance. This reduces the opportunity for the enemy to ambush the patrol.

It might be worth mentioning here that depending on the nature of the mission, the patrol might not return to the FLOT...in which case such coordination won't be necessary. Recognizing that exception, the norm is to always plan and coordinate to return.

Reentering the Forward Line of Own Troops (FLOT)

1. Return to the passage point. The patrol returns to a secure position on the far side of the FEBA using a pre-determined route. From this position the PL contacts the forward unit commander and coordinates to reenter the FLOT.

2. Render the far & near recognition signal to the forward unit commander. Once in position, the patrol makes contact with the forward unit commander/guide using the designated far recognition signal. It is the patrol's intention to make contact with the far recognition signal first. Subsequently, the patrol makes contact using the near recognition signal. The far recognition signal uses distance signaling, such as a radio broadcast, or smoke signal, or flare/light signal. The near recognition signal uses verbal contact, such as a password, or visual recognition of each other.

If for any reason contact cannot be made with the far recognition signal, the patrol dispatches a small element forward to make contact with the FLOT using the near recognition signal to coordinate our reentry.

During nighttime operations, if the patrol cannot make contact with the forward unit commander/guide using the far recognition signal, it is customary that the patrol waits in security position until daylight. Only during daylight will the patrol render a near recognition signal without first making contact with the far recognition signal.

3. Link up with the guide to reenter the FLOT through the passage lane. After the patrol makes contact with the FLOT, a security team crosses the FEBA to render the near recognition signal with the guide. A member of the security team then returns to the patrol and leads the remainder of the patrol across the FEBA to the guide waiting at the passage lane. The PL links up with the guide and counts the patrol members in *by name*. This lets the guide know that no enemy has slipped into the patrol and infiltrated their defensive line.

4. Move into the AA to debrief the patrol. The patrol moves back into the AA behind the FLOT. The patrol is debriefed either by the forward unit commander or representative of higher command. The patrol discusses the nature and findings of the mission on a "need to know basis."

II. Organization

A unit may participate in a passage of lines as either the passing or stationary force. Except for co-locating command posts and providing for guides by the stationary force, conducting a passage of lines does not require a special task organization.

The organization of the patrol depends more on the primary mission than the task of passage of lines. A forward passing unit's order of march is generally reconnaissance and security elements first.

The forward friendly unit provides a guide through friendly obstacles (mines and wire). The guide waits at this position for a pre-determined length of time in case the patrol needs to fall back through the passage lane. (Photo by Jeong, Hae-jung).

On Point

A passage of lines is a complex process at higher levels of command in which the commander must move hundreds or even thousands of troops through the forward lines of another friendly unit. When two friendly units converge upon the same space on a battlefield, there is always the potential to mistake each other for enemy. Fratricide is a very real danger in these cases, particularly at night.

For small tactical units, such as the fire team, squad, platoon, and company the process of departing and reentering the forward line is much simpler—though the danger of fratricide is the same. For this reason, the patrol leader coordinates carefully with the forward unit commander and supporting unit commander.

The process of a passage of lines serves as coordination between two units when one unit either moves forward or rearward through the defensive line of a stationary unit. More specifically, a unit may depart forward of the forward line of troops (FLOT) in order to maneuver against an enemy force. Conversely, a unit may reenter rearward of the FLOT in order to maneuver away from an enemy force.

Chap 6

Special Purpose Attacks

Ref: FM 3-90 Tactics, pp. 5-29 to 5-40.

An attack is an offensive operation that destroys or defeats enemy forces, seizes and secures terrain, or both. Movement, supported by fires, characterizes the conduct of an attack. However, based on his analysis of the factors of METT-TC, the commander may decide to conduct an attack using only fires. An attack differs from a MTC because enemy main body dispositions are at least partially known, which allows the commander to achieve greater synchronization. This enables him to mass the effects of the attacking force's combat power more effectively in an attack than in a MTC.

Special purpose attacks are ambush, spoiling attack, counterattack, raid, feint, and demonstration. The commander's intent and the factors of METT-TC determine which of these forms of attack are employed. He can conduct each of these forms of attack, except for a raid, as either a hasty or a deliberate operation.

Note: This chapter specifically discusses "special purpose attacks." Chap. 2 discusses the attack (pp. 2-13 to 2-18) and other forms of the offense.

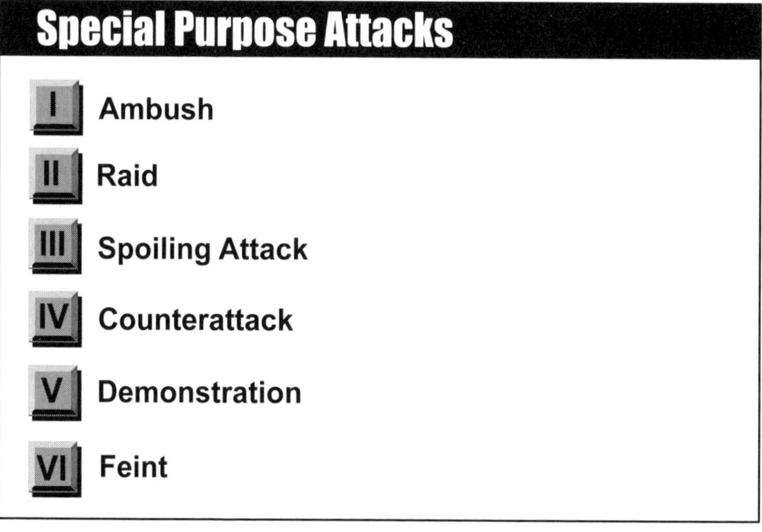

Ref: FM 3-90 Tactics, pp. 5-29 to 5-40.

I. Ambush

An ambush is a form of attack by fire or other destructive means from concealed positions on a moving or temporarily halted enemy. It may include an assault to close with and destroy the engaged enemy force. In an ambush, ground objectives do not have to be seized and held.

Note: See pp. 6-3 to 6-16 for further discussion on the ambush.

II. Raid

A raid is a form of attack, usually small scale, involving a swift entry into hostile territory to secure information, confuse the enemy, or destroy installations. It ends with a planned withdrawal from the objective area on mission completion. A raid can also be used to support operations designed to rescue and recover individuals and equipment in danger of capture.

Note: See pp. 6-17 to 6-22 for further discussion on the raid.

III. Spoiling Attack

A spoiling attack is a form of attack that preempts or seriously impairs an enemy attack while the enemy is in the process of planning or preparing to attack. The objective of a spoiling attack is to disrupt the enemy's offensive capabilities and timelines while destroying his personnel and equipment, not to secure terrain and other physical objectives. A commander conducts a spoiling attack whenever possible during friendly defensive operations to strike the enemy while he is in assembly areas or attack positions preparing for his own offensive operation or is temporarily stopped. It usually employs heavy, attack helicopter, or fire support elements to attack enemy assembly positions in front of the friendly commander's main line of resistance or battle positions.

IV. Counterattack

A counterattack is a form of attack by part or all of a defending force against an enemy attacking force, with the general objective of denying the enemy his goal in attacking. The commander directs a counterattack—normally conducted from a defensive posture—to defeat or destroy enemy forces, exploit an enemy weakness, such as an exposed flank, or to regain control of terrain and facilities after an enemy success. A unit conducts a counterattack to seize the initiative from the enemy through offensive action. A counterattacking force maneuvers to isolate and destroy a designated enemy force. It can attack by fire into an engagement area to defeat or destroy an enemy force, restore the original position, or block an enemy penetration. Once launched, the counterattack normally becomes a decisive operation for the commander conducting the counterattack.

V. Demonstration

A demonstration is a form of attack designed to deceive the enemy as to the location or time of the decisive operation by a display of force. Forces conducting a demonstration do not seek contact with the enemy.

VI. Feint

A feint is a form of attack used to deceive the enemy as to the location or time of the actual decisive operation. Forces conducting a feint seek direct fire contact with the enemy but avoid decisive engagement . A commander uses them in conjunction with other military deception activities. They generally attempt to deceive the enemy and induce him to move reserves and shift his fire support to locations where they cannot immediately impact the friendly decisive operation or take other actions not conducive to the enemy's best interests during the defense.

The principal difference between these forms of attack is that in a feint the commander assigns the force an objective limited in size, scope, or some other measure. Forces conducting a feint make direct fire contact with the enemy but avoid decisive engagement. Forces conducting a demonstration do not seek contact with the enemy. The planning, preparing, and executing considerations for demonstrations and feints are the same as for the other forms of attack.

Special Purpose Attacks

I. Ambush

Ref: FM 3-90 Tactics, pp. 5-29 to 5-34; FM 7-85 Ranger Unit Operations, chap 6; and FM 3-21.8 (FM 7-8) The Infantry Rifle Platoon and Squad, pp. 7-26 to 7-29.

An ambush is a form of attack by fire or other destructive means from concealed positions on a moving or temporarily halted enemy. It may take the form of an assault to close with and destroy the enemy, or be an attack by fire only. An ambush does not require ground to be seized or held. Ambushes are generally executed to reduce the enemy force's overall combat effectiveness. Destruction is the primary reason for conducting an ambush. Other reasons to conduct ambushes are to harass the enemy, capture the enemy, destroy or capture enemy equipment, and gain information about the enemy. Ambushes are classified by category (deliberate or hasty), formation (linear or L-shaped), and type (point, area, or antiarmor).

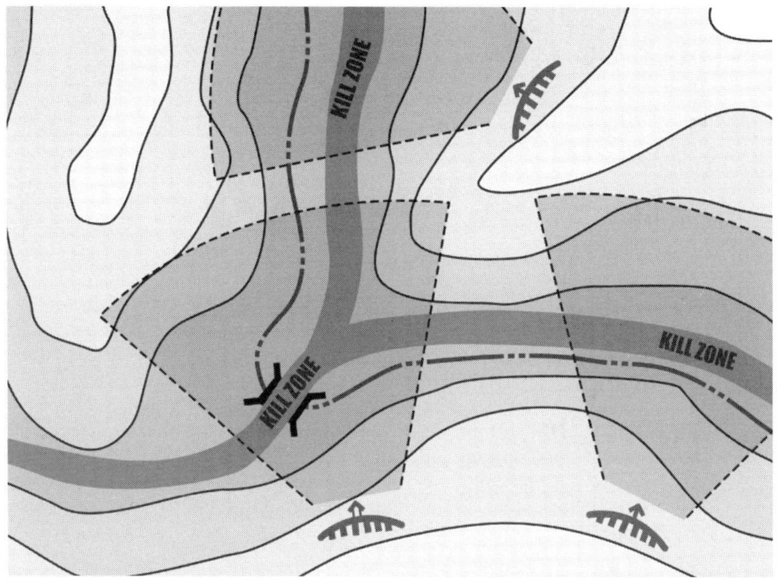

Area ambushes trap the enemy in a network of attacks from multiple concealed positions. These ambushes are carefully oriented to avoid "friendly fire" and yet maximize combat power against the enemy. (Ref: FM 7-8, chap 3, fig. 3-15).

The execution of an ambush is offensive in nature. However, a unit may be directed to conduct an ambush during offensive or defensive operations. An ambush normally consists of the following actions:

- Tactical movement to the objective rally point (ORP)
- Reconnaissance of the ambush site
- Establishment of the ambush security site
- Preparation of the ambush site
- Execution of the ambush
- Withdrawal

The intent of any ambush is to kill enemy troops and destroy enemy equipment. From a small unit perspective, how that is achieved and to what extent determines the difference in employing either a near ambush or a far ambush.

Near Ambush

The near ambush has the expressed purpose of destroying the target. This often requires an assaulting force to literally overrun the target after the initial volley of fire has inflicted tremendous damage. Again, the intent is to destroy everything.

Since the patrol will overwhelm the target, the patrol will get as close as possible to the enemy. This close proximity also means that friendly forces MUST outnumber the enemy target.

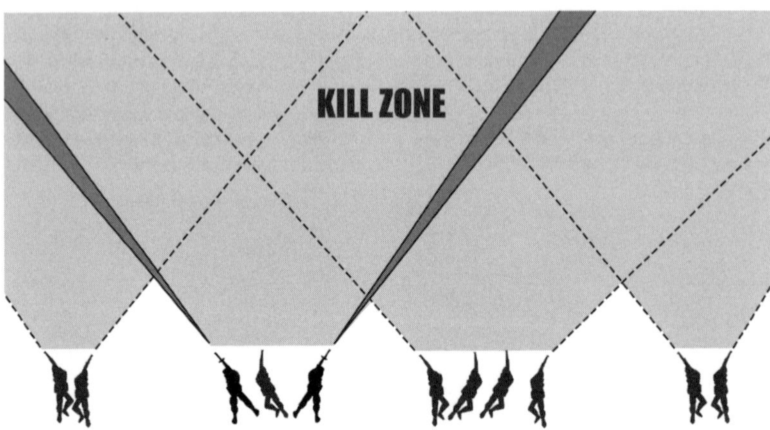

The near ambush has the express intent of overwhelming and destroying the enemy force. The near ambush masses close to the kill zone and requires careful fire coordination. The linear method offers the greatest simplicity. (Ref: FM 7-85, chap 6, fig. 6-1).

Far Ambush

The far ambush has only the purpose of injuring and/or delaying the target. This rarely ever calls for an assaulting force—since the patrol doesn't seek the complete destruction of the enemy force there is no need to risk the loss of friendly troops. The far ambush simply intends to *harass*.

A far ambush team can engage an enemy patrol of any size or type. It does not matter if the enemy force is larger than the patrol because significant distances are used, as well as natural obstacles of the terrain, and established routes of withdraw that allows the ambush patrol to escape before the enemy has time to organize an effective counterattack.

I. Organization

An ambush patrol will be broken into multiple teams, each with a very specific set of responsibilities. The Infantry platoon is normally task-organized into assault, support, and security elements for execution of the ambush.

Each team must be assigned a leader. The ambush will require special equipment for each assigned team. This equipment should be made available for the rehearsal as well, to ensure everything functions according to the execution plan. Each team has a specific set of duties.

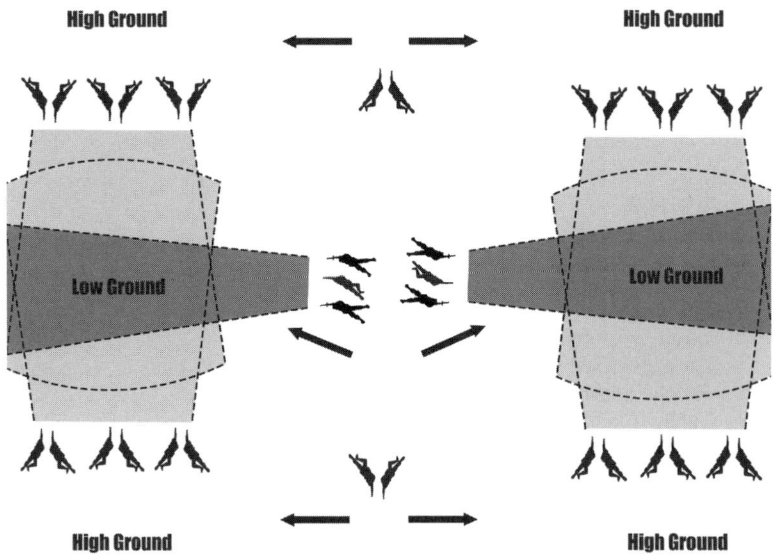

The parallel ambush method is a favorite among OPFOR militaries. It uses the high ground and plunging fires to prevent fratricide. Support teams may be used in the middle to stop the enemy advance.

The small unit leader considers the factors of METT-TC to determine the required formation:

Linear

In an ambush using a linear formation, the assault and support elements deploy parallel to the enemy's route. This position forces the enemy on the long axis of the kill zone, and subjects the enemy to flanking fire. The linear formation can be used in close terrain that restricts the enemy's ability to maneuver against the platoon, or in open terrain (provided a means of keeping the enemy in the kill zone can be effected).

L-Shaped

In an L-shaped ambush the assault element forms the long leg parallel to the enemy's direction of movement along the kill zone. The support element forms the short leg at one end of and at a right angle to the assault element. This provides both flanking (long leg) and enfilading (short leg) fires against the enemy. The L-shaped ambush can be used at a sharp bend in a road, trail, or stream. It should not be used where the short leg would have to cross a straight road or trail. The platoon leader must consider the other factors of METT-TC before opting for the L-shaped formation. Special attention must be placed on sectors of fire and surface danger zone (SDZ) of weapons because of the risk of fratricide.

V-Shaped Ambush

The V-shaped ambush assault elements are placed along both sides of the enemy route so they form a V. Take extreme care to ensure neither group fires into the other. This formation subjects the enemy to both enfilading and interlocking fire.

Note: See pp. 6-6 to 6-7 for discussion of the organization of the near ambush; pp. 6-8 to 6-9 for organization of the far ambush. See p. 6-16 for a discussion of the categories of ambushes.

A. Organization - The Near Ambush

An ambush patrol will be broken into multiple teams, each with a very specific set of responsibilities. The team must be assigned a leader. The team must also be allowed to work together at least during the rehearsals prior to the mission. This practice lets members of the patrol understand their role within that specific team, and shows how the multiple teams fit into the bigger picture of the mission.

The ambush will require special equipment for each assigned team. This equipment should be made available for the rehearsal as well, to ensure everything functions according to the execution plan.

The near ambush breaks into three teams—the security team, the support team, and the assault team. Each team has a specific set of duties, and the security and assault teams break down into further specialty teams.

The near ambush is broken into three teams, security, support, and assault. The security team is typically broken down further into a left, right, and sometimes a rear security team. (Photo by Jeong, Hae-jung).

1. The Security Team

The **security team** is responsible for the ambush's left, right, and sometimes rear security before the entire ambush is positioned. As is often the case, the security team is also assigned to specific security details while the ambush patrol maneuvers to and from the intended ambush site. Additionally, a security team will be placed in an overwatch position after the leader's recon confirms the exact site of the ambush. This security team will remain at the overwatch position while the patrol leader returns to the objective rally point (ORP) and brings the remainder of the ambush patrol forward.

The security team breaks into the "left security team" and the "right security team" at the ambush site. The security team leader will take a position with one security team or the other. In the event that a "rear security team" is required to remain at the release point, the security team leader will stay at that position.

2. The Support Team

The **support team** is responsible for delivering effective, heavy weapon fires against the enemy. The support team rarely breaks into separate teams. They are positioned in the ambush formation so that they may deliver accurate fire to the entire kill zone. The support team is typically comprised of machine gunners, grenadiers, and marksmen.

3. The Assault Team

The **assault team** is responsible for augmenting the fires of the support team against the enemy during the initial volley. This act significantly impacts the target in a physical sense, and also adds to the psychological shock of the ambush's violence of action. If a signal is given to sweep the kill zone after the initial volley of fire, the assault team must move forward to attack any surviving enemy in or around the kill zone.

Specialty Teams

The assault team also breaks into specialty teams. These teams almost always include an enemy prisoners of war (EPW) search team to look for priority intelligence requirements (PIR) such as enemy maps, orders, radio frequencies, and the like—and an aid and litter team to evacuate any friendly casualties. Additional specialty teams can include a demo team to destroy or booby-trap enemy weapons and equipment with explosives, or a grab team to take EPW.

As a general rule, the ambush patrol leader will take a position with the support team in order to better initiate and coordinate the fires of the ambush. This is just a guideline, however, and the patrol leader may determine where they are best in control.

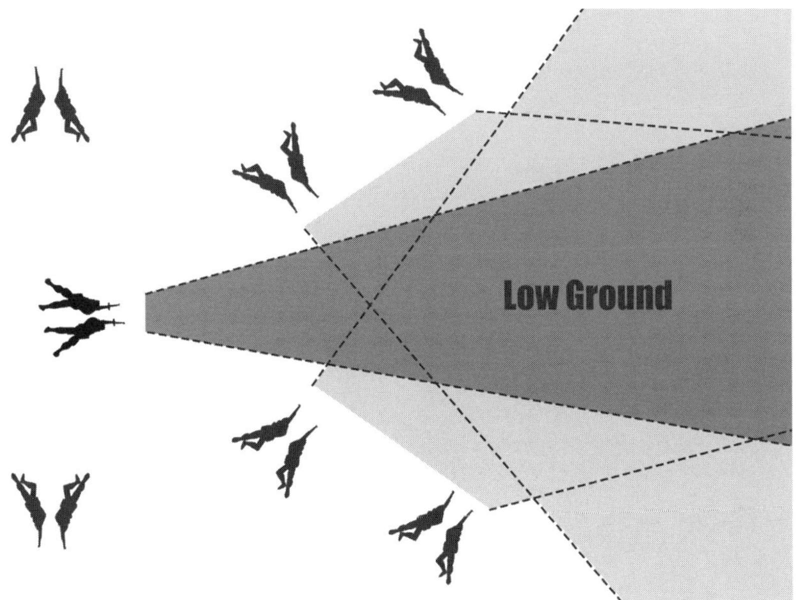

The 'V' method is commonly used when conducting near ambushes along a single draw of a ridge. By occupying the high ground of the spurs and directing fire downward, this method is extremely effective and safe. (Ref: FM 7-85, chap 6, fig. 6-3).

Special Purpose Atks

B. Organization - The Far Ambush

The far ambush breaks into only two teams—the security team and the support team. However, these teams may be spread out over large distances and assume very specific responsibilities in regards to a particular target.

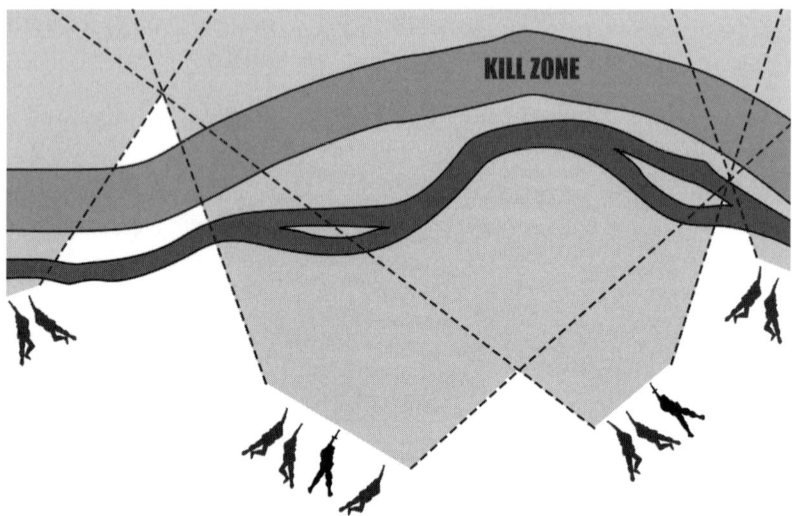

The far ambush keeps considerable distance between the ambush patrol and the enemy in the kill zone. Note that the creek offers protection from counterattack. The 'L' method is common for the far ambush. (Ref: FM 7-85, chap 6, fig. 6-2).

1. The Security Team

The **security team**, in a very similar manner to the near ambush, assumes responsibility for the far left and right sides of the far ambush formation. There is also a greater likelihood for the need of a rear security team on the far ambush to protect the multiple teams as they maneuver into their escape routes.

Also, the security team is responsible for security details as the ambush patrol moves to and from the ambush site. Again, the security team responsibilities are almost identical, regardless of whether we employ a near or far ambush. The major difference for the security team is that the far ambush requires the security teams to be very far apart from each other—often operating without visibility of each other. This takes considerable coordination in that the security teams must protect the ambush force, and ensure no friendly fire incidents occur.

2. The Support Team

The **support team** is, again, responsible for delivering effective fires against the enemy. However, in the far ambush, the support team is often broken into separate teams in order to deliver accurate fire to the entire kill zone. The support team is typically comprised of machine gunners, grenadiers, and marksmen. Depending on the type of target, the support team for a far ambush may also include missile launchers, combat engineers, and even mortar crews.

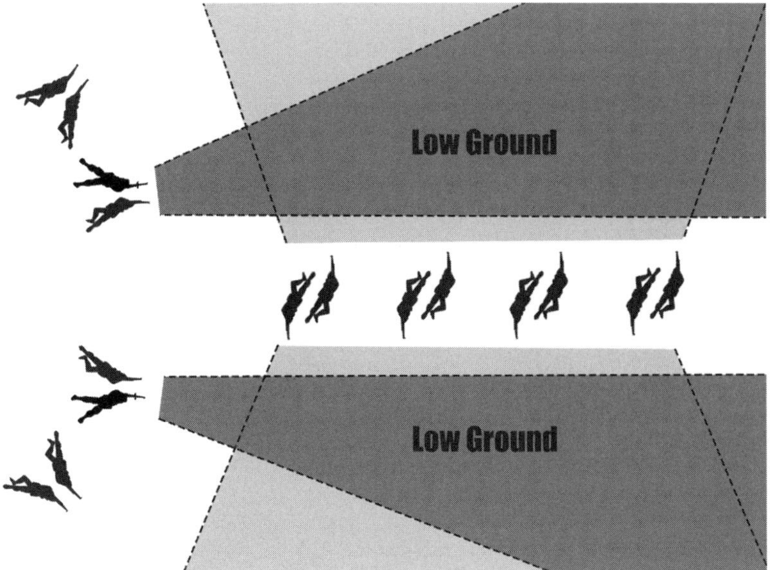

The 'T' method is a variation of the 'Z' method, but places the support teams at the same end of the ambush line. It is used for near ambushes along a spur when we are uncertain which side of the spur the enemy is traveling. (Ref: FM 7-85, chap 6, fig. 6-3).

III. Planning & Preparation

Surprise, coordinated fires, and control are the keys to a successful ambush. Surprise allows the ambush force to seize control of the situation. If total surprise is not possible, it must be so nearly complete that the target does not expect the ambush until it is too late to react effectively. Thorough planning, preparation, and execution help achieve surprise.

The commander conducts a leader's reconnaissance with key personnel to confirm or modify his plan. This reconnaissance should be undetected by the enemy to preclude alerting him. If necessary, the commander modifies the ambush plan and immediately disseminates those changes to subordinate leaders and other affected organizations. The leader's key planning considerations for any ambush include:

- Cover the entire kill zone (engagement area) by fire
- Use existing terrain features (rocks or fallen trees, for example) or reinforcing obstacles (Claymores or other mines) orienting into the kill zone to keep the enemy in the kill zone
- Determine how to emplace reinforcing obstacles on the far side of the kill zone
- Protect the assault and support elements with mines, Claymores, or explosives
- Use the security element to isolate the kill zone
- Establish rear security behind the assault element
- Assault into the kill zone to search dead and wounded, to assemble prisoners, and to collect equipment. The assault element must be able to move quickly on its own through the ambush site protective obstacles.
- Time the actions of all elements of the platoon to prevent the loss of surprise

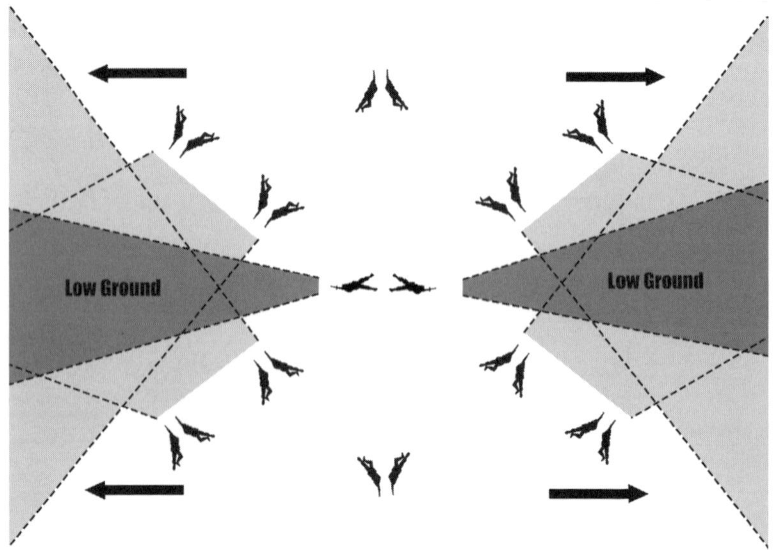

The 'X' method, as well as a close variation called the 'Z' method, is an excellent choice when the enemy may approach from multiple directions such as along converging draws or intersections. This allows the ambush team to cover multiple avenues of approach. (Ref: FM 7-85, chap 6, fig. 6-3).

A. Near Ambush

Physically, a near ambush kill zone is *close enough for the assault team to rush across*. In most types of terrain and vegetation, that means hand grenade range—35 meters. As the density of vegetation increases, the ability to rush forward decreases. In thick vegetation such as a jungle, a near ambush may need to be employed as close as 10 meters from the kill zone. Conversely, in wide-open terrain, a near ambush could be conducted =40 or even 50 meters from the kill zone. It's relative to the troop's ability to rush, taking into consideration terrain and vegetation.

In preparing a near ambush, employ obstacles on the far side of the kill zone. That is because the intent is to destroy the enemy target and not allow them to escape. These obstacles can be naturally occurring—such as a steep hill or cliff, a large body of water, or a wide open field that exposes the enemy troops as they attempt to run away. These obstacles can also be man-made—such as antipersonnel mines or well-camouflaged wire obstacles. The best technique is to employ multiple obstacles, including man-made and naturally occurring types.

B. Far Ambush

Physically, a far ambush kill zone is determined to be too far a distance to rush across. In almost all terrain, that would include distances significantly greater than 35 meters. It is true that within the most densely vegetated environment, an ambush at 50 or even 40 meters might be considered a far ambush. But typically, far ambushes make use of distances of 70 meters and up to 700 meters from the kill zone.

The far ambush is used to harass, injure, or delay the target. Due to the significant distances, there is no need to outnumber the enemy target. However, in order to effectively inflict damage, it will be beneficial to have some identification of the target. For example, is the target a supply convoy...or is it a combat patrol? Does the enemy employ armored vehicles, thin-skinned vehicles, or only foot patrols?

In preparing a far ambush, employ obstacles on the near side of the kill zone. Carefully plan and identify escape routes. The effort here is to allow the ambush patrol to escape before the enemy target recovers from the initial volley of fire and counterattacks. The obstacles in between the ambush patrol and the enemy—whether they are man-made or naturally occurring obstacles—serve to delay the enemy counterattack. The identified escape routes speed the escape and make coordination much more simplified.

III. Conducting the Ambush - A Small Unit Perspective

Fire discipline is a key part of any ambush. Fire must be withheld until the ambush commander gives the signal to initiate the ambush. That signal should be fire from the most deadly weapon in the ambush. Once initiated, the ambush unit delivers its fires at the maximum rate possible given the need for accuracy. Otherwise, the assault could be delayed, giving the target time to react and increasing the possibility of fratricide. Accurate fires help achieve surprise as well as destroy the target. When it is necessary to assault the target, the lifting or shifting of fires must be precise. The assault element does not conduct its assault until enemy fires or resistance has been negated or eliminated.

If the ambush fails and the enemy pursues the ambush force, it may have to withdraw by bounds. The ambush force should use smoke to help conceal its withdrawal. Activating limited-duration minefields along the withdrawal routes after the passage of the withdrawing ambush force can help stop or delay enemy pursuit. The commander positions the support element to assist in the withdrawal of the assault element.

Note: See pp. 6-12 to 6-13 for discussion of conducting the near ambush; pp. 6-14 to 6-15 for conducting the far ambush.

After the initial volley of fire, the commander may give the signal for the assault team to attack across the kill zone. The support team and security teams must first lift or shift their fires to prevent fratricide. (Photo by Jeong, Hae-jung).

A. Conducting the Near Ambush

The near ambush is used to destroy the enemy target. Necessarily, it is preferred that the ambush patrol outnumber the enemy by a 2:1 ratio. If they are more evenly matched, that is acceptable. To achieve numerical superiority, the PL needs to know the approximate size of the enemy patrols.

1. The patrol occupies an ORP either one terrain feature or approximately 300 meters away from the intended ambush site. The PL assembles the leader's recon team and issues a five-point contingency plan to the assistant patrol leader (APL) prior to leaving on the recon. At a minimum, the leader's recon will include the PL, a two-man security team, and either the leader of the assault team or the support team—typically the team the PLwill *not* accompany.

2. At the designated ambush site, the PL ensures that it is an appropriate terrain using the considerations of Observation, Cover & concealment, Obstacles, Key terrain, and Avenues of approach (OCOKA). The PL does this without contaminating the kill zone—meaning he shouldn't actually walk through or onto the kill zone, but should move around to view it from the far right, far left, and from the middle of the ambush formation. If the terrain is not suitable for a near ambush, the PL chooses an appropriate site nearby.

3. The PL will then post the two-man security team far back, where they are easily concealed but can still view the kill zone. This post will later become the release point. The security team sits back-to-back, with one man facing the kill zone and the other facing back in the direction of the ORP. The PL will leave these men with a five-point contingency plan and return to the ORP. The security team must monitor all enemy activity and report this to the PL upon his return. It will be critical to know if the enemy has stopped on or near the ambush site.

4. After returning to the ORP, the PL coordinates any changes to the original plan with every member of the ambush patrol. Final preparations are conducted in the ORP and the PL pulls together the patrol. The order of march will be the PL, security team, support team, and lastly the assault team. This is the exact order because the ambush must be placed into position using this sequence.

5. The PL leads the patrol to the security team at the release point. He links up the two-man security team with their security team leader. If the intended location of the left and right side security areas can be seen from the release point, the PL will have the security team leader place his teams into position. If the locations cannot be seen, the PL positions the left and right security teams, taking the Security team leader with him.

6. Once the left and right security teams are in position, the PL returns to the release point and picks up the support team. He positions them into the formation, typically in front of the release point. The PL returns back to the release point and picks up the assault team. They, too, are placed in formation and assume the opposite (left or right) side of the support team.

7. With everyone in place, the PL will take his place as the leader of either the support or the assault team, as determined in the operation order (OPORD). The PL will conduct a communication system check, and then the team awaits the enemy. Security is kept at 100 percent.

8. The ambush patrol continues to wait in position until:

- The PL gives the "end time" signal that indicates the patrol must return
- The PL gives the "no fire" signal and allows a larger enemy force to pass
- OR...the ambush is initiated

9. The ambush patrol fires upon the kill zone only when:

- The PL initiates fire against the enemy in the kill zone
- OR—the enemy discovers the ambush patrol

Special Purpose Atks

After the initial volley of fire, the commander may give the signal for the assault team to attack across the kill zone. The support team and security teams must first lift or shift their fires to prevent fratricide. (Photo by Jeong, Hae-jung).

Actions on the Objective

1. The actions on the objective will not take long. All members of the ambush patrol fire into the kill zone—regardless of whether or not they see a specific target. The only exceptions may be the security teams who may not have a clear view of the kill zone.

2. The PL gives the signal to cease fire, to shift fires, or to lift fires. At this moment, the PL decides if it is reasonably safe for the assault team to move across the kill zone.

3. If the assault team is sent across the kill zone, it conducts the following actions in this order:

- Sweep the kill zone on line, being certain to double-tap all enemy
- Secure the far side of the kill zone
- Send the necessary specialty teams back into the kill zone to search for PIR, aid friendly casualties, or to destroy enemy equipment

4. The assault team leader then gives the thumbs-up signal to the PL indicating that the far side of the kill zone is secure and that the specialty teams have finished their tasks. The assault team secures the far side of the kill zone until the PL signals to fall back.

5. The PL gives the signal for the assault team to fall back through the release point to the ORP. The assault team does this without hesitation and doesn't wait for other teams.

6. The PL gives the signal for the support team to fall back through the release point to the ORP. The support team does this immediately.

7. The PL will give the signal for the security team to fall back through the release point and move to the ORP. The PL will wait for the security team at the release point and move back to the ORP with this element. In this manner, the ambush has displaced in the exact reverse order that it was emplaced.

Specialty teams, such as the PIR search team, come from within the assault team. This is partly because the assault team tends to be the largest team on the ambush, but also because it is the only team that enters the kill zone. (Photo by Jeong, Hae-jung).

Reconsolidate & Reorganize

1. The first element to get back to the ORP is the assault team. The assault team leader forms the ORP into a 360° security area and continues to shape the ORP until a senior leader replaces him. Redistribute ammunition and water; be sure key weapons are manned.

2. All troops must be accounted for and casualties must receive medical aid. Following accountability, the PL will ask for a sensitive equipment check.

3. The PL will facilitate the dissemination of PIR to all members of the patrol. This is necessary because—should the patrol later become engaged and take casualties—the PIR must be relayed to higher command.

4. The designated route of return and plans to evacuate casualties and/or EPW will be followed in accordance with the OPORD. Continue the mission.

B. Conducting the Far Ambush

The goal in the far ambush is to *inflict damage* upon an enemy patrol. There is no requirement to overrun the target—in fact, the far ambush doesn't even have an assault team. It may help to think of the far ambush as a grandiose sniper mission.

1. The PL assembles a team to conduct the leader's recon at an ORP that has been established at an appropriate distance away from the intended ambush site. This team will include the PL and the entire security team. Prior to heading out on the recon, the PL will leave the support team leader with a five-point contingency plan.

2. The PL moves the recon team to the intended ambush site and posts the security team in a position that affords a complete view of the ambush site. Then the PL and the security team leader move to the far left, far right, and middle to determine if the terrain is appropriate, to determine where to place the security and support teams, and to identify routes of escape. Furthermore, the kill zone must have some type of natural obstacle between the enemy and the ambush patrol to slow down the enemy's counterattack. If no natural obstacle exists, then a man-made obstacle will have to be employed and camouflaged. If the terrain is inappropriate for this mission, another location must be chosen nearby.

3. The PL positions the entire security team toward the middle of the ambush line so that they can view the kill zone. This becomes the release point. The PL leaves a five-point contingency plan with the security team leader and returns to the ORP.

4. The PL disseminates any changes to the original plan to all patrol members back at the ORP. Complete final preparations and form the support team. The support team may break into sub-teams to form the order of march according to the OPORD. The PL will link up the support teams with the security team.

5. At the release point, the PL releases each element to the team leader. The security team leader places his teams as directed. The support team leader places the team(s), and the PL moves with whichever support team he decides will give him the best view of the kill zone and command of the elements.

The far ambush places high value on marksmanship skills. The support team is often broken into a series of sniper, machinegun, and rocket teams that fire into the kill zone from multiple, coordinated directions. (Photo by Jeong, Hae-jung).

6. With all elements in place, the PL conducts a communication systems check. The entire patrol will wait in place for the ambush to initiate. In the far ambush, due to the distance between elements, the left or right side security will often be the first to see the enemy element. They inform the PL on enemy movement and estimated time of arrival.

7. It is unlikely that the enemy will detect the ambush patrol in a far ambush mission. Still, the same rules apply to the far ambush that applies to the near ambush:

- The PL gives the "time" signal that indicates the patrol must return
- The PL gives the "no fire" signal and allows a large enemy team to pass
- OR...the ambush is initiated

8. The ambush patrol fires upon the kill zone only when:

- The PL initiates fire against the enemy in the kill zone, OR
- if the enemy discovers the ambush patrol

Actions on the Objective

1. The actions on the objective depend upon the enemy's ability to react. The far ambush continues until the enemy escapes from the kill zone, the enemy begins a counterattack, or the PL is satisfied with the effect or the ambush. Do not fire all ammunition. The patrol still has to escape. Combat leaders must keep in mind that the longer the patrol stays, the more vulnerable the patrol becomes to enemy counterattack.

2. Upon the signal to cease fire, the support teams automatically withdraw to the ORP using the designated escape route. There is no need to pass through the release point. This will waste time due to the distance between elements.

3. The PL travels with one of the support teams. When he calculates that he has passed the release point, he signals the security team to withdraw. The security team leader rallies his team in a concealed area behind the release point to make certain to account for the entire team. Then the security team proceeds to the ORP.

Escape routes are an important consideration for any ambush, but they are absolutely vital to the far ambush. Once the far ambush has achieved its effect, defilades, ravines, and draws are used as escape routes. (Photo by Jeong, Hae-jung).

Reconsolidate & Reorganize

1. The PL arrives back at the ORP and forms into a 360° security area until all patrol members are assembled. Ammunition and water are distributed as needed. Key weapons are manned. Casualties receive medical aid.

2. Once every member is accounted for, the PL asks for a sensitive equipment check. Patrol members count their assigned sensitive equipment (weapons, radios, night vision devices, etc.) by physically touching the item.

3. Far ambushes also attempt to gain PIR and all observations are quickly disseminated. The designated route of return and plans to evacuate casualties are conducted according to the OPORD. Continue the mission.

IV. Ambush Categories

Ambushes are classified by category (deliberate or hasty), formation (linear or L-shaped), and type (point, area, or antiarmor). The leader determines the category of ambush through an analysis of the factors of METT-TC. Typically, the two most important factors are time and enemy. The leader's key planning considerations for any ambush include the following:

- Cover the entire kill zone (engagement area) by fire
- Use existing terrain features (rocks or fallen trees, for example) or reinforcing obstacles (Claymores or other mines) orienting into the kill zone to keep the enemy in the kill zone
- Determine how to emplace reinforcing obstacles on the far side of the kill zone
- Protect the assault and support elements with mines, Claymores, or explosives
- Use the security element to isolate the kill zone
- Establish rear security behind the assault element
- Assault into the kill zone to search dead and wounded, to assemble prisoners, and to collect equipment. The assault element must be able to move quickly on its own through the ambush site protective obstacles.
- Time the actions of all elements of the platoon to prevent the loss of surprise

Deliberate

A deliberate ambush is a planned offensive action conducted against a specific target for a specific purpose at a predetermined location. When planning a deliberate ambush, the leader requires detailed information on the—

- Size and composition of the targeted enemy unit
- Weapons and equipment available to the enemy
- Enemy's route and direction of movement
- Times that the targeted enemy unit will reach or pass specified points along the route

Hasty

A hasty ambush is conducted when a unit makes visual contact with an enemy force and has time to establish an ambush without being detected. The conduct of the hasty ambush should represent the execution of disciplined initiative within the parameters of the commander's intent. The actions for a hasty ambush should be established in a unit SOP and rehearsed so Soldiers know what to do on the leader's signal.

Area Ambush

An area ambush (more than one point ambush) is not conducted by a unit smaller than a platoon. This ambush works best where enemy movement is restricted. Once the platoon is prepared, the area ambush is conducted the same as a point ambush. The dominating feature of an area ambush is the amount of synchronization between the separate point ambushes.

Area ambushes require more planning and control to execute successfully. Surprise is more difficult to achieve due to the unit's dispersion in the AO. Having more than one ambush site increases the likelihood of being detected by the enemy or civilians. This major disadvantage is offset by the increased flexibility and sophistication available to the leader.

Point Ambushes

Point ambushes are set at the most ideal location to inflict damage on the enemy. Such ambushes must be able to handle being hit by the enemy force from more than one direction. The ambush site should enable the unit to execute an ambush in two or three main directions. The other directions must be covered by security that gives early warning of enemy attack.

Special Purpose Attacks

II. Raid

Ref: FM 3-90 Tactics, pp. 5-38 to 5-39 and FM 7-85 Ranger Unit Operations, chap 5.

The raid is a special purpose attack that falls under the category of strike operations. Raiding patrols infiltrate well into enemy territory. This means the raiding force can expect to be outnumbered, outgunned, and far from help. A successful raid is the hallmark tactic of special operational forces and a crowning achievement for any combat unit. No tactical maneuver requires a more advanced set of skills—intelligence gathering through reconnaissance, brilliant planning, accurate rehearsals, and individual and team skill craft that is the envy of others.

A raid is a limited-objective form of attack entailing swift entry into hostile terrain. A raid operation always ends with a planned withdrawal to a friendly location upon the completion of the assigned mission. It is not intended to hold terrain.

There are many reasons to conduct raids. A patrol might be tasked to destroy key enemy equipment or facilities, temporarily seize key terrain, gather intelligence items, or liberate personnel. While each of these missions differs from the next, they each entail a set of basic considerations.

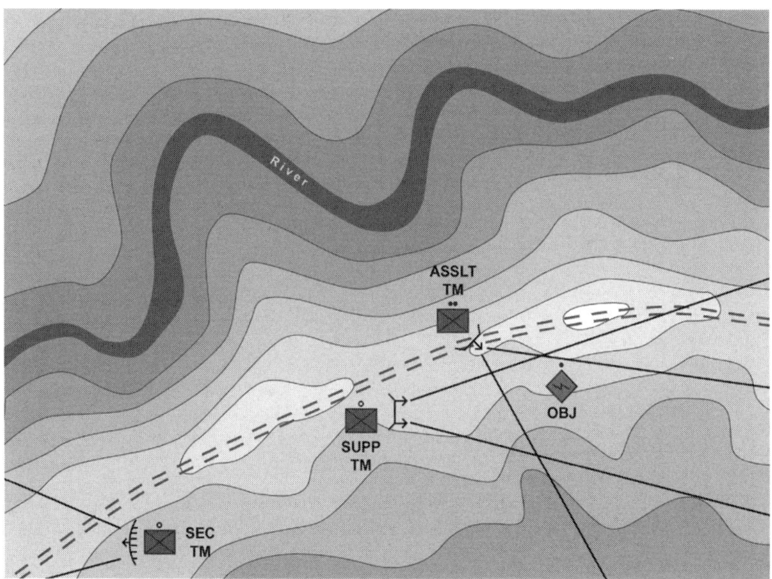

The raid has the same basic teams as the ambush—security, support, and assault. The principle difference is that the raid is conducted on established, stationary targets, whereas the ambush is used on moving or temporarily halted targets. (Ref: FM 7-85, chap 5, fig. 5-1).

I. Organization

In a very similar manner as the ambush force, the raiding force breaks down into three main elements: the security team, the support team, and the assault team.

1. Security Team

The security team is most commonly deployed to the left, right and sometimes rear of the raiding formation as it is deployed around the objective. They carry rifles, light machineguns, anti-personnel mines and possibly some anti-armor capabilities. Their main purpose is to isolate the target, prevent any enemy reinforcements, and to seal the escape of any enemy running from the objective.

2. Support Team

The **support team** is commonly deployed center of the raiding formation in such a manner that they have a clear view of the objective. They carry heavier mass-casualty producing weapons, such as machineguns, grenade launchers, or missiles. This team is primarily responsible for the shock effect, as well as inflicting as many casualties upon the enemy as possible to ensure the success of the assaulting team.

3. Assault Team

The assault team is deployed as closely to the objective as stealth and coordinated fire support allow. They are lightly armed with rifles and carbines but may have special equipment. This team is responsible for the destruction, capture, or liberation of the target. Upon assaulting across the objective, they are also the most exposed—and least armed element of the raid.

After the leader's recon, the patrol leader leaves a 2-man security team overlooking the objective from a concealed position. This position later becomes the release point for the raid. The PL returns to the ORP to finalize plans. (Photo by Jeong, Hae-jung).

Raids also have sub-groups within the assault team. Examples of these specialty teams would include grab teams for abduction, prisoner search teams for intelligence requirements, aid & litter teams for wounded, demolition or explosive ordinance disposal (EOD) teams, and possibly even chemical biological radiological and nuclear (CBRN) recovery teams.

The assault team moves into position last. The assault team is lightly armed and may require special equipment for breaching obstacles. After the support team shifts fire, the assault team sweeps the objective and destroys the enemy. (Photo by Jeong, Hae-jung).

II. Planning & Preparation

The main differences between a raid and other attack forms are the limited objectives of the raid and the associated withdrawal following completion. Raids might be conducted in daylight or darkness, within or beyond supporting distance of the parent unit. When the area to be raided is beyond supporting distance of friendly lines, the raiding party operates as a separate force. A specific objective is normally assigned to orient the raiding unit. During the withdrawal, the attacking force should use a route or axis different from that used to conduct the raid itself.

The raid requires the most up-to-date information, which aids in the development of the intelligence preparation of the battlespace (IPB). This translates into effective maneuver control measures, fire control measures, and nothing less than a brilliant plan that makes ample use of stealth and timing. Rehearsals are an essential part of the raid preparations.

The enemy will likely have good communications with reinforcements in the immediate vicinity, making the raid patrol all the more vulnerable to a counterattack. This fact dictates that severe time constraints exist from the moment the raid begins, until the moment the patrol withdraws from the objective.

A raid will be much more successful if the patrol has the element of surprise. To maximize this surprise, the raid is conducted at a time when the enemy is least likely to expect an attack. Attack when visibility is limited and, if possible, attack from an unexpected avenue of approach—such as from seemingly impassable terrain. This requires in depth knowledge of the terrain surrounding the objective as well.

III. Conducting the Raid - A Small Unit Perspective

Surprise, firepower, and a tenacious attack stun and disorient the enemy. The psychological effect of violence should not be underestimated. If the enemy on the objective believe that the raid patrol is actually much larger due to the use of massed firepower and violence, the enemy is less likely to stand and defend against the assaulting team. Furthermore, after the patrol has withdrawn from the objective, the enemy will pursue the raid patrol much less aggressively if they believe the patrol is very large.

The ORP must be secured. The patrol leader leaves the assistant patrol leader in the ORP with a security force. The rest of the patrol will drop any unnecessary gear at the ORP, and return to the ORP after the raid is complete. (Photo by Jeong, Hae-jung).

A. Infiltrate to the Objective

1. After infiltrating into enemy territory and the objective rally point (ORP) has been properly occupied and secured, the patrol leader (PL) conducts a leader's recon of the objective. At a minimum, the PL takes a two-man security team, and the leader of the support or assault team—whichever one the PL will *not* be positioned with during the raid. It generally is considered a good idea to bring all three element leaders, if possible.

2. The PL leaves a contingency plan with the assistant patrol leader (APL) in the ORP before departing. The leader's recon conducts a physical inspection of the objective, making certain that everything is as planned. If not, the PL improvises any change to the plan...and since there will be no time or space for rehearsals, the option to change the plan should only be used in extreme circumstances.

3. The PL leaves a two-man security team with communication and a contingency plan. The security team is positioned in such a manner that they maintain constant observation of the objective (this spot will later become the release point) to ensure that enemy reinforcements do not arrive and that the target doesn't leave. The PL and element leader(s) move back to the ORP.

4. The PL issues any changes to the plan in the ORP and finalizes all preparations. Picking up the rest of the patrol, the PL leads them out of the ORP and towards the release point in the following order:

- PL leads at point
- Security team
- Support team
- Assault team pulls up the drag

The patrol leader moves the patrol forward to link up with the release point. From the release point the patrol waits while the security teams carefully and quietly move to their assigned locations. (Photo by Jeong, Hae-jung).

5. Upon reaching the release point, the PL checks with the on-site security team to make certain everything is okay. The PL then links the entire security team up with the leader and gives them time to move into their designated position. Unlike the ambush, the PL does NOT have the option of positioning each element. On a raid, the elements have all rehearsed exhaustively on where to go. Time must be allowed for each team to stealthily position themselves.

6. The PL releases the support team next and may travel with that element if he has not assigned himself to the assault team. The assault team takes position last and due to the close proximity of their position to the objective, they must be given ample time to move.

7. All elements wait for the signal to commence fire. This may be designated by:

- A fixed time, OR
- A designated signal, OR
- The PL may issue the "No Fire" signal (in which case the patrol withdraws)

B. Actions on the Objective

Just as with the ambush, the initiating volley of fire must physically and psychologically overwhelm the enemy force. Upon the initiating shot, every member of the patrol immediately opens fire on the objective. Failure to immediately suppress the enemy means failure for the raid patrol. If the enemy gains the initiative, the patrol will likely be destroyed.

The support team takes position after the security team sets into place. Because the support team carries crew-served weapons that are heavy, more time must be allotted for their movement. (Photo by Jeong, Hae-jung).

1. After effectively devastating the objective with a heavy volume of fire, the PL gives a designated signal to lift or shift fires. Now, a common misconception is that the term "lift or shift" fires actually means "cease-fire."

Shifting fires means that the support team's direction of fire will shift either left or right in order to suppress fleeing or reinforcing enemy. If shifting of fires cannot be done safely, then **lifting** fires means the support team will continue to fire harmlessly over everyone's heads.

2. The assault team begins their choreographed attack across the objective. The assault team crosses the objective in pre-arranged buddy teams and...

- Double-taps all enemy combatants
- Secures the far side of the objective, AND
- Conducts the sub-tasks of the specialty teams

3. Once the specialty teams are finished with the assigned tasks, the assault team leader gives the PL the signal that they have accomplished the task and are ready to move.

4. The PL then gives three designated signals. The first notifies the assault team to fall back through the release point to the ORP. The second notifies the support team to do the same. The third signal notifies the security team to fall back via their designated route to the ORP.

5. In the ORP, subordinate leaders reconsolidate and reorganize the patrol. The APL accounts for all members and equipment. All crew served weapons and priority equipment is reassigned if there have been casualties. Friendly casualties are cared for in accordance with the operations order (OPORD). Water and ammunition is redistributed.

6. The patrol then falls back to a pre-designated position, usually one terrain feature back from the ORP. The patrol stops to disseminate all information and PIR regarding the raid amongst every patrol member. This is done prior to returning to the FEBA.

Once the raid has been successfully executed, the patrol moves to an extraction point. The key to achieving elusiveness for a raiding patrol is a stealthy infiltration, and a highly mobile extraction. (Dept. of Army photo by Michael Guillory).

On Point

A raid is a surprise attack to temporarily overwhelm stationary enemy targets, usually deep within enemy territory. Raids are conducted for a multitude of reasons—most commonly to seize or destroy enemy assets, collect valuable information, or rescue personnel aligned with our cause.

A simplified chain of command is an essential organizational requirement. A raid usually requires a force carefully tailored to neutralize specific enemy forces operating in the vicinity of the objective and to perform whatever additional functions are required to accomplish the objective of the raid. These additional functions can consist of the demolition of bridges over major water obstacles or the recovery of an attack helicopter pilot shot down forward of the forward line of own troops (FLOT). The commander incorporates any necessary support specialists during the initial planning stage of the operation.

When a commander and his staff plan a raid, they develop COAs that meet ethical, legal, political, and technical feasibility criteria. Planners require precise, time-sensitive, all-source intelligence. The planning process determines how C2, sustainment, target acquisition and target servicing will occur during the raid. Techniques and procedures for conducting operations across the FLOT, given the specific factors of METT-TC expected to exist during the conduct of the raid, are also developed. The commander and his staff develop as many alternative COAs as time and the situation permit. They carefully weigh each alternative. In addition to those planning considerations associated with other offensive operations, they must determine the risks associated with conducting the mission and possible repercussions.

Time permitting, all elements involved in a raid should be fully rehearsed in their functions. The key elements in determining the level of detail and the opportunities for rehearsal prior to mission execution are time, OPSEC, and deception requirements.

Special Purpose Attacks

III. Swarming Attack

Ref: Compiled from "Swarming on the Battlefield: Past, Present, and Future" by Sean Edwards. Copyright 1993-2000 by Rand Corporation. Reproduced with permission of Rand Corporation via Copyright Clearance Center.

The swarming attack is a specialized form of attack that uses distributed, autonomous forces that converge at a single point to mass an attack against the enemy. Numerical superiority over an opponent is not required either to attack or to operate in large geographical areas of operation (AO). Instead, numerical superiority is required only at the local point of engagement.

Swarming attacks do not work for all situations, but are well suited for low intensity conflicts. For this reason, the swarming attack is the preferred offensive tactic within insurgencies and counter-insurgency (COIN) operations. This tactic is used both by guerilla forces attempting to assert dominance over a regional conflict and by the host nation and/or international military forces that leverage military power to coerce such guerilla and insurgent forces back to a peaceful diplomatic solution.

Editor's note: Discussion in this section is based on "Swarming on the Battlefield: Past, Present, and Future," a monograph produced as part of a study on swarming and the future of conflict conducted by RAND's National Defense Research Institute (a federally funded research and development center sponsored by OSD, the Joint Staff, the unified commands, and the defense agencies). Readers should note that "swarming" is not doctrinally recognized per se by the U.S. Army, nor is it addressed in current field manuals or texts. However, readers may find the conceptual framework useful for insight/discussion with application in certain tactical scenarios such as one might find in counterinsurgency or nontraditional operations. (Photo by Jeong, Hae-jung).

The swarming attack seeks to destroy an enemy target through a series of pulsating, coordinated attacks from multiple directions. The effort is not necessarily to defeat the enemy in a single attack, but through a series of attacks that disorient and erode the enemy force. There are two recognized methods of swarming attacks:

- **Massed swarming**—the force begins as a massed unit and then breaks apart to swarm against an identified target
- **Dispersed swarming**—the force is geographically dispersed from the start of the mission and converges to attack once a target is identified.

Dispersed swarming is the more effective of the two methods since the attacking force never presents a massed target for the enemy to engage. However, dispersed swarming takes the greatest planning and coordinating efforts because the force is never co-located for the planning and rehearsal phase. Furthermore, while both methods of swarming attacks require considerable reliance upon the junior leader, the dispersed swarm method involves autonomous teams. Dispersed swarming operations also require advanced leadership competencies. Without it, coordination and synchronization will not be achieved.

Due to the reasons previously cited, dispersed swarming is typically reserved for military units larger than the platoon—typically at least at the battalion level. Companies and platoons more commonly make use of massed swarming. Admittedly, this decision is situation-dependent.

The swarming attack requires three characteristics for success:

- Elusiveness
- Standoff capability
- Situational awareness

Elusiveness can be achieved either through mobility or concealment. Standoff capability requires advanced communication and targeting systems coupled with long-range firepower. And situational awareness is achieved through an acute understanding of the Strength, Weaknesses, Opportunities, and Threats (SWOT) of both friendly forces and enemy forces. Situational awareness takes into consideration the factors of Mission, Enemy, Terrain and weather, Time, Troops available, and Civilians on the battlefield (METT-TC).

I. Organization

The battalion breaks into multiple direct action cells of three to five troops, plus multiple combat service and combat service and support cells. These cells can be assembled for direct action as a company, platoon, or even squad. When assembled as a platoon, these cells typically form into six fireteams. One fire team is held in reserve with a small command team. And all fireteams are equipped with radios or cell phones for communication.

While swarming attacks are conducted by autonomous or semi-autonomous cells, they still are lead by the unifying vision of a single commander. As such, the swarming attack requires:

- Autonomy
- Mobility
- Communication
- Synchronization

Highly desirable for the swarming attack are weapons that allow the swarming force to attack from significant distances. This inflicts damage and disorients the enemy. (Dept. of Army photo by Gary L. Kieffer).

A. Autonomy

The swarming attack differs significantly from a conventional attack or MTC in that the attacking force is dispersed along a much greater geographical area. This dispersing has two advantageous effects. First, it does not offer the enemy a massed target to engage with mass-casualty producing weapons. Second, it allows the swarming attack force to gather more human intelligence because the patrol is spread out over such a large area.

Admittedly, this type of formation goes against the massed, linear hierarchy of command mindset. That is why the swarming attack falls under the category of special purpose attacks. Like the raid and the ambush, the swarming attack hits the enemy in an unpredictable space, time, and manner. The nature of such specialized attacks relies on the decentralized and independent operations of a small military force.

The swarming attack also relies on a well-communicated commander's intent. This is because the small team leader will often find be faced with a situation in which the original plan is no longer feasible. In such situations, the swarming attack leans heavily on the philosophy of *Auftragstaktik*—the notion that the junior leader may make decisions that might even appear to be in direct conflict with the original order, in-so-much as she is trying to achieve the commander's expressed goal for the mission. That is why the commander's intent is so critical for such specialized missions.

Decentralized and autonomous units require small unit commanders who are capable and have the latitude to make their own decisions within the framework of the commander's intent. Yet, swarming forces must be constantly aware of the location and presence of friendly units—thus the reliance upon communication and synchronization. Otherwise, swarming forces inadvertently attack one another.

B. Mobility

All things being equal, a small team travels faster than a large team. This is the essence of the swarming attack's mobility.

If the patrol has helicopter lift capabilities then the swarming attack will be exponentially faster than the enemy's ability to respond. The same could be said for the enemy, if they have some type of vehicle support. So, if the enemy has the upper hand in mobility, ultimately friendly forces will have to try to mitigate the enemy's advantage.

If the enemy has helicopters and the friendly force does not, use the heavy canopy of the jungle to hide patrol movement. If the enemy has wheeled vehicles and the friendly force does not, use the channeling effects of the city to expose the enemy's movements. If the enemy has tracked armored vehicles and the friendly force does not, conduct operations in the steep mountains where tanks cannot pass.

In any case, for the swarming attack, friendly forces will operate as small, highly mobile teams. These patrols must adjust quickly to the changing battlefield and constantly seek the position of advantage.

Swarming attacks use mobility to remain elusive. When the resources are available and the terrain is permissive, mobility is used to strike quickly and then withdraw in a pulsing action. (Dept. of Army photo by Heidi Holston).

C. Communication

Swarming attacks place great emphasis on communication and targeting technologies. Dependence upon technology has produced as many battlefield failures as it has successes. Even when successful, technological advantages are always temporary. Still, the need to locate the enemy can be satisfied in part by technology. So, too, is the need to communicate effectively in order to coordinate the converging, attacking, and dispersing swarming force.

Without adequate communication technology, the synchronization between elements of a swarming attack takes place through line-of-sight communication, such as hand and arm signals and runners. These methods of communication are slow and likely will not produce the tempo of operations necessary to defeat a modern, disciplined military.

D. Synchronization

The swarming attack must simultaneously hit the enemy from multiple vantage points. After dispersing again, the attacking cells will regroup and reform back into separate teams and, again, simultaneously re-attack to achieve the pulsing effect. All of this requires synchronization.

Synchronization is achieved through:

- Established communication networks
- Coordinated zones of influence
- Pre-positioned supply caches and rally points
- Pre-positioned casualty/evacuation points
- Standardized equipment and weapon systems
- Shared supplies within the swarming network

II. Planning & Preparation

One of the greatest concerns and challenges of the swarming attack is to prevent "friendly fire" incidents. This will take considerable planning and organization if the friendly forces are to avoid inflicting casualties against its own troops—while attacking the enemy in a synchronized manner from multiple vantage points.

The patrol will form into a massed swarming attack (it is unlikely that a platoon would conduct a dispersed swarming attack). A map overlay is used to assign a parallel axis of movement for each fire team. Typically, a platoon conducting a swarming attack will divide the platoon's advance into five separate axis of movement. That is one per fire team, with the last fire team following in reserve with the command team. This means five axis are sketched into the platoon's direction of advance.

The fireteams act independently. As such, radio communication will be paramount in establishing situational awareness. Phase lines are sketched onto the map overlay. These phase lines intersect each axis of movement at fairly regular patterns and each fire team leader must communicate their position as they cross each designated phase line.

Pre-determined rally points must be designated on the map overlay. These should include easy-to-locate terrain features that are naturally suited to defense. Rally points are used to coordinate movements, halts, and will act as an ORP from which to pulse the swarming attack.

Brevity codes must be assigned for each of these organizational concerns—names for each fire team's axis of movement, names for each phase line, and names for each rally point. These codes are used to continue the swarming attack, change missions, or withdraw. Brevity codes and radio frequencies must be distributed to all members of the patrol and used for sake of operational security.

III. Conducting a Swarming Attack

The swarming attack seeks an asymmetric battle. When the enemy's defenses are strong, attack their patrols and disrupt their sleep patterns with attacks during the day and night. When the enemy's defenses are passive, attack along their lines and seek the path of least resistance. When the enemy sends out large patrols to conduct attacks, attack the weakened defensive line once the larger patrols have departed.

Swarming is conceptually broken into four stages: locate, converge, attack, and disperse. The swarming attack must sustain a pulsing tempo. Swarming forces must be able to come together on target rapidly and with great stealth, then disperse again and reform for a new pulse. It is critical that swarming forces converge and attack simultaneously!

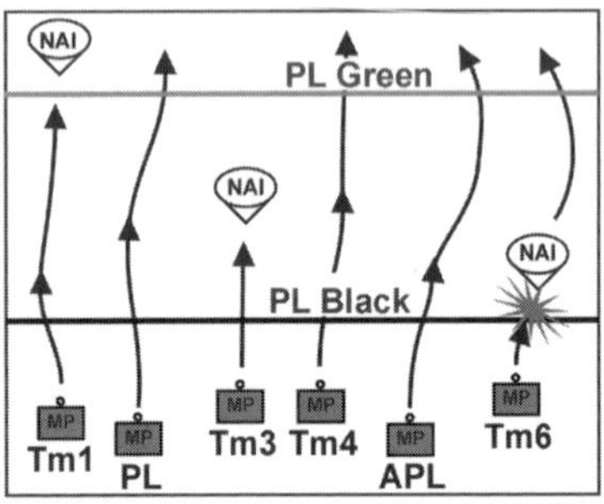

1. Locate

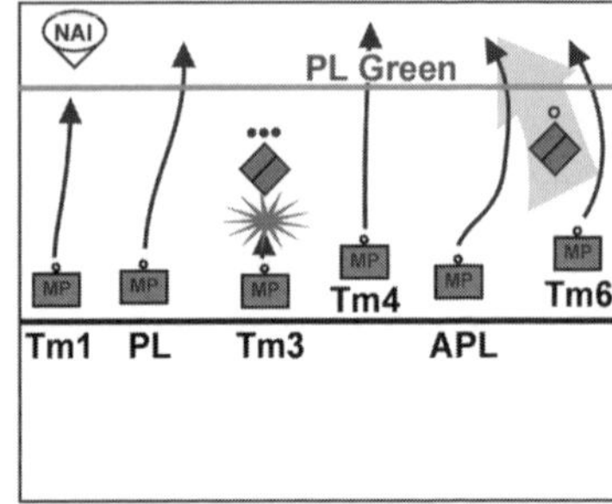

2. Converge

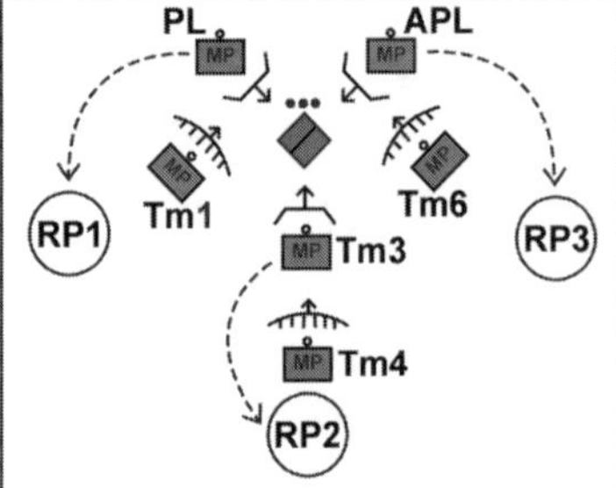

3. Attack

Massed swarming attacks function similar to a MTC, but without a main force. Each team is assigned a lane and areas of interest. The enemy is attacked by fire, while baited ambushes are set. (Ref: Swarming on the Battlefield, Rand 2000, fig. 5-1).

1. Locate

The commander resides with a command team and directs the actions of the individual patrols using the maneuver control measures identified on the map. As a patrol comes into contact with the enemy, the greatest care must be taken to *avoid* an engagement. If the point patrol—that patrol with visual contact of the enemy—becomes engaged in a firefight, they cannot continue to develop the situation. That means the patrol fails in its responsibility to function as an Intelligence, Surveillance, and Reconnaissance (ISR) asset. Furthermore, it is highly unlikely that the tiny point patrol will be able to effectively fix the enemy to any location. More likely, the massive enemy force will quickly destroy that patrol. If the patrol does become decisively engaged, they must break contact and seek a new vantage point to continue reporting on the enemy.

2. Converge

Once informed as to the enemy position, the commander must determine whether this is the high priority target, a low priority target, or a decoy. If the commander determines

Special Purpose Atks

this to be a priority target, he will inform the other patrols to quickly converge on the target using the maneuver control references. The effort is to mass the multiple patrols into an appropriate formation for an attack.

The Barbed Bull Horn (5 points) formation makes use of multiple vantage points with which to conduct an attack by fire against the enemy position. Additionally, each of these vantage points serves as a "baited ambush"—attempting to lure the enemy into a kill zone if the enemy gives chase.

Swarming attacks use the most primitive to the most advanced means of gaining situational awareness. Only when the enemy situation is known can their weakness be exploited. (Photo by Jeong, Hae-jung).

3. Attack

The commander gives the order to attack, synchronizing the assaults. This serves to disrupt the enemy because attack by fire comes from multiple directions. The enemy is confused as to the direction of the primary attack. Since physical assaults occur only when it is an advantage against weakened targets of opportunity, the objective of the swarming force is rarely ever immediately apparent to the enemy force.

When the enemy takes offensive action against one of the friendly force's swarming patrols, that patrol will yield their position and move through the prepared kill zone of the supporting patrol waiting in ambush.

In fact, it is desirable to give ground as the enemy approaches. That way the enemy force giving pursuit is lured into the waiting kill zone. Once the enemy becomes bogged down and loses their forward momentum, the patrols must be directed again to take up multiple vantage points and attack by fire.

4. Disperse

The commander directs swarming attacks to employ multiple patrols in a hit-and-run style that requires these small teams to immediately fall back to designated positions. The commander and patrol leaders base the pulsing of the swarming attack on what the enemy is doing and where they are currently located.

As the attack continues, the commander must rally and rest individual patrols at locations he will designate using the assigned maneuver control measures. The commander and multiple independent patrol leaders must retain or regain visual contact between the pulsed attacks.

Each patrol acts independently during swarming attacks, though their efforts are coordinated. Small unit leaders must be very well trained or experienced, and afforded considerable autonomy. (Photo by Jeong, Hae-jung).

They look for the enemy's strengths and weaknesses—and the commander employs his forces against the enemy weakness.

5. Pulse

The swarming attack will continue until the commander recognizes the signs of culmination. Signs of culmination may include the defeat or surrender of the entire enemy force. Conversely, it may mean that the enemy has escaped detection and moved out of the AO, or that friendly patrols have exhausted the troops, supplies, or munitions, or that the enemy's actions have begun to caused friendly forces to lose the majority of the engagements.

When signs of culmination are recognized, the commander must direct the patrols to withdraw and transition to another form of combat operation.

On Point

Swarming operations are ideal for COIN operations. Guerillas must remain elusive, operating as small, highly mobile teams that are dispersed over a large area. Swarming forces physically cover a greater geographic area than the traditionally massed attack force, and are more likely to pick up battlefield intelligence. A swarming network dispersed over a large area can perform frequent and random reconnaissance and can quickly react to suspected areas of enemy activity.

Swarming doctrine is not new. Alexander the Great had to contend with such swarming attacks by the Scythian horse archers. In fact, the principal characteristics of swarming doctrine are common to many other combat operations.

The swarming attack functions much like the reserve force in a mobile defense. While swarming attacks assume an offensive mode, the principal characteristics of the swarming attack and mobile defense have remarkable similarities and compliment each other in tactical symmetry.

Essential to swarming attacks are the characteristics of elusiveness, situational awareness, and standoff weaponry. History has shown that standoff weaponry is not as essential—though it is extremely desirable in that the swarming force may deliver a decisive blow with such weaponry. However, if the swarming attack's elusiveness or situational awareness is compromised, the swarming attack is doomed to failure against a well-disciplined enemy.

The patrol's communication systems are paramount to achieving situational awareness, as well as synchronization. Extra care must be taken to prevent the communication system from being compromised. Likewise, the enemy's targeting systems present the biggest danger to the patrol's elusiveness. These targeting systems must be impaired, mitigated, or destroyed.

I. Small Unit Operations in Urban Areas

Ref: FM 3-21.8 (FM 7-8) The Infantry Rifle Platoon and Squad, pp. 7-36 to 7-47. For a more detailed discussion on urban operations see FM 3-06.11.

Infantry platoons conduct operations in urban areas using the same principles applicable to other offensive operations. This section explains the general tactics, techniques, and procedures used for a limited attack in an urban area.

Depending on the scale of the operation, Infantry platoons or squads may be required to conduct any or all of the find, fix, fight, and follow-through functions. Leaders should expect trouble in the process of determining the exact location of the enemy and should anticipate enemy knowledge of their movements prior to arriving in the objective area. (Dept. of Army photo by Richard Rzepka, 101st Airborne).

I. Find

The compartmentalized nature of urban terrain, limited observation and fields of fire, and the vast amounts of potential cover and concealment mean that defenders can disperse and remain undetected. The origin of enemy gunfire can be difficult to detect, because distance and direction become distorted by structures. The nature of urban conflicts makes it more difficult for leaders to exercise command and control verbally, and for Soldiers to pass and receive information. Situational understanding is normally limited to the platoon's immediate area.

II. Isolate the Building

The fix function has two aspects: isolating the objective to prevent interference from the outside (while preventing enemy from exiting), and separating forces on the objective from each other (denying mutual support and repositioning). This is accomplished by achieving fire superiority and seizing positions of advantage.

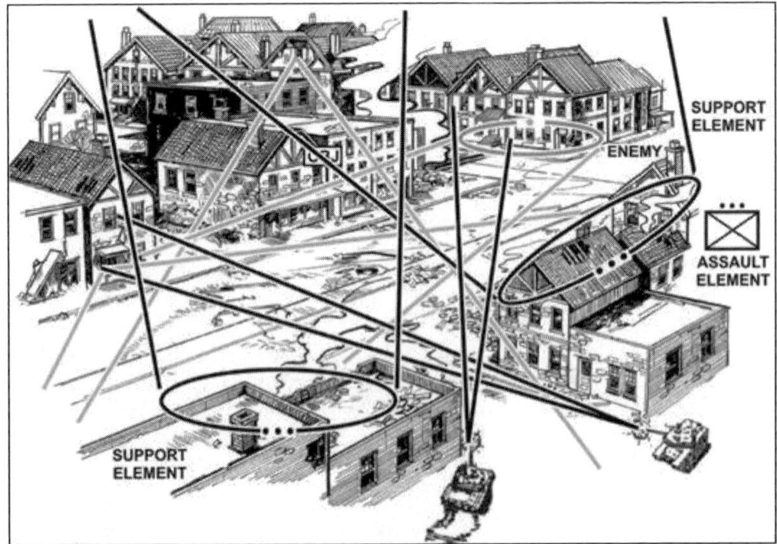

Cordon

A cordon is a line of troops or military posts that enclose an area to prevent passage. The Infantry platoon normally conducts a cordon as part of a larger unit. It is established by positioning one or more security elements on key terrain that dominates avenues of approach in and out of the objective area. The overall goal is the protection of the maneuver element, and to completely dominate what exits or enters the objective area. This requires a detailed understanding of avenues of approach in the area. There are many techniques used to facilitate isolation including, blocking positions, direct fire (precision and area), indirect fire, roadblocks, checkpoints, and observation posts. The same techniques can be used to cordon and search a small urban area (such as a village) surrounded by other terrain.

Ideally these positions are occupied simultaneously, but a sequential approach can also be useful. Limited visibility aids can be used in the establishment and security of the cordon. The security element can either surround the area while the maneuver element simultaneously moves in, or it can use a sequential technique in which they use stealth to get into position before the actual assault.

Plans should be developed to handle detained personnel. Infantrymen will normally provide security and accompany police and intelligence forces who will identify, question, and detain suspects. Infantry may also conduct searches and assist in detaining suspects, but their principal role is to reduce any resistance that may develop and to provide security for the operation. Use of force is kept to a minimum unless otherwise directed.

III. Assault a Building

Squads and platoons, particularly when augmented with engineers, are the best organized and equipped units in the Army for breaching protective obstacles; gaining access to buildings; and assaulting rooms, hallways, and stairways. Although there are specific drills associated with fighting in buildings, the overall assault is an operation, not a drill. During planning, the leader's level of detail should identify each window (aperture, opening, or firing port) in his sector fortifications. He should then consider assigning these as a specific TRP when planning fires.

Critical Tasks

There are a number of critical tasks that need emphasis for Infantry platoons assaulting a building:

- Isolate the building
- Gain and maintain fire superiority inside and outside the building
- Gain access to the inside of the building
- Move inside the building
- Seize positions of advantage
- Control the tempo

A. Entering the Building

After establishing suppression and obscuration, leaders deploy their subordinates to secure the near side and then, after gaining access, secure the far side. Gaining access to the inside of the building normally requires reducing protective obstacles.

Units gain access by using either a top or bottom entry. The entry point is the same thing as a point of penetration for an obstacle breach and as such is a danger area. The entry point will become the focus of fires for any enemy in a position to fire at it. It is commonly referred to as the "fatal funnel." Leaders ensure they have established measures to ensure the assault team has fire superiority when moving through the fatal funnel. Grenades (ROE determines fragmentation or concussion) are used to gain enough of a window of opportunity until the assault element can employ its small arms fire.

Top Entry

The top of a building is ordinarily considered a position of advantage. Entering at the top and fighting downward is the preferred method of gaining access to a building for a number of reasons. First, just as in operations on other types of terrain, it is easier to own the high ground and work your way down than it is to fight your way up when the enemy owns the high ground. Second, an enemy forced down to ground level may be tempted to withdraw from the building and expose himself to the fire of covering units or weapons. Third, the ground floor and basements are normally more heavily defended. Finally, the roof of a building is ordinarily weaker than the walls (and therefore easier to penetrate).

Top entry is only feasible when the unit can gain access to an upper floor or rooftop. Rooftops are danger areas when surrounding buildings are higher and forces can be exposed to fire from those buildings. Soldiers should consider the use of devices and other techniques that allow them upper level access without using interior stairways. Those devices and techniques include, but are not limited to, adjacent rooftops, fire escapes, portable ladders, and various Soldier-assisted lifts. For more information on top entry breaching, see FM 3-06.11.

Bottom Entry

Entry at the bottom is common and may be the only option available. When entering from the bottom, breaching a wall to create a "mousehole" is the preferred method because doors and windows may be booby-trapped and covered by fire from inside the structure. There are many ways to accomplish this, including employing CCMS, SLM, demolitions, hand tools, machine guns, artillery fire, and tank fire. The actual technique used depends on the ROE, assets available, building structure, and the enemy situation. If the assault element must enter through a door or window, it should enter from a rear or flank position after ensuring the entry point is clear of obstacles.

Secure the Near and Far Side of the Point of Penetration

Infantry platoons use the following drill for gaining access to the building. The steps of this drill are very similar to those drills described in Section IX to secure the near and far side of the point of penetration—

- The squad leader and the assault fire team move to the last covered and concealed position near the entry point
- The squad leader confirms the entry point
- The platoon leader or squad leader shifts the support fire away from the entry point
- The support-by-fire element continues to suppress building and adjacent enemy positions as required
- Buddy team #1 (team leader and automatic rifleman) remain in a position short of the entry point to add suppressive fires for the initial entry
- Buddy team #2 (grenadier and rifleman) and the squad leader move to the entry point. They move in rushes or by crawling.
- The squad leader positions himself where he can best control his teams
- Buddy team #2 position themselves against the wall to the right or left of the entry point.
- On the squad leader command of COOK OFF GRENADES (2 seconds maximum), the Soldiers employing the grenades shout, FRAG OUT, and throw the grenades into the building. (If the squad leader decides not to use grenades, he commands, PREPARE TO ENTER—GO!)
- Upon detonation of both grenades (or command GO), the buddy team flows into the room/hallway and moves to points of domination engaging all identified or likely enemy positions.
- Both Soldiers halt and take up positions to block any enemy movement toward the entry point.
- Simultaneously, buddy team #1 moves to and enters the building, joins buddy team #2, and announces, CLEAR.
- The squad leader remains at the entry point and marks it IAW unit SOP. He calls forward the next fire team with, NEXT TEAM IN.
- Once the squad has secured a foothold, the squad leader reports to the platoon leader, FOOTHOLD SECURE. The platoon follows the success of the seizure of the foothold with the remainder of the platoon.

When using a doorway as the point of entry, the path of least resistance is initially determined on the way the door opens. If the door opens inward, the Soldier plans to move away from the hinged side. If the door opens outward, he plans to move toward the hinged side. Upon entering, the size of the room, enemy situation, and obstacles in the room (furniture and other items) that hinder or channel movement become factors that influence the number one man's direction of movement.

B. Clearing Rooms

Ref: FM 3-21.8 (FM 7-8) The Infantry Rifle Platoon and Squad, pp. 7-40 to 7-42.

Although rooms come in all shapes and sizes, there are some general principles that apply to most room clearing tasks. For clearing large open buildings such as hangars or warehouses, it may be necessary to use subordinate units using a line formation while employing traveling or bounding overwatch. These methods can effectively clear the entire structure while ensuring security.

Room clearing techniques differ based on METT-TC, ROE, and probability of non-combatants inside the building. If there are known or suspected enemy forces, but no noncombatants inside the building, the platoon may conduct high intensity room clearings. If there are known or suspected noncombatants within the building, the platoon may conduct precision room clearings. High intensity room clearing may consist of fragmentation grenade employment and an immediate and high volume of small arms fire placed into the room, precision room clearing will not.

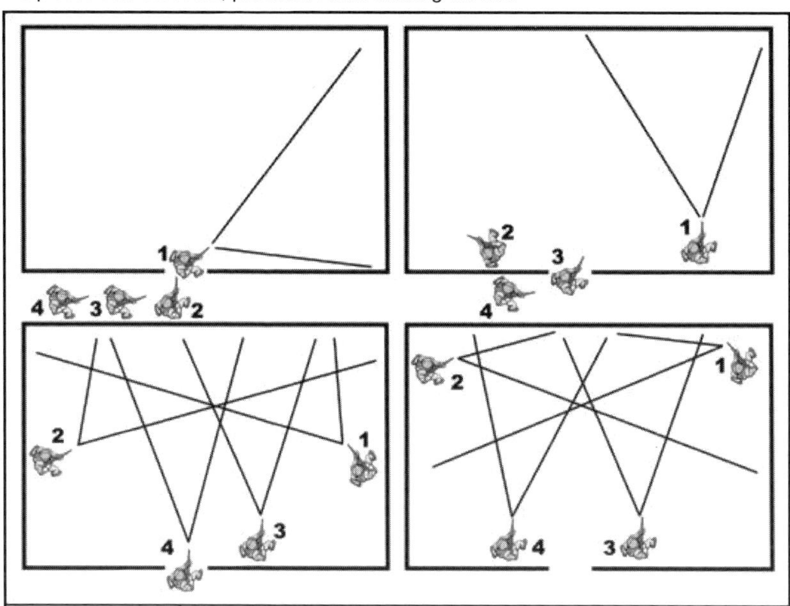

• **#1 Man**. The #1 man enters the room and eliminates any immediate threat. He can move left or right, moving along the path of least resistance to a point of domination—one of the two corners and continues down the room to gain depth.

• **#2 Man**. The #2 man enters almost simultaneously with the first and moves in the opposite direction, following the wall. The #2 man must clear the entry point, clear the immediate threat area, and move to his point of domination.

• **#3 Man**. The #3 man simply moves in the opposite direction of the #2 man inside the room, moves at least 1 meter from the entry point, and takes a position that dominates his sector.

• **#4 Man**. The #4 man moves in the opposite direction of the #3 man, clears the doorway by at least 1 meter, and moves to a position that dominates his sector.

Once the room is cleared, the team leader may order some team members to move deeper into the room overwatched by the other team members. The team leader must control this action. In addition to dominating the room, all team members are responsible for identifying possible loopholes and mouseholes. Cleared rooms should be marked IAW unit SOP.

C. Moving in the Building

Ref: FM 3-21.8 (FM 7-8) The Infantry Rifle Platoon and Squad, pp. 7-42 to 7-46. See also pp. 2-32 to 2-33 for discussion of clearing as a tactical mission task.

Movement techniques used inside a building are employed by teams to negotiate hallways and other avenues of approach.

Diamond Formation (Serpentine Technique)

The serpentine technique is a variation of a diamond formation that is used in a narrow hallway. The #1 man provides security to the front. His sector of fire includes any enemy Soldiers who appear at the far end or along the hallway. The #2 and #3 men cover the left and right sides of the #1 man. Their sectors of fire include any enemy combatants who appear suddenly from either side of the hall. The #4 man (normally carrying the M249) provides rear protection.

Vee Formation (Rolling-T Technique)

The rolling-T technique is a variation of the Vee formation and is used in wide hallways. The #1 and #2 men move abreast, covering the opposite side of the hallway from the one they are walking on. The #3 man covers the far end of the hallway from a position behind the #1 and #2 men, firing between them. The #4 man provides rear security.

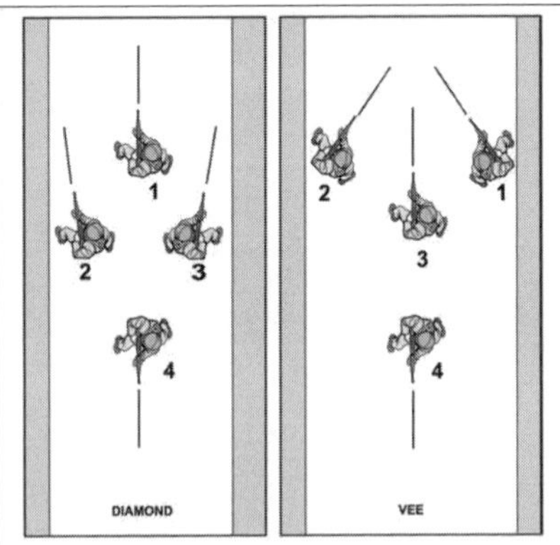

1. Clearing Hallway Junctions

Hallway intersections are danger areas and should be approached cautiously. Figure 7-13 depicts the fire team's actions upon reaching a "T" intersection when approaching along the "cross" of the "T".

The unit is using the diamond (serpentine) formation for movement (Figure 7-13 A).

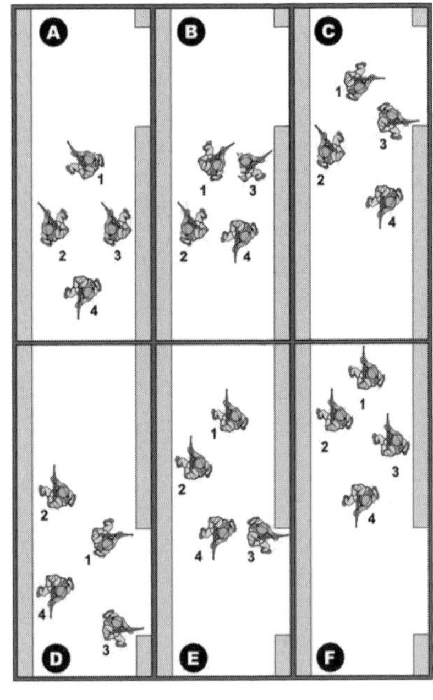

To clear a hallway—

- The team configures into a modified 2-by-2 (box) formation with the #1 and #3 men abreast and toward the right side of the hall. The #2 man moves to the left side of the hall and orients to the front, and the #4 man shifts to the right side (his left) and maintains rear security. (When clearing a right-hand corner, use the left-handed firing method to minimize exposure [Figure 7-13 B]).
- The #1 and #3 men move to the edge of the corner. The #3 man assumes a low crouch or kneeling position. On signal, the #3 man, keeping low, turns right around the corner and the #1 man, staying high, steps forward while turning to the right. (Sectors of fire interlock and the low/high positions prevent Soldiers from firing at one another [Figure 7-13 C]).

Urban Ops & Fortifications

- The #2 and #4 men continue to move in the direction of travel. As the #2 man passes behind the #1 man, the #1 man shifts to his left until he reaches the far corner (Figure 7-13 D).
- The #2 and #4 men continue to move in the direction of travel. As the #4 man passes behind the #3 man, the #3 man shifts laterally to his left until he reaches the far corner. As the #3 man begins to shift across the hall, the #1 man turns into the direction of travel and moves to his original position in the diamond (serpentine) formation (Figure 7-13 E).
- As the #3 and #4 men reach the far side of the hallway, they, too, assume their original positions in the serpentine formation, and the fire team continues to move (Figure 7-13 F).

2. Clearing a "T" Intersection

Figure 7-14 depicts the fire team's actions upon reaching a "T" intersection when approaching from the base of the "T". The fire team is using the diamond (serpentine) formation for movement (Figure 7-14 A).

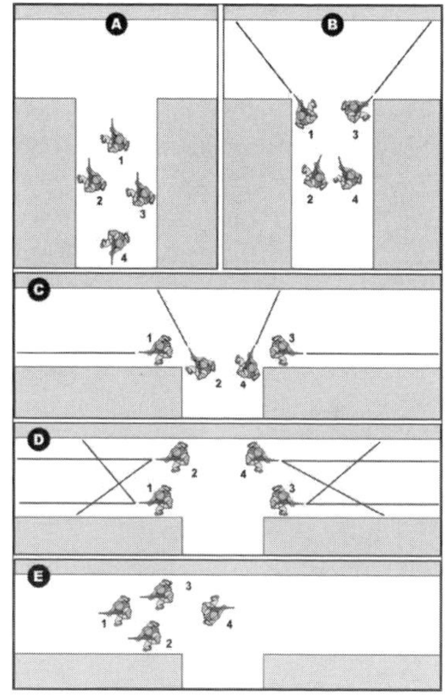

- The team configures into a 2-by-2 (box) formation with the #1 and #2 men left and the #3 and #4 men right. (When clearing a right-hand corner, use the left-handed firing method to minimize exposure [Figure 7-14 B]).
- The #1 and #3 men move to the edge of the corner and assume a low crouch or kneeling position. On signal, the #1 and #3 men simultaneously turn left and right respectively (Figure 7-14 C).
- At the same time, the #2 and #4 men step forward and turn left and right respectively while maintaining their (high) position. (Sectors of fire interlock and the low/high positions prevent Soldiers from firing at another [Figure 7-14 D]).
- Once the left and right portions of the hallway are clear, the fire team resumes the movement formation (Figure 7-14 E). Unless security is left behind, the hallway will no longer remain clear once the fire team leaves the immediate area.

3. Clearing Stairwells and Staircases

Stairwells and staircases are comparable to doorways because they create a fatal funnel. The danger is intensified by the three-dimensional aspect of additional landings. The ability of units to conduct the movement depends upon which direction they are traveling and the layout of the stairs. Regardless, the clearing technique follows a basic format:

- The leader designates an assault element to clear the stairs
- The unit maintains 360-degree, three-dimensional security in the vicinity of the stairs.
- The leader then directs the assault element to locate, mark, bypass, and or clear any obstacles or booby traps
- The assault element moves up (or down) the stairway by using either the two-, three-, or four-man flow technique, providing overwatch up and down the stairs while moving. The three-man variation is preferred.

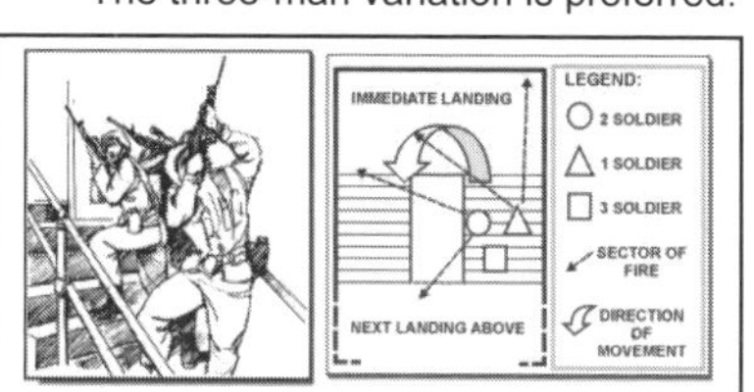

IV. Follow Through

After securing a floor (bottom, middle, or top), selected members of the unit are assigned to cover potential enemy counterattack routes to the building. Priority must be given initially to securing the direction of attack. Security elements alert the unit and place a heavy volume of fire on enemy forces approaching the unit.

Units must guard all avenues of approach leading into their area. These may include—

- Enemy mouseholes between adjacent buildings
- Covered routes to the building
- Underground routes into the basement
- Approaches over adjoining roofs or from window to window

Units that performed missions as assault elements should be prepared to assume an overwatch mission and to support another assault element.

To continue the mission—

- Momentum must be maintained. This is a critical factor in clearing operations. The enemy cannot be allowed to move to its next set of prepared positions or to prepare new positions.
- The support element pushes replacements, ammunition, and supplies forward to the assault element
- Casualties must be evacuated and replaced
- Security for cleared areas must be established IAW the OPORD or TSOP
- All cleared areas and rooms must be marked IAW unit SOP
- The support element must displace forward to ensure that it is in place to provide support (such as isolation of the new objective) to the assault element

The compartmentalized nature of urban terrain, limited observation and fields of fire, and the vast amounts of potential cover and concealment mean that defenders can disperse and remain undetected. The origin of enemy gunfire can be difficult to detect, because distance and direction become distorted by structures. (Dept. of Army photo by Spc. Kieran Cuddihy).

II. Attacking Fortified Areas

Ref: FM 3-21.8 (FM 7-8) The Infantry Rifle Platoon and Squad, pp. 7-48 to 7-53.

Fortifications are works emplaced to defend and reinforce a position. Time permitting, enemy defenders build bunkers and trenches, emplace protective obstacles, and position mutually supporting fortifications when fortifying their positions. Soldiers who attack prepared positions should expect to encounter a range of planned enemy fires to include small arms fire, mortars, artillery, antitank missiles, antitank guns, tanks, attack aviation, and close air support. Attacking forces should also expect a range of offensive type maneuver options to include spoiling attacks, internal repositioning, counterattacks, and withdrawing to subsequent defensive positions. Spoiling attacks will attempt to disrupt the attacker's momentum and possibly seize key terrain. If driven out of their prepared positions, enemy troops may try to win them back by hasty local counterattacks or through deliberate, planned combined arms counterattacks. If forced to withdraw, the enemy forces may use obstacles, ambushes, and other delaying tactics to slow down pursuing attackers.

The attack of a fortified position follows the basic principles of tactical maneuver. However, greater emphasis is placed upon detailed planning, special training and rehearsals, increased fire support, and the use of special equipment.

The deliberate nature of defenses requires a deliberate approach to the attack. These types of operations are time consuming. Leaders must develop schemes of maneuver that systematically reduce the area. Initially, these attacks should be limited in scope, focusing on individual positions and intermediate terrain objectives. Leaders must establish clear bypass criteria and position destruction criteria and allocate forces to secure cleared enemy positions. Failure in this will likely result in enemy reoccupying the positions, isolating lead elements, and ambushes.

Characteristics

The intense, close combat prevalent in trench clearing is remarkably similar to fighting in built up areas. Comparable characteristics include:

- **Restricted Observation and Fields of Fire**. Once the trench is entered, visibilities may be limited to a few meters in either direction. This compartmentalization necessarily decentralizes the engagement to the lowest level.
- **Cover and Concealment**. The nature of a trench system allows covered movement of both friendly and enemy forces. To prevent being flanked or counterattacked, junctions, possible entry points, and corners should be secured.
- **Difficulty in Locating the Enemy**. The assault element may come under fire from multiple mutually supporting positions in the trench or a nearby position. The exact location of the fire may be difficult to determine. Supporting elements should be capable of locating, suppressing, or destroying such threats.
- **Close Quarters Fighting**. Because of the close nature of the trench system, Soldiers should be prepared to use close quarters marksmanship, bayonet, and hand-to-hand fight techniques.
- **Restricted Movement**. Trench width and height will severely restrict movement inside the system. This will ordinarily require the assault element to move at a low crouch or even a crawl. Sustainment including ammunition resupply, EPW evacuation, casualty evacuation, and reinforcement will also be hampered.
- **Sustainment**. The intensity of close combat in the trench undoubtedly results in increased resource requirements.

I. Find

Finding the enemy's fortified positions relates back to the position's purpose. There are two general reasons to create fortified positions. The first includes defending key terrain and using the position as a base camp, shelter, or sanctuary for critical personnel or activities. This type of position is typically camouflaged and difficult to locate. When U.S. forces have air superiority and robust reconnaissance abilities, enemy forces will go to great lengths to conceal these positions. Sometimes the only way to find these enemy positions is by movement to contact. When Infantry platoons or squads encounter a previously unidentified prepared enemy position, they should not, as a general rule, conduct a hasty attack until they have set conditions for success.

The second general purpose for fortified positions is to create a situation in which the attacker is required to mass and present a profitable target. This type of position normally occurs in more conventional battles. These positions can be relatively easy to find because they occupy key terrain, establish identifiable patterns, and generally lack mobility.

Attacking fortified positions requires thorough planning and preparation based on extensive reconnaissance.

II. Fix

An enemy in fortified defenses has already partially fixed himself. This does not mean he will not be able to maneuver or that the fight will be easy. It does mean that the objective is probably more defined than with an enemy with complete freedom of movement. Fixing the enemy will still require measures to prevent repositioning to alternate, supplementary, and subsequent positions on the objective and measures to block enemy counterattack elements.

III. Finish (Fighting Enemies in Fortifications)

Finishing an enemy in prepared positions requires the attacker to follow the fundamentals of the offense-surprise, concentration, tempo, and audacity to be successful.

The actual fighting of enemy fortifications is clearly an Infantry platoon unit function because squads and platoons, particularly when augmented with engineers, are the best organized and equipped units in the Army for breaching protective obstacles. They are also best prepared to assault prepared positions such as bunkers and trench lines. Infantry platoons are capable of conducting these skills with organic, supplementary, and supporting weapons in any environment.

Leaders develop detailed plans for each fortification, using the SOSRA technique to integrate and synchronize fire support and maneuver assets. Although there are specific drills associated with the types of fortifications, the assault of a fortified area is an operation, not a drill. During planning, the leader's level of detail should identify each aperture (opening or firing port) of his assigned fortification(s) and consider assigning these as a specific target when planning fires. Contingency plans are made for the possibility of encountering previously undetected fortifications along the route to the objective, and for neutralizing underground defenses when encountered.

A. Securing the Near and Far Side—Breaching Protective Obstacles

To fight the enemy almost always requires penetrating extensive protective obstacles, both antipersonnel and antivehicle. Of particular concern to the Infantrymen are antipersonnel obstacles. Antipersonnel obstacles (both explosive and nonexplosive) include, wire entanglements; trip flares; antipersonnel mines; field expedient devices (booby traps, nonexplosive traps, punji sticks); flame devices; rubble; warning devices; CBRN; and any other type of obstacle created to prevent troops from entering a position. Antipersonnel obstacles are usually integrated with enemy fires close enough to the fortification for adequate enemy surveillance by day or night, but beyond effective hand grenade range. Obstacles are also used within the enemy position to compartmentalize the area in the event outer protective barriers are breached. See Appendix F for more information on obstacles.

The following steps are an example platoon breach:

- The squad leader and the breaching fire team move to the last covered and concealed position near the breach point (point of penetration)
- The squad leader confirms the breach point
- The platoon leader or squad leader shifts the suppressing element away from the entry point
- The fire element continues to suppress enemy positions as required
- Buddy team #1 (team leader and the automatic rifleman) remains in a position short of the obstacle to provide local security for buddy team #2
- The squad leader and breaching fire team leader employ smoke grenades to obscure the breach point
- Buddy team #2 (grenadier and rifleman) moves to the breach point. They move in rushes or by crawling
- The squad leader positions himself where he can best control his teams.
- Buddy team #2 positions themselves to the right and left of the breach point near the protective obstacle
- Buddy team #2 probes for mines and creates a breach, marking their path as they proceed
- Once breached, buddy team #1 and buddy team #2 move to the far side of the obstacle and take up covered and concealed positions to block any enemy movement toward the breach point. They engage all identified or likely enemy positions.
- The squad leader remains at the entry point and marks it. He calls forward the next fire team with, "Next team in."
- Once the squad has secured a foothold, the squad leader reports to the platoon leader, "Foothold secure." The platoon follows the success of the seizure of the foothold with the remainder of the platoon.

B. Knocking Out Bunkers

The term bunker in this discussion covers all emplacements having overhead cover and containing apertures (embrasures) through which weapons are fired. The two primary types are reinforced concrete pillboxes, and log bunkers. There are two notable exploitable weaknesses of bunkers.

First, bunkers are permanent, their location and orientation fixed. Bunkers cannot be relocated or adjusted to meet a changing situation. They are optimized for a particular direction and function. The worst thing an Infantry platoon or squad can do is to approach the position in the manner it was designed to fight.

Second, bunkers must have openings (doors, windows, apertures, or air vents). There are two disadvantages to be exploited here. First, structurally, the opening is the weakest part of the position and will be the first part of the structure to collapse if engaged. Second, a single opening can only cover a finite sector, creating blind spots.

C. Assaulting Trench Systems

Ref: FM 3-21.8 (FM 7-8) The Infantry Rifle Platoon and Squad, pp. 7-51 to 7-53.

Trenches are dug to connect fighting positions. They are typically dug in a zigzagged fashion to prevent the attacker from firing down a long section if he gets into the trench, and to reduce the effectiveness of high explosive munitions. Trenches may also have shallow turns, intersections with other trenches, firing ports, overhead cover, and bunkers. Bunkers will usually be oriented outside the trench, but may also have the ability to provide protective fire into the trench.

The trench provides defenders with a route that has frontal cover, enabling them to reposition without the threat of low trajectory fires. However, unless overhead cover is built, trenches are subject to the effects of high trajectory munitions like the grenade, grenade launcher, plunging machine gun fire, mortars, and artillery. These types of weapon systems should be used to gain and maintain fire superiority on defenders in the trench.

The trench is the enemy's home, so there is no easy way to clear it. Their confined nature, extensive enemy preparations, and the limited ability to integrate combined arms fires makes trench clearing hazardous for even the best trained Infantry. If possible, a bulldozer or plow tank can be used to fill in the trench and bury the defenders. However, since this is not always feasible, Infantry units must move in and clear trenches.

1. Entering the Trenchline

To enter the enemy trench the platoon takes the following steps:

- The squad leader and the assault fire team move to the last covered and concealed position near the entry point
- The squad leader confirms the entry point
- The platoon leader or squad leader shifts the base of fire away from the entry point
- The base of fire continues to suppress trench and adjacent enemy positions as required
- Buddy team #1 (team leader and automatic rifleman) remains in a position short of the trench to add suppressive fires for the initial entry
- Buddy team #2 (grenadier and rifleman) and squad leader move to the entry point. They move in rushes or by crawling (squad leader positions himself where he can best control his teams).
- Buddy team #2 positions itself parallel to the edge of the trench. Team members get on their backs
- On the squad leader command of COOK OFF GRENADES (2 seconds maximum), they shout, FRAG OUT, and throw the grenades into the trench
- Upon detonation of both grenades, the Soldiers roll into the trench, landing on their feet and back-to-back. They engage all known, likely or suspected enemy positions.
- Both Soldiers immediately move in opposite directions down the trench, continuing until they reach the first corner or intersection
- Both Soldiers halt and take up positions to block any enemy movement toward the entry point
- Simultaneously, buddy team #1 moves to and enters the trench, joining buddy team #2. The squad leader directs them to one of the secured corners or intersections to relieve the Soldier who then rejoins his buddy at the opposite end of the foothold.
- At the same time, the squad leader rolls into the trench and secures the entry point.
- The squad leader remains at the entry point and marks it. He calls forward the next fire team with, NEXT TEAM IN
- Once the squad has secured a foothold, the squad leader reports to the platoon leader, FOOTHOLD SECURE. The platoon follows the success of the seizure of the foothold with the remainder of the platoon.

The leader or a designated subordinate must move into the trench as soon as possible to control the tempo, specifically the movement of the lead assault element and the movement of follow-on forces. He must resist the temptation to move the entire unit into the trench as this will unduly concentrate the unit in a small area. Instead,, he should ensure the outside of the trench remains isolated as he maintains fire superiority inside the trench. This may require a more deliberate approach. When subordinates have reached their objectives or have exhausted their resources, the leader commits follow-on forces. Once stopped, the leader consolidates and reorganizes.

The assault element is organized into a series of three-man teams. The team members are simply referred to as number 1 man, number 2 man, and number 3 man. Each team is armed with at least one M249 and one grenade launcher. All men are armed with multiple hand grenades.

The positioning within the three-man team is rotational, so the men in the team must be rehearsed in each position. The number 1 man is responsible for assaulting down the trench using well aimed effective fire and throwing grenades around pivot points in the trenchline or into weapons emplacements. The number 2 man follows the number 1 man closely enough to support him but not so closely that both would be suppressed if the enemy gained local fire superiority. The number 3 man follows the number 2 man and prepares to move forward when positions rotate.

While the initial three-man assault team rotates by event, the squad leader directs the rotation of the three-man teams within the squad as ammunition becomes low in the leading team, casualties occur, or as the situation dictates. Since this three-man drill is standardized, three-man teams may be reconstituted as needed from the remaining members of the squad. The platoon ldr controls the rotation between squads using the same considerations as the squad leaders.

2. Clearing the Trenchline

Once the squad has secured the entry point and expanded it to accommodate the squad, the rest of the platoon enters and begins to clear the designated section of the enemy position. The platoon may be tasked to clear in two directions if the objective is small. Otherwise, it will only clear in one direction as another platoon enters and clears in the opposite direction.

The lead three-man team of the initial assault squad moves out past the security of the support element and executes the trench clearing drill. The number 1 man, followed by number 2 man and number 3 man, maintains his advance until arriving at a pivot, junction point, or weapons emplacement in the trench. He alerts the rest of the team by yelling out, POSITION or, JUNCTION, and begins to prepare a grenade. The number 2 man immediately moves forward near the lead man and takes up the fire to cover until the grenade can be thrown around the corner of the pivot point. The number 3 man moves forward to the point previously occupied by number 2 and prepares for commitment.

If the lead man encounters a junction in the trench, the platoon leader should move forward, make a quick estimate, and indicate the direction the team should continue to clear. This will normally be toward the bulk of the fortification or toward command post emplacements. He should place a marker (normally specified in the unit TSOP) pointing toward the direction of the cleared path. After employing a grenade, the number 2 man moves out in the direction indicated by the platoon leader and assumes the duties of the number 1 man. Anytime the number 1 man runs out of ammunition, he shouts, MAGAZINE, and immediately moves against the wall of the trench to allow the number 2 man to take up the fire. Squad leaders continue to push uncommitted teams forward, securing bypassed trenches and rotating fresh teams to the front. Trenches are cleared in sequence not simultaneously.

3. Moving in a Trench

Once inside, the trench teams use variations of the combat formations to move. These formations are used as appropriate inside buildings as well. The terms hallway and trench are used interchangeably. The column (file) and box formations are self explanatory. The line and echelon formations are generally infeasible.

Ideally the team is able to destroy the bunker with standoff weapons and HE munitions. However, when required, the fire team can assault the bunker with small arms and grenades. A fire team (two to four men) with HE and smoke grenades move forward under cover of the suppression and obscuration fires from the squad and other elements of the base of fire. When they reach a vulnerable point of the bunker, they destroy it or personnel inside with grenades or other hand-held demolitions. All unsecured bunkers must be treated as if they contain live enemy, even if no activity has been detected from them. The clearing of bunkers must be systematic or the enemy will come up behind assault groups. To clear a bunker—

- The squad leader and the assault fire team move to the last covered and concealed position near the position's vulnerable point
- The squad leader confirms the vulnerable point
- The platoon leader/squad leader shifts the base of fire away from the vulnerable point
- The base of fire continues to suppress the position and adjacent enemy positions as required
- Buddy team #1 (team leader and the automatic rifleman) remain in a position short of the position to add suppressive fires for buddy team #2 (grenadier and rifleman)
- Buddy team #2 moves to the vulnerable point. They move in rushes or by crawling
- One Soldier takes up a covered position near the exit
- The other Soldier cooks off a grenade (2 seconds maximum), shouts, FRAG OUT, and throws it through an aperture
- After the grenade detonates, the Soldier covering the exit enters and clears the bunker
- Simultaneously, the second Soldier moves into the bunker to assist Soldier #1
- Both Soldiers halt at a point of domination and take up positions to block any enemy movement toward their position
- Buddy team #1 moves to join buddy team #2
- The team leader inspects the bunker, marks the bunker, and signals the squad leader
- The assault squad leader consolidates, reorganizes, and prepares to continue the mission

IV. Follow Through

The factors for consolidation and reorganization of fortified positions are the same as consolidation and reorganization of other attacks. If a fortification is not destroyed sufficiently to prevent its reuse by the enemy, it must be guarded until means can be brought forward to complete the job. The number of positions the unit can assault is impacted by the—

- Length of time the bunkers must be guarded to prevent reoccupation by the enemy
- Ability of the higher headquarters to resupply the unit
- Availability of special equipment in sufficient quantities
- Ability of the unit to sustain casualties and remain effective

As part of consolidation, the leader orders a systematic search of the secured positions for booby traps and spider holes. He may also make a detailed sketch of his area and the surrounding dispositions if time allows. This information will be helpful for the higher headquarters intelligence officer or if the unit occupies the position for an extended length of time.

Patrols & Patrolling

Ref: FM 3-21.8 (FM 7-8) The Infantry Rifle Platoon and Squad, pp. 9-2 to 9-9 and The Ranger Handbook, chap. 5.

The two categories of patrols are combat and reconnaissance. Regardless of the type of patrol being sent out, the commander must provide a clear task and purpose to the patrol leader. Any time a patrol leaves the main body of the unit there is a possibility that it may become engaged in close combat.

Patrol missions can range from security patrols in the close vicinity of the main body, to raids deep into enemy territory. Successful patrolling requires detailed contingency planning and well-rehearsed small unit tactics. The planned action determines the type of patrol. (Dept. of Army photo by Sgt. Ben Brody).

Combat Patrols

Patrols that depart the main body with the clear intent to make direct contact with the enemy are called combat patrols. The three types of combat patrols are raid patrols, ambush patrols (both of which are sent out to conduct special purpose attacks), and security patrols.

Reconnaissance Patrols

Patrols that depart the main body with the intention of avoiding direct combat with the enemy while seeing out information or confirming the accuracy of previously-gathered information are called reconnaissance patrols. The most common types reconnaissance patrols are area, route, zone, and point. Leaders also dispatch reconnaissance patrols to track the enemy, and to establish contact with other friendly forces. Contact patrols make physical contact with adjacent units and report their location, status, and intentions. Tracking patrols follow the trail and movements of a specific enemy unit. Presence patrols conduct a special form of reconnaissance, normally during stability or civil support operations.

Note: See also p. 4-12 for discussion of patrols in support of stability operations.

I. Organization of Patrols

A patrol is organized to perform specific tasks. It must be prepared to secure itself, navigate accurately, identify and cross danger areas, and reconnoiter the patrol objective. If it is a combat patrol, it must be prepared to breach obstacles, assault the objective, and support those assaults by fire. Additionally, a patrol must be able to conduct detailed searches as well as deal with casualties and prisoners or detainees.

The leader identifies those tasks the patrol must perform and decides which elements will implement them. Where possible, he should maintain squad and fire team integrity.

Squads and fire teams may perform more than one task during the time a patrol is away from the main body or it may be responsible for only one task. The leader must plan carefully to ensure that he has identified and assigned all required tasks in the most efficient way. (Dept. of Army photo by Sgt. Ben Brody).

A patrol is sent out by a larger unit to conduct a specific combat, reconnaissance, or security mission. A patrol's organization is temporary and specifically matched to the immediate task. Because a patrol is an organization, not a mission, it is not correct to speak of giving a unit a mission to "Patrol."

The terms "patrolling" or "conducting a patrol" are used to refer to the semi-independent operation conducted to accomplish the patrol's mission. Patrols require a specific task and purpose.

A commander sends a patrol out from the main body to conduct a specific tactical task with an associated purpose. Upon completion of that task, the patrol leader returns to the main body, reports to the commander and describes the events that took place, the status of the patrol's members and equipment, and any observations.

If a patrol is made up of an organic unit, such as a rifle squad, the squad leader is responsible. If a patrol is made up of mixed elements from several units, an officer or NCO is designated as the patrol leader. This temporary title defines his role and responsibilities for that mission. The patrol leader may designate an assistant, normally the next senior man in the patrol, and any subordinate element leaders he requires.

A patrol can consist of a unit as small as a fire team. Squad- and platoon-size patrols are normal. Sometimes, for combat tasks such as a raid, the patrol can consist of most of the combat elements of a rifle company. Unlike operations in which the Infantry platoon or squad is integrated into a larger organization, the patrol is semi-independent and relies on itself for security.

Every patrol is assigned specific tasks. Some tasks are assigned to the entire patrol, others are assigned to subordinate teams, and finally some are assigned to each individual. An individual will have multiple tasks and subtasks to consider and carry out.

1. Pointman, Dragman, and Security Team

Security is everyone's responsibility. Having noted that, every patrol has a troop walking in front. This troop is called the pointman. He is responsible for making sure the patrol does not walk into enemy ambushes, minefields, or similar. The pointman has forward security. Sometimes a patrol will send the pointman with another patrol member to walk a short distance forward of the patrol.

Also, every patrol has someone who is last in the formation. This troop is called the dragman. He is responsible for making sure that no patrol members are left behind. He also makes sure that the enemy doesn't surprise the patrol from the rear unnoticed.

The security team is responsible for specifically pulling security to the left and right of the patrol. This is a critical task when crossing danger areas, so a specific team is identified to conduct this task.

2. Clearing Team

The clearing team crosses the danger area once the security team is in place. The clearing team has the specified responsibility of visually clearing and physically securing the far side of a danger area. It's important so another team is designated to conduct this task.

3. Compass & Pace Team

Obviously someone needs to make sure the patrol is headed in the right direction and that we don't travel too far. This is the job of the compassman and paceman. Typically the compass and pace team is positioned immediately behind the pointman. Additionally, a secondary compass and pace team is usually located in the back half of the patrol.

4. Command Team

The PL and a radio operator (RTO) make up the command team for most patrols. Doctrinally speaking, the APL is also part of this team but the APL is normally positioned near the very rear of the formation to help the dragman and ensure no patrol member is left behind.

5. Aid & Litter Team

Someone has to help pull wounded buddies out of harms way. There are usually two members of each fire team designated as aid and litter teams. These teams are spread throughout the patrol and have the responsibility of carrying and employing extra medical aid gear.

6. Enemy Prisoner of War (EPW) Search Team

EPW teams are responsible for controlling enemy prisoners IAW the five S's and the leader's guidance. These teams may also be responsible for accounting for and controlling detainees or recovered personnel.

7. Tracking Team

There are many different specialty teams that might be assigned to a patrol. Trackers are just one such resource. Explosive ordinance details (EOD) are another. Trackers are unique, however, because they are generally positioned just ahead of the pointman on the patrol.

8. Support Team

The support team is outfitted with heavy, crew-served weapons on the patrol. Of course, reconnaissance patrols usually do not make use of a support team. But when a support team is required, it will be positioned to the center of the patrol.

9. Assault & Breach Team

Reconnaissance rarely ever needs an assault team. The assault team may be dispersed throughout the patrol, but ideally is situated toward the rear. This is because the assault team is typically placed on the objective last.

II. Planning & Conducting a Patrol

Leaders plan and prepare for patrols using troop leading procedures and an estimate of the situation. They must identify required actions on the objective, plan backward to the departure from friendly lines, then forward to the reentry of friendly lines.

The patrol leader will normally receive the OPORD in the battalion or company CP. Because patrols act semi-independently, move beyond the direct-fire support of the parent unit, and often operate forward of friendly units, coordination must be thorough and detailed.

Patrol leaders may routinely coordinate with elements of the battalion staff directly. Unit leaders should develop tactical SOPs with detailed checklists to preclude omitting any items vital to the accomplishment of the mission.

Items coordinated between the leader and the battalion staff or company commander include:

- Changes or updates in the enemy situation
- Best use of terrain for routes, rally points, and patrol bases
- Light and weather data
- Changes in the friendly situation
- The attachment of Soldiers with special skills or equipment (engineers, sniper teams, scout dog teams, FOs, or interpreters)
- Use and location of landing or pickup zones
- Departure and reentry of friendly lines
- Fire support on the objective and along the planned routes, including alternate routes
- Rehearsal areas and times. The terrain for the rehearsal should be similar to that at the objective.
- Special equipment and ammunition requirements
- Transportation support, including transportation to and from the rehearsal site
- Signal plan—call signs frequencies, code words, pyrotechnics, and challenge and password

As the patrol leader completes his plan, he considers the following elements.

- Essential and supporting tasks. The leader ensures that he has assigned all essential tasks to be performed on the objective, at rally points, at danger areas, at security or surveillance locations, along the route(s), and at passage lanes.
- Key travel and execution times. The leader estimates time requirements for movement to the objective, leader's reconnaissance of the objective, establishment of security and surveillance, compaction of all assigned tasks on the objective, movement to an objective rally point to debrief the patrol, and return through friendly lines.
- Primary and alternate routes. The leader selects primary and alternate routes to and from the objective. Return routes should differ from routes to the objective.
- Signals. The leader should consider the use of special signals to include arm-and-hand signals, flares, voice, whistles, radios, visible and nonvisible lasers.
- Challenge and password outside of friendly lines. The challenge and password from the SOI must not be used when the patrol is outside friendly lines.
- Location of leaders. The leader considers where he, the platoon sergeant, and other key leaders should be located for each phase of the patrol mission. The platoon sergeant is normally with the following elements for each type of patrol:
  - In a raid or ambush, he normally controls the support element.
  - On an area reconnaissance, he normally supervises security in the objective rally point (ORP).
  - On a zone reconnaissance, he normally moves with the reconnaissance element that sets up the link-up point.
- Actions on enemy contact. The leader's plan must address actions on chance, to include:
  - Handling of seriously wounded & KIAs
  - Prisoners captured as a result of chance contact who are not part of the planned mission

The following provides an overview of considerations when conducting a patrol:

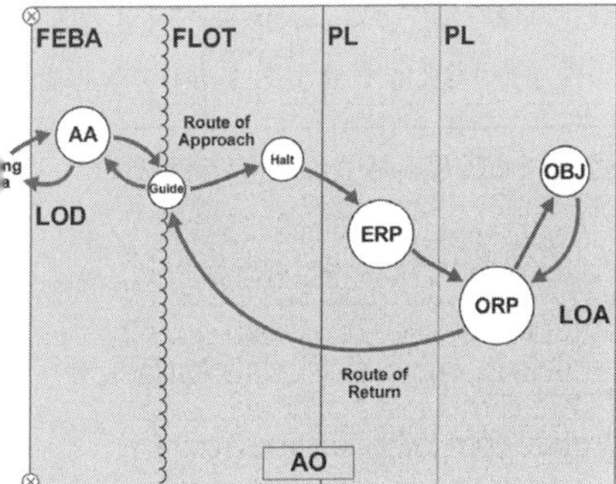

Patrol planning starts in a staging area. At the AA, a passage lane is coordinated through the FLOT, and the patrol conducts a listening halt past the FEBA. Movement to and from the OBJ is reported via phase lines. (Ref: FM 7-8, chap 3, section I).

1. Occupy Assembly Area (AA)

The patrol marches to and gathers in a designated AA behind the forward line of troops (FLOT). This area allows final preparation—everyone must be accounted for and in the correct uniform, with the correct gear, having the correct information, etc.

2. Coordinate the Passage of Lines

Once all troops are accounted for, the FLOT guide links up with the PL. This coordination includes the normal contingency plans, including the near and far recognition signals, and how long the guide should wait on the far end of the obstacles should the patrol need to return unexpectedly.

3. Depart the Forward Line of Troops (FLOT)

The PL calls the assistant patrol leader (APL) forward to count the troops out through the forward obstacles with the guide. Once through the FLOT, the APL takes up a position in the rear of the patrol's formation. En route rally points (ERP) are identified as a fallback point if there is trouble along the route.

4. Establish a Listening Halt

The PL pauses the patrol and forms a 360-degree security. When it's safe to continue, the patrol will resume its march.

5. Occupy the Objective Rally Point (ORP)

The last stop prior to the objective is the ORP. This is where all plans are finalized and execution of actions on the objective begins. Maintain noise and light discipline.

6. Move through the Release Point (RP)

A security team is positioned forward where the patrol will begin their recon. This is the release point. From this point the PL releases authority to the subordinate leaders to achieve their tasks.

7. Conduct Actions on the Objective (OBJ)

Actions on the objective will vary depending on whether the patrol is a reconnaissance or a combat patrol. These actions should be clearly delineated and rehearsed by team members.

8. Reoccupy the ORP

The mission is almost over. Back in the ORP is where the patrol members disseminate any necessary information about the mission and make final coordination for the route back to the AA behind the FLOT.

9. Reenter the FLOT

The PL conducts a far recognition signal with the FLOT. This typically involves a simple radio call, but it can also be a flare, gong, or smoke signal. The patrol lets the FLOT know the patrol is returning so that the patrol is not mistaken for enemy activity. The PL stops the patrol in a security halt and moves forward with a security team to give the near recognition signal.

Once the near recognition is established, the security team returns to the security halt and leads the patrol to the guide. The PL counts each member in by name.

10. Reoccupy the AA

The PL should render his patrol report to the commander. This report may be verbal or written, simple, or elaborate depending on the situation and the commander's requirements. Continue the mission; reorganize and reconstitute.

III. Elements of a Combat Patrol

There are three essential elements for a combat patrol: security; support; and assault. The size of each element is based on the situation and the analysis of METT-TC.

1. Assault Element

The assault element is the combat patrol's decisive effort. Its task is to conduct actions on the objective. The assault element is responsible for accomplishing the unit's task and purpose. This element must be capable (through inherent capabilities or positioning relative to the enemy) of destroying or seizing the target of the combat patrol. Tasks typically associated with the assault element include:

- Conduct of assault across the objective to destroy enemy equipment, capture or kill enemy, and clearing of key terrain and enemy positions
- Deployment close enough to the objective to conduct an immediate assault if detected
- Being prepared to support itself if the support element cannot suppress the enemy
- Providing support to a breach element in reduction of obstacles (if required)
- Planning detailed fire control and distribution
- Conducting controlled withdrawal from the objective

Additional tasks/special purpose teams assigned may include search teams, prisoner teams, demolition teams, breach team, and aid and litter teams.

2. Support Element

The support element suppresses the enemy on the objective using direct and indirect fires. The support element is a shaping effort that sets conditions for the mission's decisive effort. This element must be capable, through inherent means or positioning relative to the enemy, of supporting the assault element. The support force can be divided into two or more elements if required.

The support element is organized to address a secondary threat of enemy interference with the assault element(s). The support force suppresses, fixes, or destroys elements on the objective. The support force's primary responsibility is to suppress enemy to prevent reposition against decisive effort. The support force—

- Initiates fires and gains fire superiority with crew-served weapons and indirect fires
- Controls rates and distribution of fires
- Shifts/ceases fire on signal
- Supports the withdrawal of the assault element

3. Security Element

The security element(s) is a shaping force that has three roles. The first role is to isolate the objective from enemy personnel and vehicles attempting to enter the objective area. Their actions range from simply providing early warning, to blocking enemy movement. This element may require several different forces located in various positions. The patrol leader is careful to consider enemy reserves or response forces that, once the engagement begins, will be alerted. The second role of the security element is to prevent enemy from escaping the objective area. The third role is to secure the patrol's withdrawal route.

There is a subtle yet important distinction for the security element. All elements of the patrol are responsible for their own local security. What distinguishes the security element is that they are protecting the entire patrol. The security element is organized to address the primary threat to the patrol—being discovered and defeated by enemy forces prior to execution of actions on the objective. To facilitate the success of the assault element, the security element must fix or block (or at a minimum screen) all enemy security or response forces located on parts of the battlefield away from the raid.

Patrols & Patrolling

I. Traveling Techniques

Ref: FM 7-92 Infantry Reconnaissance Platoon and Squad (Airborne, Air Assault, Light Infantry), chap 3; and FM 3-19.4 Military Police Leader's Handbook, chap 7.

Traveling techniques can be used with any of the attack formations. In essence, these techniques are concerned with the distances between troops and units while moving. The critical factor of any movement technique is that the patrol leader (PL) can see the subordinate leaders and vise versa. This is because most of the communication and coordination is achieved through hand and arm signals—which requires line of sight.

The first technique, traveling, is used primarily for walking a patrol down a road or path in fairly secured areas. Patrols use the traveling technique when enemy contact is unlikely.

The second technique, traveling overwatch, is the most common technique employed when moving troops in unsecured areas. Patrols use the traveling overwatch when enemy contact is likely.

The third technique, bounding overwatch, is the preferred technique when security is the most important factor. Patrols use the bounding overwatch when enemy contact is expected.

Note: See following pages (pp. 7-8 to 7-9) for further discussion.

The squad is the essential fire and maneuver element. US Army squads include two fire teams, while Marine squads include three fire teams made up of a rifleman, automatic rifleman, grenadier, and team leader. A squad with as few as seven troops can be split into two fire teams and a squad leader. (Photo by Jeong, Hae-jung).

Traveling Techniques

I. Traveling

1. The patrol is massed together as one entity for ease of command and control (C2). This technique allows for speed of movement.

2. Troops are spaced five meters apart. If marching on a road, two lines are formed with troops staggered left and right. This creates a distance of ten meters between the troops on one side of the road, but still only five meters behind or in front of the troop to the opposite side of the road.

3. The patrol disperses to the left and right in the event of attack. This technique permits very little deterrence to the effectiveness of mass-casualty producing weapons, but does concentrate the troops for a massed assault in the event of a near ambush.

The traveling technique is used when enemy contact is unlikely. Marching troops by road is often the most efficient means of travel. As such, this technique mitigates our vulnerability if attacked. (Photo by Jeong, Hae-jung).

II. Traveling Overwatch

1. The patrol is separated into two or more elements. This technique is also fast. It has considerably more security and the flexibility for each element to maneuver in support of another if attacked. However, the PL losses some of the control in that each element is now commanded by a subordinate leader. The PL maintains contact with these leaders.

2. There is still five meters between troop, and the troops are staggered in two lines when roads are used. However, a distance of *at least* 20 meters is maintained between each element.

3. The patrol disperses left and right in the event of attack. This technique has improved security in its ability to deter the effect of mass-casualty producing weapons and has further advantages in regard to its ability to disperse and overwhelm a near or far ambush.

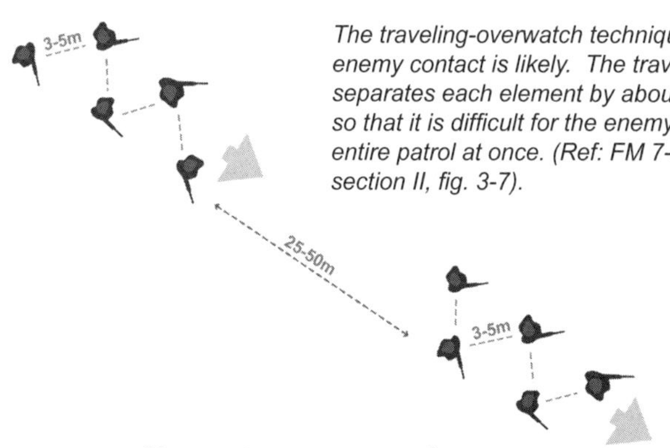

The traveling-overwatch technique is used when enemy contact is likely. The traveling overwatch separates each element by about 25 meters so that it is difficult for the enemy to attack an entire patrol at once. (Ref: FM 7-92, chap 3, section II, fig. 3-7).

III. Bounding Overwatch

1. The patrol is separated into two elements. This technique compromises speed for greater security and control.

2. The forward element halts in a position that offers the best observation of the terrain in front of the patrol. This element becomes the "overwatch" position. The position must offer some cover or concealment.

3. The trail element (behind the forward element) then bounds forward, either slightly left or right of the overwatch position.

4. Once the bounding element has successfully passed through the terrain, they take up a position that offers the best observation of the terrain in front of them. The bounding element now becomes the overwatch position and the old overwatch bounds forward.

5. This process is repeated until the patrol reaches its objective, or the PL selects another movement technique due to an improved security situation.

6. If the patrol comes under fire, the bounding overwatch becomes quick and violent. The overwatch position conducts suppressive fires while the PL directs the bounding element to either conduct a hasty attack against the enemy or break contact.

The bounding-overwatch technique is used explicitly when enemy contact is expected. The effort is to allow maximum use of combat power in the direction of movement, while exposing our smallest force to any potential enemy. (Photo by Jeong, Hae-jung).

On Point

Avoid confusing movement with maneuver. Maneuver is defined as "Movement supported by fire to gain a position of advantage over the enemy." At company level, the two overlap considerably. Tactical movement differs from maneuver, however, because maneuver is movement while in contact, but tactical movement is movement in preparation for contact. The process by which units transition from tactical movement to maneuver is called "actions on contact."

Troops must move. That's the nature of warfare. The trick is employing the appropriate technique to the present level of danger. Contact with the enemy is either unlikely, likely, or expected. Each technique allows for defensive fires in reaction to the enemy. The PL must consider the coordination of these fires in the planning phase.

The PL takes into consideration the factors of speed, control, and security. So, while bounding overwatch offers excellent control and security, it can be slow. On the other end of the spectrum is traveling, which maintains top speed and control, but dangerously lacks security. Somewhere in the middle of that continuum is the traveling overwatch, which offers adequate speed and security, but somewhat compromises the PL's control over the formation.

Keeping this in mind, the PL assesses the situation to determine the emphasis on speed, control, and security. In essence, the PL considers the appropriate distance between troops and subordinate elements.

Many issues factor into this consideration. Is the patrol moving troops in a secured area? Is it crossing rough or heavily vegetated terrain? Is the patrol moving at nighttime or daytime light conditions? How soon does the patrol need to be at its destination? How many troops are in this patrol—a fairly large unit, or a smaller one?

The most important consideration the PL takes into account is whether or not enemy contact is unlikely, likely, or expected.

Subordinate elements must not become so spread apart that they can no longer support each other. Weapon systems have finite ranges. In truth, weapon systems are more commonly limited by rugged or heavily vegetated terrain. In these cases, the distances between subordinate elements is even less. The PL chooses the appropriate technique for the given situation. Subordinate leaders enforce strict adherence to the assigned interval distances between troops and elements.

It is unrealistic to always move troops with the highest level of security, the bounding overwatch. The troops become easily fatigued and movement is slowed to an unreasonable pace. Conversely, it's unrealistic to always use the least amount of security, the traveling technique, in order to capitalize on speed.

Patrols & Patrolling

II. Attack Formations

Ref: FM 3-21.8 (FM 7-8) The Infantry Rifle Platoon and Squad, chap. 3 and 9; and FM 7-92 Infantry Reconnaissance Platoon and Squad (Airborne, Air Assault, Light Infantry), chap 3.

Squad formations include the squad column, the squad line, and the squad file. These formations are building blocks for the entire element. What that means is that the smallest element, the fire team, may be in a wedge while the larger element, such as the squad or platoon may be in another formation. It is quite possible to have fireteams in wedges, squads in columns, and the platoon in line—all at the same time. Additionally, this section will discuss a couple variations including the diamond and the staggered column.

Leaders attempt to maintain flexibility in their formations. Doing so enables them to react when unexpected enemy actions occur. (Dept. of Army photo by Senior Airman Steve Czyz).

Fire Team Formations

The term fire team formation refers to the Soldiers' relative positions within the fire team. Fire team formations include the fire team wedge and the fire team file. Both formations have advantages and disadvantages. Regardless of which formation the team employs, each Soldier must know his location in the formation relative to the other members of the fire team and the team leader. Each Soldier covers a set sector of responsibility for observation and direct fire as the team is moving. To provide the unit with all-round protection, these sectors must interlock.

The team leader adjusts the team's formation as necessary while the team is moving. The distance between men will be determined by the mission, the nature of the threat, the closeness of the terrain, and by the visibility. As a general rule, the unit should be dispersed up to the limit of control. This allows for a wide area to be covered, makes the team's movement difficult to detect, and makes them less vulnerable to enemy ground and air attack. Fire teams rarely act independently. However, in the event they do, they use a perimeter defense to ensure all-around security.

The squad leader adjusts the squad's formation as necessary while moving, primarily through the three movement techniques. The squad leader exercises command and control primarily through the two team leaders and moves in the formation where he can best achieve this. The squad leader is responsible for 360-degree security, for ensuring the team's sectors of fire are mutually supporting, and for being able to rapidly transition the squad upon contact.

The squad leader designates one of the fire teams as the base fire team. The squad leader controls the squad's speed and direction of movement through the base fire team while the other team and any attachments cue their movement off of the base fire team. This concept applies when not in contact and when in contact with the enemy.

Weapons from the weapons squad (a machine gun or a Javelin) may be attached to the squad for the movement or throughout the operation. These high value assets need to be positioned so they are protected and can be quickly brought into the engagement when required. Ideally, these weapons should be positioned so they are between the two fire teams.

Attack Formation Considerations

The decision on which formation to use comes down to four considerations:

- C2
- Maneuverability
- Firepower forward
- Protection of the flanks

Each formation offers distinct advantages over the other and employing the right formation for the situation allows the patrol to be very aggressive. However, stealth is still the preferred mode, allowing the unit get as close as possible.

A squad forms into a file with fireteams in wedges. This formation places the smallest footprint forward, while still maximizing the fire team's combat power. (Photo by Jeong, Hae-jung).

I. Attack Formations - The Line

The line formation places excellent firepower forward, employing virtually 100 percent of the unit's weapon systems to the front. Additionally, C2 is easily achieved along a line formation, making the line an excellent choice for frontal assaults against the enemy.

To execute the squad line, the squad leader designates one of the teams as the base team. The other team cues its movement off of the base team. This applies when the squad is in close combat as well. From this formation, the squad leader can employ any of the three movement techniques or conduct fire and movement.

The disadvantages include a lack of maneuverability, difficulty in changing direction, and an almost complete inability to protect the flank. Regardless of the interval distance between each troop in the line formation, they are literally lined up in a side-by-side fashion. This means that only the last troop on either flank can engage an enemy force to the sides of this formation.

Troops stand abreast of each other to form the line—with key leaders situated in the middle or just behind the formation. This formation is effective when we expect to gain fire superiority to the immediate front. (Photo by Jeong, Hae-jung).

1. All troops are formed into a rank, side-by-side. Each troop faces forward and has essentially a 90° sector of fire. Subordinate leaders maintain control over the formation, careful not to allow any portion of the line formation to get ahead of the others. This could risk fratricide or at the very least, mask the fires of friendly troops.

2. Hand and arm signals are the preferred method of communication. Communication is passed left and right along the formation. This means that every sixth step of the left foot, each troop should look left and right to see if any information is being passed along the line formation.

3. When any one member of the formation stops, every member halts. Each member takes a knee upon the formation's halt facing forward. The troop on the far left and right face out accordingly. After five minutes, each patrol member drops their rucksack and assumes a prone position until the signal to move out is given.

II. Attack Formations - The File

The squad file has the same characteristics as the fire team file. In the event that the terrain is severely restrictive or extremely close, teams within the squad file may also be in file. This disposition is not optimal for enemy contact, but does provide the squad leader with maximum control. If the squad leader wishes to increase his control over the formation he moves forward to the first or second position. Moving forward also enables him to exert greater morale presence by leading from the front, and to be immediately available to make key decisions. Moving a team leader to the last position can provide additional control over the rear of the formation

The file formation lends great ease of C2, maneuvers almost as easily as the individual troop, and can employ virtually every weapon to either flank.

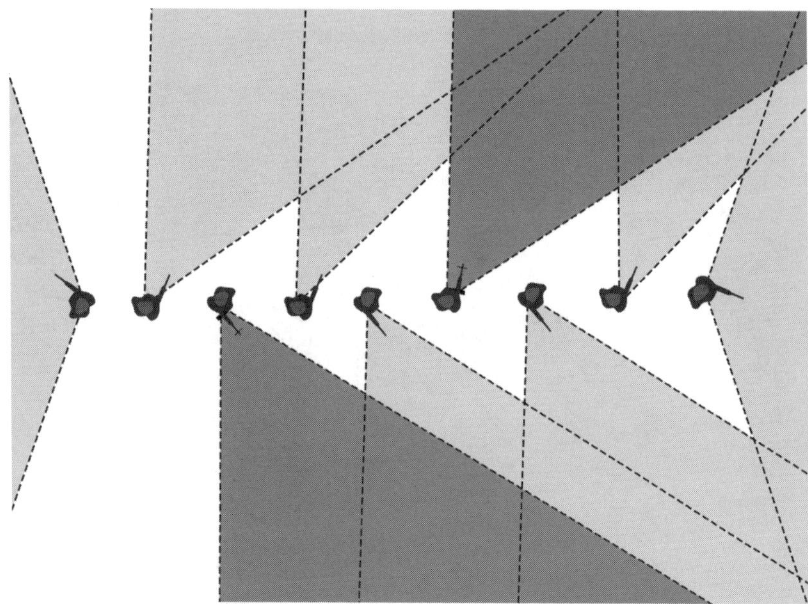

The file formation allows for the best command and control of troops. It is also the easiest formation to maneuver. And while it has ample security to the flanks, it makes poor use of combat power forward or to the rear—where it is very vulnerable. (Ref: FM 7-92, chap 3, sect II, fig. 3-5).

The file is an excellent choice for moving through difficult terrain. Because C2 is communicated so easily, the file is also ideal for moving in times of limited visibility, such as nighttime. In battle, the file also has advantages. The file is a difficult formation to ambush because it permits the use of virtually every single weapon system to either flank. Additionally, this formation is ideal for penetrating or flanking an enemy position because, as the file comes perpendicular to the enemy position, a left or right turn allows every troop to employ their weapon against the enemy. In this case, the file transforms into a line formation—which is excellent for attacking forward.

A disadvantage of the file formation is its inability to place adequate fires forward or backward of the formation. Troops behind the pointman cannot fire forward without the risk of hitting their own troops. If the enemy is able to place significant fires upon the file formation, this can prove to be disastrous.

Execution

1. This formation is constructed by having each troop follow the pointman in single file.

2. The pointman's sector of fire is the 120º field of view to his front. The second man in line must monitor a 90º sector of fire to the left of the formation. The third man in the line must monitor a 90º sector of fire to the right of the formation, and so on. The sectors of fire are staggered left and right for every member of the patrol except the dragman. The dragman's sector of fire is a 120° field of view to the rear of the formation.

3. Hand and arm signals are the preferred method of communication. Communication is passed up and down the formation. This means that every sixth step of the left foot, each troop should turn around to see if any information is being passed UP the column formation.

4. When any one member of the formation stops, every member halts. Typically, each member takes a knee upon the formation's halt. After three minutes, each patrol member takes a couple steps in the direction they are facing (their sector of fire). This clears the center path for leaders and key teams to use. After five minutes, each patrol member drops their rucksack and assumes a prone position until the signal to move out is given.

Each troop follows behind the pointman to form the file—like ducks in a row. Each troop is assigned a sector of observation alternating left and right. The dragman watches rearward. This formation places excellent fires to the flank. (Photo by Jeong, Hae-jung).

Variation: The Staggered Column

When the patrol uses a road or developed path, they will form two lines, one on each side of the road. This is achieved by alternately assuming a position based on the opposite side of the road for the man in front of you. More simply, if the pointman takes the left side, the next troop takes the right, and the next troop takes the left, and so on. This forms two columns, one to the right side of the road and to the left side of the road. Otherwise, the staggered column functions exactly like the column file.

III. Attack Formations - The Wedge

Offsetting each troop behind the pointman forms the wedge. The wedge permits excellent firepower forward and to either flank. A version known as the modified wedge places the last man in the formation all the way back, and positioned behind the pointman. This is also called the diamond. (Photo by Jeong, Hae-jung).

The wedge is the basic formation for the fire team. The interval between Soldiers in the wedge formation is normally 10 meters. The wedge expands and contracts depending on the terrain. Fire teams modify the wedge when rough terrain, poor visibility, or other factors make control of the wedge difficult. The normal interval is reduced so all team members can still see their team leader and all team leaders can still see their squad leader. The sides of the wedge can contract to the point where the wedge resembles a single file. Soldiers expand or resume their original positions when moving in less rugged terrain where control is easier.

In this formation the fire team leader is in the lead position with his men echeloned to the right and left behind him. The positions for all but the leader may vary. This simple formation permits the fire team leader to lead by example. The leader's standing order to his Soldiers is: "Follow me and do as I do." When he moves to the right, his Soldiers should also move to the right. When he fires, his Soldiers also fire. When using the lead-by-example technique, it is essential for all Soldiers to maintain visual contact with the leader.

The wedge formation is somewhat of a compromise between the line and column formations. The wedge formation scores high in terms of firepower forward and protection of the flanks. It also scores moderately in maneuverability.

Using the wedge formation, the patrol can still employ almost all of the weapons forward against an enemy force. Additionally, since about half of all weapons can be instantly brought to bear to either flank, this formation proves to be very difficult to ambush or flank. While pivoting the formation is a bit difficult—especially in steep or heavily vegetated terrain—it is far easier to maneuver the wedge than the line formation.

Execution

1. This formation is constructed by offsetting each troop to the left and right of the pointman. This forms a wide, inverted "V".

2. The pointman's sector of fire is, again, the 120º field of view to his front. The next two members in the formation, behind the pointman's position and offset to the left and right, monitor a 90º sector of fire that begins directly forward and covers their immediate left or right, respectively. This is also true for the last troop(s) in the formation, being offset one more time to the left or right of the troops in front of them. There is no rear sector of fire because subsequent fireteams follow behind.

3. Hand and arm signals are the preferred method of communication. Communication is passed up and down the formation. This means that every sixth step of the left foot, each troop should turn inward to see if any information is being passed along the wedge formation.

4. While it is acceptable to temporarily halt the wedge formation—in which each troop takes a knee—it is inadvisable to halt troops for any length of time in this formation. That is because C2 is very difficult to achieve and soon troops and subordinate leaders lose situational awareness. If a long stop is required, the PL designates another attack formation before halting the patrol or the PL rallies the patrol into a security halt.

The squad wedge with the fireteams in wedge (when three fireteams are used) makes maximum use of the squad's firepower forward and to the flanks. (Photo by Jeong, Hae-jung).

Variation: The Diamond

The diamond formation, also known as the "modified wedge", is an acceptable alternative to the wedge. If there are four members of the fire team, simply place the fourth troop, last in line, directly behind the pointman. If there are five members of the fire team, place the fire team leader in the very middle of the formation…also in line with the point and dragman.

Be warned that the diamond formation will not allow a maximum deployment of the fire team's weaponry against targets forward of the patrol. However, it still allows an acceptable percentage of the weapons to be brought to bear against an enemy force in front and to the flanks of the formation. The trade-off is that with the diamond formation, the fire team may move with more speed, change directions with more ease, and provide 360º of security for itself.

On Point

Combat formations are composed of two variables: lateral frontage, represented by the line formation; and depth, represented by the column formation. The advantages attributed to any one of these variables are disadvantages to the other. Leaders combine the elements of lateral frontage and depth to determine the best formation for their situation. In addition to the line and column/file, the other five types of formations—box; vee; wedge; diamond; and echelon—combine these elements into varying degrees. Each does so with different degrees of emphasis that result in unique advantages and disadvantages

Attack formations are designed to allow the maximum use of the patrol's weaponry, while limiting the patrol's exposure to the enemy. Every troop in the formation knows their sector of fire according to their position within the formation. The PL selects the appropriate formation based on considerations of C2, maneuverability, firepower forward of the formation, and protection of the formation's flanks.

Each tactical situation is unique and the patrol is not restricted to just one formation or another. Employ all of them if necessary. Generally, it is better to use the attack formation that allows optimal command and control to maneuver within striking distance of the enemy. At that time the patrol may need to change attack formations in order obtain the greatest security and make maximum use of the patrol's firepower.

The final consideration might be called "follow through." It is important that the patrol is not exhausted to the point that they cannot continue the mission. Use the right formation for the given situation.

Security Checks While on Patrol

Patrol members must assist their patrol leader by applying basic patrolling techniques consistently. This gives the team leader more time to concentrate on assisting the patrol leader in the conduct of the patrol. Team members should concentrate on maintaining spacing, formation, alertness, conducting 5 and 20 meter checks and taking up effective fire positions without supervision.

5 and 20 Meter Checks

Every time a patrol stops, it should use a fundamental security technique known as the 5 and 20 meter check. The technique requires every patrol member to make detailed, focused examinations of the area immediately around him, and looking for anything out of the ordinary that might be dangerous or significant. Five meter checks should be conducted every time a patrol member stops. Twenty meter checks should be conducted when a patrol halts for more than a few minutes.

Soldiers should conduct a visual check using unaided vision, and by using the optics on their weapons and binoculars. They should check for anything suspicious, and anything out of the ordinary. This might be as minor as bricks missing from walls, new string or wire run across a path, mounds of fresh dirt, or any other suspicious signs. Check the area at ground level through to above head height.

When the patrol makes a planned halt, the patrol leader identifies an area for occupation and stops 50 meters short of it. While the remainder of the patrol provides security, the patrol leader carries out a visual check using binoculars. He then moves the patrol forward to 20 meters from the position and conducts a visual check using optics on his weapon or with unaided vision.

Before actually occupying the position, each Soldier carries out a thorough visual and physical check for a radius of 5 meters. They must be systematic, take time and show curiosity. Use touch and, at night, white light if appropriate.

Any obstacles must be physically checked for command wires. Fences, walls, wires, posts and the ground immediately underneath must be carefully felt by hand, without gloves.

III. Crossing a Danger Area

Ref: FM 3-21.8 (FM 7-8) The Infantry Rifle Platoon and Squad, pp. 3-33 to 3-37 and FM 7-93 Long-Range Surveillance Unit Operations, appendix J.

Crossing danger areas can be achieved through one of a series of battle drills designed to get the patrol to the far side of the danger area with the very least amount of exposure, and the maximum amount of necessary firepower positioned to deflect an enemy attack. In essence, the patrol will be moving from one concealed position to another, getting through the danger area as safely and as quickly as possible.

Types of Danger Areas

Danger areas fall into two categories, linear and open. Each category has two subcategories, big and small. The numerous types of danger areas require that patrols have multiple methods in their bag of tricks to get safely across the danger area.

Roads, paths, creeks, and open fields present opportunities for ambush and sniping missions. Natural and man-made obstacles allow for fairly long sectors of fire because they are relatively clear.

A patrol leader (PL) must assess is which type of danger area the patrol is presented with. Ideally, the patrol circumvents a danger area—that is, the patrol goes around. However, linear danger areas rarely leave that option. Instead, the patrol must traverse these danger areas by crossing them.

So, the PL has to assess the type and relative size of the danger area. Also, the PL has to assess the likelihood of enemy contact. It's a pretty quick mental checklist:

- Linear vs. Open
- Big vs. Small
- Time Constraints

If the patrol is moving through territory with significant enemy presence, hopefully the PL allotted a realistic amount of time to conduct the mission. The patrol employs a more deliberate method of crossing the danger area, one that offers maximum protection to the front and flanks. For a linear danger area, this might mean the heart-shaped method. For an open danger area, this might mean the box method.

If, on the other hand, the patrol is moving quickly through territory with sparse enemy presence and time is of a high priority, then the patrol employs a method of crossing the danger area that makes maximum use of speed as a form of security, with minimal protection to the front and flanks. For a linear danger area, this might mean the patch-to-the-road method. For an open danger area, this might mean the bypass method.

The size of the danger area must also be considered. Even in the case of patrolling through territory with sparse enemy presence, if the danger area is too large to use speed as a form of security...it may be best to use a method that offers a greater form of security.

The platoon leader or squad leader decides how the unit will cross based on the time he has, size of the unit, size of the danger area, fields of fire into the area, and the amount of security he can post. An Infantry platoon or squad may cross all at once, in buddy teams, or one Soldier at a time. A large unit normally crosses its elements one at a time. As each element crosses, it moves to an overwatch position or to the far-side rally point until told to continue movement.

I. Patch-to-the-Road Method

Using this method, a nine-man squad should be able to cross the danger area in ten seconds or less. *Speed is a form of security.* This method also allows the column formation to be maintained, which means greater control and communication for the PL.

1. The point man brings the patrol to a halt and signals that he has come upon a danger area. The PL comes forward to view the danger area, assesses the situation, and selects a method of negotiating the danger area.

2. If the patch-to-the-road method is selected, the PL communicates this to the team with the appropriate hand and arm signal. The entire patrol closes the intervals between members shoulder-to-shoulder. The patrol members must actually touch each other. This is done even during daylight hours. This will allow a very fast pace when crossing and prevent a break in contact.

3. The two-man security team moves from the rear of the formation up to the front. At the PL's signal, the first security troop steps up to the danger area only as far as he needs to look left and right. If the road is clear of enemy presence, the troop takes a position so he can view down the road to his right. In this position, his unit patch (on the upper part of his left arm sleeve) will be facing toward the middle of the road. Thus, the method is called "patch-to-the-road."

This method uses speed as the primary form of security. A left and right security overwatch is provided locally. At the patrol leader's signal, the rest of the patrol move in file across the danger area. (Photo by Jeong, Hae-jung).

4. As soon as the security troop on the near side of the danger area levels his weapon down the road, the second member of the security team immediately rushes across the danger area and takes up a position to view down the opposite direction of the road. At this point, both team members have their unit arm patches facing toward the middle of the road and they are pointing in the *opposite direction.*

5. As soon as the security troop is on far side if the danger area levels his weapon down the road, this signals the PL to stand the remaining patrol members and RUN across the danger area. This is done literally by holding onto the gear of the troop to the front.

6. As the last troop passes the near side security troop, he firmly says, "Last man." An acceptable alternative is to tap the security troop on the shoulder. In either case, this indicates to the security troop to stand up and run across the danger area behind the patrol.

7. The security troop will say firmly, "Last man", to the far side security troop or tap him on the shoulder. This lets that troop know to follow behind.

8. Now the entire patrol is back in its original marching order on the far side of the objective.

It is important that as the pointman initially crosses the danger area, that he makes a quick dash into the tree line to visually inspect the space the patrol will occupy. The *only reason to stop the patrol in the danger area* is if the pointman determines the far side tree line is booby-trapped. Even if the enemy has set up a near ambush, the patrol must assault through. No one stays in the danger area.

The potential danger here is that the security team troops become distracted from the mundane task of overwatching their sector. This is especially true if some snag holds up the process and the security team is forced to stand overwatch down the road for more that the allotted ten seconds.

It takes considerable discipline and lots of rehearsals to keep troops facing down a linear danger area, partially exposing themselves and generally feeling vulnerable when there is a hold-up such as another member tripping while running across the road, or getting caught on a fence wire, or dropping an unsecured piece of equipment and then doubling back to retrieve it. What generally happens at that point is that one or both of the security team members become agitated and turns to look to see what's going on in middle of the road instead of maintaining a vigilant overwatch of their sector.

Contingency Plan

Ideally, if the enemy does show up when the patrol is crossing a danger area, the security team will fire first. Or if there is on-coming traffic, the security team will shout a warning to the other patrol to momentarily halt and hide. This signal means no one else should attempt to cross the danger area. So it is imperative that the security team realizes they are to keep a vigilant overwatch of the danger area until:

- The patrol successfully traverses the danger area
- They are directed to hide from on-coming traffic
- Or the patrol becomes engaged in a firefight

If there is a break in contact due to traffic or contact with the enemy, each patrol must establish a method of link-up. Typically, if the patrol becomes separated, the patrol will rendezvous at the last designated en-route rally point (ERP).

II. Heart-Shaped Method

If the patrol has to pass through a linear danger area in territory with significant enemy activity, or if the linear danger area is simply too large to cross quickly with the patch-to-the-Road method, then the PL needs to select a method with the greatest amount of security the patrol can mass. The Heart-shaped method takes about three to five minutes even for a squad-sized patrol. It also has a tendency to scramble the order of march and requires a great command and control. But, if rehearsed thoroughly, these issues can be mitigated.

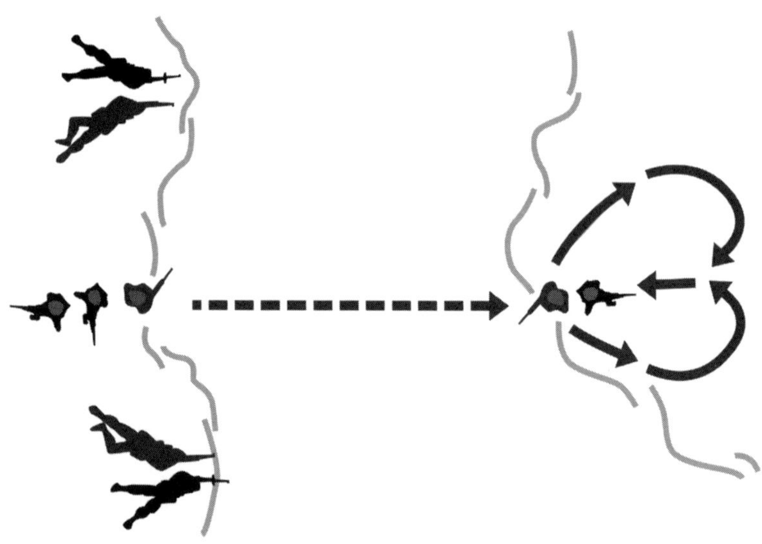

Crossing danger areas with this method makes maximum use of security and combat power. However, the heart-shaped method is time consuming. (Ref: FM 7-8, chap 2, section III, fig. 2-27).

1. The point man brings the patrol to a halt and signals he has come upon a danger area. The PL comes forward to view the danger area, assesses the situation, and selects a method of negotiating the danger area.

2. If the heart-shaped method is selected, the PL physically places a security team approximately 20~50 meters down to the right and places another security team 20~50 meters down to the left. The exact distance depends on the terrain and visibility of the danger area. The PL returns to the main body of the patrol.

3. The PL now sends a third security team to the far side, across the danger area. The PL does not go with the far-side security team. Instead, the PL points out an easily recognized object on the far side that is in line with the patrol's direction of movement.

4. This team will cross the danger area as the situation dictates—perhaps at a run, perhaps at a crawl. They have immediate fire support from the left and right side security teams.

5. Once concealed within the far side tree line, the security team conducts a quick listening halt to determine if the enemy is in the immediate area. If enemy are detected, the security team carefully makes its way back to the patrol and informs the PL of the situation.

6. If no enemy is detected, the far side security team physically inspects an area large enough for the entire patrol to fit. This is achieved by walking a designated distance into the tree line. Once they have walked the designated distance, members turn away from each other and pace off a determined distance to check the flanks. The security members then move back toward their original listening halt position. When looking at the path from a bird's eye perspective, it looks as though the security team has cut a heart-shaped path into the tree line. Thus it earned the name "heart-shaped."

7. When the security team has reassembled and determined the far-side security team free from enemy presence, they give the PL the "thumbs up" hand & arm signal. This lets the PL know the far side is secure and that the far-side security team is monitoring the danger area.

8. At this point, the PL leads the remainder of the patrol, minus the left and right security teams, across the field using the same path as the far-side security team took earlier. The left and right security teams continue to monitor the danger area.

9. When the patrol is safely on the far side of the danger area, the PL will signal by hand or by radio for the left and right security teams to cross the danger area, using the same path.

Contingency Plan

If the patrol is compromised while crossing the danger area, the patrol will rendezvous back at the last ERP. However, the patrol cannot simply run away and leave elements of the patrol still in the danger area. Without support, these troops would be killed or captured. Smoke canisters are employed to screen withdrawing troops and the left and right security teams place suppressive fires on the enemy until all patrol members have withdrawn. Once the patrol has withdrawn, the left and right security teams withdraw.

III. Bypass Method

The previously mentioned methods, patch-to-the-road and the heart-shaped, are all fine and well. But what if it is simply too dangerous to cross an open danger area? The patrol doesn't want to unnecessarily expose the patrol to enemy observation or fire. That could bring the mission to a quick end; especially if the patrol isn't suppose to make contact in the first place. In these cases, it's best to use the bypass. The bypass takes considerable time, but offers the greatest degree of stealth.

The bypass method is used for isolated danger areas, such as open meadows. The patrol takes several 90-degree turns until coming back on azimuth. The lateral distance is not added to the route pace count. (Photo by Jeong, Hae-jung).

1. After halting the patrol and signaling a danger area, the pointman and the PL confirm the patrol's direction of advance using a prominent feature as a point of reference on the far side of the danger area. This may be an easily recognized terrain feature, such as a rise or dip in the terrain, or it may be an easily recognized landmark, such as a tall tree, or a large boulder.

2. The PL estimates the distance to the far side of the danger area using visual techniques or the map. That distance is added to their present pace count.

3. Then, ignoring the pace count and compass bearing, the patrol simply follows the pointman as he skirts the danger area, keeping safely inside the tree line until the patrol gets to the designated feature on the far side of the danger area.

4. Here the pointman assumes the previous direction of advance and the patrol takes up the new pace count.

If the open danger area is so incredibly large that the patrol cannot even see the far side, one option is to deal with this terrain as "significantly thinning vegetation" instead of as a danger area. In such cases, the patrol assumes a wedge formation and significantly increases the interval between patrol members and subordinate teams. The patrol continues to move along the direction of advance in this manner until the terrain changes.

IV. Box Method

An alternative plan is the "box method" which is really a type of navigation technique that is closely related to the bypass. This method is more scientific in its execution and employs dead-reckoning skills.

1. After the pointman halts the patrol, the PL moves forward and confirms that the danger area is too large to see any prominent features on the far side.

2. The PL either adds 90° to the current direction of advance if he wants to turn the patrol to the right, or subtracts 90° from the current direction of advance if he wants to turn the patrol to the left. The new direction is issued to the lead team and pointman.

3. The patrol continues on the new direction of advance being careful to keep a pace count to record the distance traveled in this new direction. The patrol halts when the danger area is no longer visible.

4. The PL now assumes the old direction of advance for a distance that is greater than the length of the danger area. This information is confirmed on the map—since the far side of the danger area could not be visibly observed.

5. Again, the lead team and pointman pay careful attention to the distance traveled. Once the patrol has covered the prescribed distance, the pointman halts the patrol.

6. The PL now does the reverse of the earlier left or right turn. That is, the PL either adds 90° to the current direction of advance if he wants to turn the patrol back to the right, or subtracts 90° from the current direction of advance if he wants to turn the patrol back to the left.

7. When the patrol has traveled the same lateral distance as their first turn, mathematically speaking, the patrol is back on the original direction of advance. The patrol assumes the old direction of advance and takes up the new pace count. The entire danger area has been bypassed.

This method takes the patrol off route. This option can be selected only if the patrol has ample time to conduct the Box method and if the diverging route does not take the patrol out of the AO.

V. Crossing Large Open Areas

If the large open area is so large that the platoon cannot bypass it due to the time needed to accomplish the mission, a combination of traveling overwatch and bounding overwatch is used to cross the large open area. The traveling overwatch technique is used to save time. The squad or platoon moves using the bounding overwatch technique at any point in the open area where enemy contact may be expected. The technique may also be used once the squad or platoon comes within range of enemy small-arms fire from the far side (about 250 meters). Once beyond the open area, the squad or platoon re-forms and continues the mission.

On Point

When analyzing the terrain (in the METT-TC analysis) during the TLP, small unit leaders may identify danger areas. When planning the route, the leader marks the danger areas on his overlay. The term danger area refers to any area on the route where the terrain could expose the platoon to enemy observation, fire, or both. If possible, the platoon leader plans to avoid danger areas, but sometimes he cannot. When the unit must cross a danger area, it does so as quickly and as carefully as possible. During planning, the leader designates near-side and far-side rally points. If the unit encounters an unexpected danger area, it uses the en route rally points closest to the danger area as far-side and near-side rally points.

Examples of danger areas include—

- **Open Areas**. Conceal the platoon on the near side and observe the area. Post security to give early warning. Send an element across to clear the far side. When cleared, cross the remainder of the platoon at the shortest exposed distance and as quickly as possible.
- **Roads and Trails**. Cross roads or trails at or near a bend, a narrow spot, or on low ground.
- **Villages**. Pass villages on the downwind side and well away from them. Avoid animals, especially dogs, which might reveal the presence of the platoon.
- **Enemy Positions**. Pass on the downwind side (the enemy might have scout dogs). Be alert for trip wires and warning devices.
- **Minefields**. Bypass minefields if at all possible, even if it requires changing the route by a great distance. Clear a path through minefields only if necessary.
- **Streams**. Select a narrow spot in the stream that offers concealment on both banks. Observe the far side carefully. Emplace near- and far-side security for early warning. Clear the far side and then cross rapidly but quietly.
- **Wire Obstacles**. Avoid wire obstacles (the enemy covers obstacles with observation and fire).

Each danger area is unique and the PL will determine the manner in which the patrol overcomes each obstacle. The situation on the ground can change dramatically from what we see on a map. For instance, a linear danger area on the map might actually turn out to be a massive open danger area. Similarly, open danger areas on the map may actually be so overgrown that they present no danger area at all.

Enemy Contact at Danger Areas

An increased awareness of the situation helps the platoon leader control the platoon when it makes contact with the enemy. If the platoon makes contact in or near the danger area, it moves to the designated rally points. Based on the direction of enemy contact, the leader still designates the far- or near-side rally point. During limited visibility, he can also use his laser systems to point out the rally points at a distance. If the platoon has a difficult time linking up at the rally point, the first element to arrive should mark the rally point with an infrared light source. This will help direct the rest of the platoon to the location. During movement to the rally point, position updates allow separated elements to identify each other's locations. These updates help them link up at the rally point by identifying friends and foes.

IV. Establishing a Security Halt

Ref: FM 7-8 (FM 7-8) The Infantry Rifle Platoon and Squad, chap. 3 and 9.

Regardless of the mission, every patrol must halt at different locations along the route. This type of security halt is called the en route rally point (ERP). In addition to the ERP, every patrol makes a final stop prior to the assigned objective. This is done to coordinate between elements and make final preparations for actions on the objective. This type of security halt is called the objective rally point (ORP).

When the patrol halts, take a knee. Standing upright may draw fire. Troops face in the opposite directions forming 360-degree security. (Photo by Jeong, Hae-jung).

The ORP and ERP are security halts that afford 360° of security for the patrol as the patrol stops along its route toward the objective. Security halts provide concealment from enemy observation while plans and equipment are adjusted. The operative description for the security halt is *disciplined.* Noise and light discipline is strictly enforced.

The ERP is either occupied or at least designated along the route. Ideally, it is designated at easily recognized terrain or landmarks that offer cover and concealment. Again, the ERP does not need to be occupied...but it is still designated en route. The ERP may also be pre-designated in the plan.

The ORP is always pre-designated in the plan. It is placed far enough away from the enemy objective that the patrol can conduct final preparations and planning before conducting actions on the objective.

When halted longer than several minutes, take a step or two out and go to a prone position. This automatically forms a 'cigar-shaped' perimeter with the PL in the center. (Photo by Jeong, Hae-jung).

The patrol needs to stay safely concealed from the enemy's view and far enough that the noise of the patrol's final preparations won't be heard.

A rule of thumb is to remain 300 meters away or one terrain feature. Keeping one sizable terrain feature between the ORP and the objective significantly reduces the chance that the patrol will be detected. However, if the terrain is rather open, the ORP is kept at least 300 meters away from the objective. In practice, this decision really depends more on the type of terrain, the size of the patrol, and the nature of the patrol's final preparations.

As for the ERP, the only consideration regarding when and where to stop would be concealment.

I. Cigar-Shaped Method

Security halts are either taken by force or a leader's recon is sent forward to assess the anticipated site. The ERP is almost exclusively taken by force because there are so many unpredictable reasons for establishing an ERP. The drill that is most suitable for the ERP security halt is the "cigar-shaped" method.

The ORP, on the other hand, is a planned security halt and generally requires a leader's recon of the site to determine its suitability. In this case, the drill that is most suitable for the ORP is the "wagon wheel" method.

A small patrol often walks directly up to the ERP or ORP security halt. This practice is known as occupying by force. The implications are that if the enemy is detected near the security halt, the patrol either engages the enemy or quietly withdraws to a new position.

1. Upon reaching a desired location for the security halt, the patrol leader (PL) halts the patrol. During halts, all troops automatically take a knee.

2. The PL indicates to the patrol members that they are in a security halt. Each patrol member faces either left or right in an alternating pattern and takes two steps outward to form a cigar-shaped perimeter. The pointman, dragman, and PL are exempt from this maneuver and remain kneeling where they initially stopped. This leaves the PL in the center, the pointman at 12 o'clock, and the dragman at the 6 o'clock position.

3. Subordinate leaders then ensure each man is behind adequate cover and assigned a sector of fire. At a minimum, the 3, 6, 9, and 12 o'clock positions must be maintained and covering their sector of fire.

4. The PL pulls any necessary leaders to the center in order to confirm or adjust plans. If this security halt is an ORP, the PL begins work priorities for the ORP.

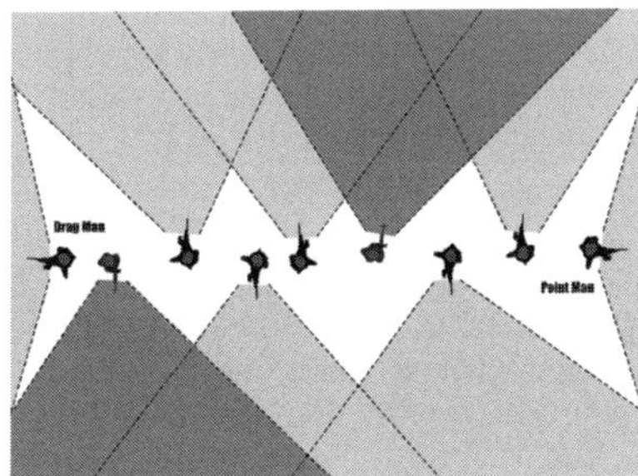

All troops should take a kneeling position upon a halt to lower their profile. They continue to face in their primary direction for security purposes—affording 360-degree security. (Ref: FM 7-8, chap 5, annex B, appendix 5, para 2-a).

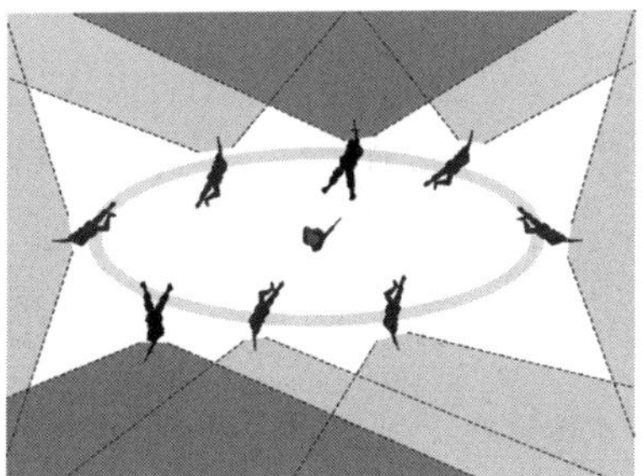

The 'cigar shape' is formed when troops take a step forward in the direction they are facing. They look for cover such as a thick tree or stone for frontal protection and assume a prone position. (Ref: FM 7-8, chap 5, annex B, appendix 5, para 2-b).

II. Wagon Wheel Method

This drill is used almost exclusively for occupying the ORP security halt. Developed in the jungles of Southeast Asia, this drill works well in areas of dense vegetation because it allows the PL to see where each troop is located. The effort is to get the entire patrol in a circular formation and this takes a bit more work than the cigar-shaped method. Care must be taken in selecting the ORP site, as well as occupying it with the least amount of noise and commotion.

This method of forming the ORP is one of the most simple. After a security team is placed as the anchor, the entire patrol plays "follow the leader" in a big circle. Once the circle is complete, the PL adjusts the circle evenly.

The wagon wheel method is conducted by having the patrol leader simply walk in a circle around the area of the intended ORP. Troops are adjusted once the circle is complete. Typically a machinegunner sits at 12 and 6 o'clock. (Photo by Jeong, Hae-jung).

1. The patrol assumes an ERP security halt approximately 100 meters out from the planned ORP site. A leader's recon is then conducted forward at the ORP site to make certain the terrain is appropriate for use.

2. The leader's recon typically involves four members of the patrol—the PL, a compass man, and a two-man security team. Before leaving the ERP, the PL issues the assistant patrol leader (APL) a contingency plan and coordinates for their return.

3. Once the leader's recon has reached the designated ORP site, the PL determines if the site is appropriate or selects another site nearby.

4. The PL places the two-man security back to back at the 6 o'clock position of the ORP. The security team will be left at the ORP to watch the objective and to guide the remainder of the patrol into position. The PL will leave a contingency plan with the security team before the PL and the compass man return to pick up the rest of the patrol.

5. The PL and the point man return to the rest of the patrol back in the security halt. The patrol resumes its marching order, and since the compass man has already been to the ORP and back, he can lead the patrol right to the security team at the 6 o'clock position. The patrol halts once the compass man links up with the security team and the PL moves forward.

6. From the 6 o'clock position the PL leads the patrol in a large circular path around the perimeter of the ORP. This forms the patrol into a large circle through an exercise of "follow the leader."

7. Once the circle has been completed, the subordinate leaders adjust the exact positions of the members to offer the best cover and to provide 360° sectors of fire.

8. The PL pulls subordinate leaders to the center in order to confirm or adjust plans. The PL sets work priorities in motion for the ORP.

This variation of the wagon wheel method requires a bit more coordination and is typically only used for larger patrols. Three elements make up three legs of the ORP—from 2 to 6 o'clock, from 6 to 10 o'clock, and from 10 to 2 o'clock. Machinegunners are typically placed at each apex. (Photo by Jeong, Hae-jung).

III. Priorities of Work at the Objective Rally Point

Regardless of the method used, once the ORP has been established, there is work to do. The ORP is merely a security halt where the patrol can finalize its preparations for the mission. Some of the work priorities are conducted concurrently; some may not be necessary at all.

1. Security is always the first priority. The ORP never falls lower than 50 percent security. That means that whatever task is necessary, half of the patrol maintains a vigilant guard of their sectors of fire.

2. A leader's recon is conducted. The leader's recon is optional and depends on the nature of the mission. The leader's recon team leaves and re-enters through the 12 o'clock position. It is coordinated with the patrol members in the ORP. Typically, the APL remains in the ORP while the PL, the security team leader, and a security team conduct the recon.

3. All special equipment is prepared. The patrol doesn't prepare explosives, anti-armor weapons, or conduct radio checks while sitting in position on the objective. That is too much noise and activity and the enemy would certainly see or hear the patrol.

4. Plans are finalized or altered. The leader's recon may come back with information that either slightly or dramatically alters the plan of the mission. Or, sometimes the failure of special equipment may require some improvising. In any case, these adjustments are made in the ORP and every member must be informed.

5. Weapons are prepared. Weapons are cleaned if the patrol made contact while en route to the ORP, or if the movement to the ORP took considerable time and moved through a notably dirty environment—such as fording a river or being inserted onto a sandy beach. Still, no more than 50 percent of the patrol members do this at one time. The other 50 percent pulls security.

6. Sleep and eating plans are initiated. If the situation dictates, the ORP may implement an eating and sleeping schedule. Fifty percent security is maintained, always.

On Point

Units conducting tactical movement frequently make temporary halts. These halts range from brief to extended periods of time. For short halts, platoons use a cigar-shaped perimeter intended to protect the force while maintaining the ability to continue movement. When the platoon leader decides not to immediately resume tactical movement, he transitions the platoon to a perimeter defense. The perimeter defense is used for longer halts or during lulls in combat.

There are many reasons a patrol may stop. The patrol leader might need to confirm the patrol's position on the map, the patrol periodically needs to listen and observe new surroundings, and the patrol may need a rest or to make final coordination prior to actions on the objective.

Security halts offer 360° of security when the patrol stops along its route toward the objective. Security halts provide concealment from enemy observation while plans and equipment are adjusted.

En Route Rally Point (ERP)

The ERP is a security halt along the route. Ideally, it is quickly recognizable on the ground in case the patrol needs to return to it. The ERP is rarely pre-designated, but is assigned or occupied along the route. When the ERP is occupied, it is almost always taken by force. The cigar-shaped method is well suited for this.

Objective Rally Point (ORP)

The ORP is the last stop prior to the objective, where the patrol can come together to coordinate with other friendly elements, to finalize the mission plans, and to rest prior to conducting actions on the objective. The ORP may be occupied by force—in which case the cigar-shaped method is used. More commonly, the ORP is first inspected by a leader's recon and then the patrol is carefully maneuvered into position. In this case, the wagon-wheel method is used.

The ORP is a point out of sight, sound, and small-arms range of the objective area. It is normally located in the direction that the platoon plans to move after completing its actions on the objective. The ORP is tentative until the objective is pinpointed. Actions at or from the ORP include—

- Issuing a final FRAGO
- Disseminating information from reconnaissance if contact was not made
- Making final preparations before continuing operations
- Accounting for Soldiers and equipment after actions at the objective are complete
- Reestablishing the chain of command after actions at the objective are complete

If the ORP is occupied under limited visibility, the method of occupation is rehearsed prior to the patrol's movement. Noise and light discipline are paramount.

Which method choosen to occupy a security halt depends on the terrain, the mission, and the number of troops available. Every combat mission will include security halts. Security is paramount.

V. Establishing a Hide Position

Ref: FM 7-93 Long-Range Surveillance Unit Operations, app. E.

Hide positions are primarily used for surveillance teams during reconnaissance operations. The recon team uses the hide position to rest troops while keeping them concealed. The troops can then be rotated to the surveillance position during their shift. Often the hide and surveillance site are combined. Hide positions may be subterranean or above ground.

However, hide positions are also used by small patrols operating for extended periods of time beyond the forward edge of battle area (FEBA). Such hide positions can be temporarily employed for many reasons. Perhaps the patrol entailed a march that could not be achieved in a single day or, more commonly, the patrol itself is of such a small size that a patrol base is neither feasible nor necessary. In these cases, the patrol can opt to implement a hide position in order to plan and rest.

Considerations

The hide position is similar to the patrol base in that it is a security perimeter that uses concealment for its primary defense. However, the hide position is not a patrol base. It is only a place to rest or observe.

There are several key differences between the hide position and the patrol base:

- No one departs or re-enters the hide position (No missions are conducted)
- It is intended for no more than 12 hours of use and is vacated
- Hide positions are never re-used due to risk of detection by the enemy
- Fighting positions are not built up

The hide position offers 360° security in that the entire patrol is positioned in a tight formation facing outward. The patrol is so close they act as a single fighting position, as few as two men can easily maintain security. The hide position does not require any communication system other than word of mouth and visual contact with other troops.

The hide position is established ideally no closer that 300 meters or a terrain feature away from an enemy force. Hide positions are intentionally placed in the most inhospitable terrain, such as in thick patches of thorn bushes or jagged rock formations. Although a bit uncomfortable, this terrain discourages enemy patrols.

The patrol leader (PL) designates the approximate location of the hide position on a map, or the PL may designate a condition under which the patrol establishes a hide position—such as after patrolling for a set number of hours or days. If the patrol is small, the PL may occupy the hide position by force.

For a medium sized patrol, the patrol establishes a security halt and sends a leader's recon forward to identify the hide position. At any rate, the PL indicates to the patrol that they are in hide position.

Establishing a Hide Position

I. Back-to-Back Method

This method is more practical for wooded and heavily vegetated terrain. When seated, the security team can observe of the likely avenues of approach or escape. This could not be achieved if the security team were laying in the prone in heavy vegetation. And frankly, if the patrol is exhausted enough that it has to use the hide position, placing the watch team on their bellies is just asking for trouble. An exhausted troop is much more likely to fall asleep lying down than sitting up—no matter how disciplined.

When a hide position is placed in a heavily vegetated area without decent observation, the two troops pulling security will sit back-to-back to form a 360-degree security position. The rest of the troops rest head-to-toe until it is their turn. (Photo by Jeong, Hae-jung).)

1. The patrol members come shoulder to shoulder, take a knee and face left and right in an alternating pattern. All patrol members drop their rucksacks.

2. Half of the patrol members are designated to ready their sleeping bags and mats while the other half pull security. Once the first members have readied their sleeping positions as comfortably as possible, they sit on their equipment and pull security while the other members ready their sleeping bags and mats. No tents are pitched, no early warning devices are implemented, and no fighting positions are prepared.

3. The PL determines how many members of the patrol will pull security and what the duration and schedule of the guard shifts will be. Typically, hide positions require at least two troops to pull security at a time.

4. Since no anti-personnel mines or trip flares are used, CS canisters or fragmentation grenades are given to the first guard shift and then passed to subsequent guards. If the enemy does walk near the patrol, great discipline must be enforced to allow the enemy to pass by. In the unlikely case that the enemy walks up on the hide position, grenades are used while the patrol makes a quick escape. Direct fire should be avoided at night since

the muzzle flashes from the rifles and machine guns will disclose the patrol's position.

5. Radios are handled in a similar manner—passed from guard shift to guard shift—to be keep in touch with higher command. If the hide position is occupied during nighttime hours, night vision devices are also passed from guard shift to guard shift.

II. Star Method

The star method is used for flat, open terrain such as a desert, high mountain tundra, or grasslands. In this type of terrain, the patrol lies on the ground to lower their profiles.

When the vegetation permits a decent field of observation, the troops lay prone to form a star. Two troops on opposite sides of the formation pull security while others sleep. They kick their buddies to an alert status if a threat approaches. (Photo by Jeong, Hae-jung).

1. The patrol comes shoulder-to-shoulder and the PL instructs them to form into the star. The troops lay in the prone and interlock their ankles. This allows the security team to kick the man to their left and right to an alert status without making noise.

2. Half of the patrol members are designated to ready their sleeping bags and mats while the other half pull security. This responsibility changes hands while the other half of the patrol readies their sleeping bags and mats. Again, no tents are pitched due to being easily visible; however, rain tarps may be used to cover the patrol's sleeping bags.

3. The PL determines how many members of the patrol will pull security and what the duration and schedule of the guard shifts will be. Typically, hide positions require at least two troops to pull security at a time. Also, the two-man watch team will not be positioned right next to each other, but on opposite sides of the formation.

4. It might prove to be a daunting task to find terrain that is difficult to traverse in middle of the grassland prairie. The best a patrol could do would be to place a far distance between it and the enemy position and blend into the vastness of the countryside. Also, due to the ease of enemy movement in the open terrain, the PL may opt to use early warning devices or anti-personnel mines to slow an enemy attack.

On Point

Hide positions provide reasonable security to rest a small or medium-sized patrol. However, when patrols become tired, undisciplined or lazy, hidings are often overused due to the low requirement of security.

The type of hide or surveillance site employed depends on METT-TC. Improvement of camouflage, at a minimum, must be continuous while occupying the site.

Hidings have their purposes, but attempting to use a hide position as a replacement for the patrol base places the patrol in great danger. These two security positions have completely different functions. If a larger patrol needs rest, the PL must establish a patrol base or a tactical assembly area and implement a sleep plan.

Site Selection

The team leader initially selects the tentative sites during the planning phase. He selects the sites by physical reconnaissance (stay-behind), aerial observation, photographs, line-of-site data, soil and drainage data, or map reconnaissance. At a minimum, the team leader selects primary and alternate hide sites, and primary and alternate surveillance sites. Before the team occupies the sites, the team leader conducts a physical reconnaissance of the tentative site chosen during planning. If necessary, the team leader moves the site to a better location.

When selecting a site, the leader should consider the following aspects:

- Line of sight to target
- Within a range that can be supported by available observation equipment to meet the reporting requirements
- Overhead concealment and cover
- Away from natural lines of drift
- Away from roads, trails, railroad tracks, and major waterways
- Defendable for a short time
- Primary and alternate hasty exits
- Concealed serviceable entrance; little noise getting into and out of the hide site
- METT-TC in relation to other site positions (hide, surveillance, communication sites)
- Not near man-made objects
- Downwind of inhabited areas
- Not dominated by high ground, but takes advantage of high ground

Site Sterilization

Before departing hide and surveillance locations, team members must ensure sites and routes have been sterilized.

- Personnel carry out all foreign debris
- If possible, they do not bury waste or trash. Animals will uncover trash and expose it to enemy patrols. If trash is buried, the team buries it 18 to 24 inches deep in sealed containers or covers the scent by using CS or lime.
- The team sterilizes the sites using displaced earth. They use the site to bury overhead material, which contrasts with the surrounding area
- The team camouflages the area by blending the site with local surroundings
- As team members withdraw from the site, they ensure routes are camouflaged to prevent detection

Chap 8

VI. Establishing a Patrol Base

Ref: FM 3-21.8 (FM 7-8) The Infantry Rifle Platoon and Squad, chap. 9 and The Ranger Handbook, pp. 5- 19 to 5-22.

A patrol base is a position set up when the patrol unit halts for an extended period. When the unit must halt for a long time in a place not protected by friendly troops, it takes active and passive security measures. The time the patrol base may be occupied depends on the need for secrecy. It should be occupied only as long as necessary, but not for more than 24 hours--except in an emergency. The unit should not use the same patrol base more than once.

The patrol base is a temporary, forward, static position out of which a patrol conducts a series of missions. It offers cover and concealment from enemy observation. Security is maintained at 360° inside the patrol base, and while there is no requirement to maintain 100 percent security at all times, the percentage of troops maintaining security is kept at a level that work priorities will allow.

Patrol bases are typically used--

- To avoid detection by eliminating movement
- To hide a unit during a long detailed reconnaissance
- To perform maintenance on weapons, equipment, eat and rest
- To plan and issue orders
- To reorganize after infiltrating on an enemy area
- To establish a base from which to execute several consecutive or concurrent operations

The goal is to go undetected by the enemy; the patrol base is never used for more than 24 hours. The patrol base is a temporary position that uses concealment as its primary defense. As such, there is no need to develop fighting positions, bunkers, or trench systems. However, to provide a minimal amount of cover, some build up of the patrol base defenses should be tolerated. Entrenching tools and machetes make a good deal of noise. Barricades are preferable to digging, but hasty fighting positions or 'shell scrapes' are generally permitted.

Site Selection

The leader selects the tentative site from a map or by aerial reconnaissance. The site's suitability must be confirmed and secured before the unit moves into it. Plans to establish a patrol base must include selecting an alternate patrol base site. The alternate site is used if the first site is unsuitable or if the patrol must unexpectedly evacuate the first patrol base.

The rule of thumb on where to place a patrol base dictates no closer than 500 meters from the enemy force, or better yet, to maintain a major terrain feature between the enemy and the patrol base. To further conceal the position and the number of foot trails leading back to the patrol base, all subsequent patrols depart and re-enter the patrol base at the 6 o'clock position.

Establishing a Patrol Base - The Triangle Method

The triangle method is excellent for patrols with three elements (i.e. three fireteams, three squads, three platoons). A crew-served weapon is placed at each of the three apexes of the triangle—6, 10 and 2 o'clock. In this manner, no matter which direction the enemy approaches the patrol base, at least two crew-served weapons are brought to bear on the attacking force.

1. The patrol leader (PL) establishes an objective rally point (ORP) within 300 meters of the anticipated patrol base site. The PL conducts a leader's recon of the patrol base site, leaving a contingency plan with the assistant patrol leader (APL) back in the ORP. The leader's recon includes the PL, compass man, and a six-man security team.

The perimeter is formed in four phases. ***Phase One:*** *The patrol leader determines the direction of greatest threat as 12 o'clock, then sets security teams at the 6, 10, and 2 o'clock positions. (Ref: FM 7-8, chap 3, section V, fig. 3-22).*

2. Once the PL has inspected the site and is satisfied with the patrol base site (or has chosen a suitable alternative) the PL leaves a two-man security team at the 2, 6, and 10 o'clock positions of the patrol base with a contingency plan. Each security team is placed back to back. The PL and compass man move back to the ORP.

3. They rendezvous with the rest of the patrol in the ORP and inform them of any change of plan. The compass man is now familiar enough with the terrain to lead the patrol forward to the patrol base. If this is done at night, the security team member facing back towards the patrol must have a visual reference for the point man— a chemical light stick, flashlight, or illuminated compass lens. The compass man will link the security team with the rest of the patrol at the 6 o'clock position of the patrol base.

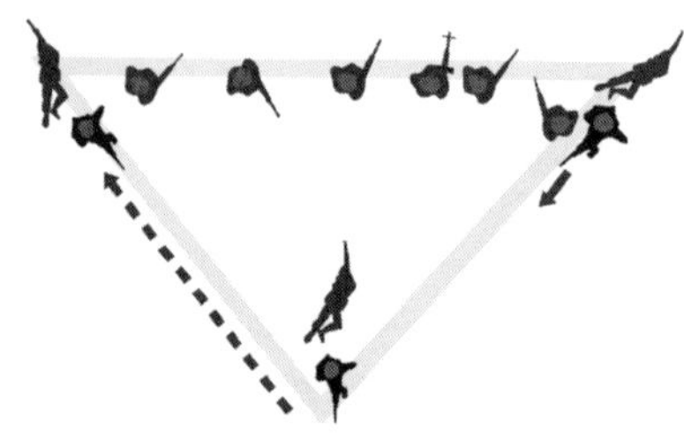

Phase Two: *The patrol leader walks the first squad from 6 o'clock to 10 o'clock, and then places them in a line from the 10 o'clock to the 2 o'clock position. The troops face out toward the enemy threat. (Ref: FM 7-8, chap 3, section V, fig. 3-22).*

4. The PL then leads the first element from the 6 o'clock position, up to the 10 o'clock position. He then walks that first element from the 10 o'clock to 2 o'clock positions and physically places each member of the element in a straight line between the two security teams. The PL then returns to the 6 o'clock position.

5. Waiting at 6 o'clock is the second element of the patrol. The PL walk the second element from the 6 o'clock to the 10 o'clock positions and physically places each member of the element in a straight line between these two security teams. The PL returns again to the 6 o'clock position.

6. The third element waits at the 6 o'clock security team position. The PL links up with the third element and walks them in a straight line between the 6 o'clock and the 2 o'clock position, physically placing each member of the element.

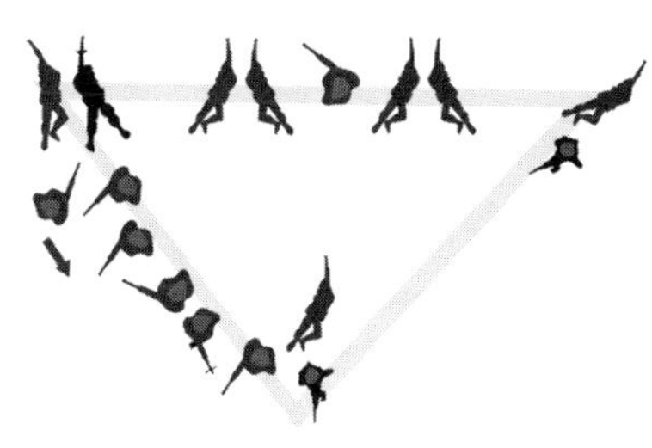

Phase Three: *The patrol leader returns to the 6 o'clock position to walk the second squad in a line between the 6 o'clock on the 10 o'clock positions. Troops must link up with the apex to their left and right. (Ref: FM 7-8, chap 3, section V, fig. 3-22).*

7. The PL moves to the center of the patrol base to establish the command post (CP). The PL coordinates his subordinate leaders to be sure they are all aware of each other's location and tied into each other's left and right line.

Phase Four: *The PL meets the last squad at the 6 o'clock position and walks them in a line between the 6 o'clock and 2 o'clock positions. Each apex is assigned a crew-served weapon, and the command post is center. (Ref: FM 7-8, chap 3, section V, fig. 3-22).*

Planning Considerations

Leaders planning for a patrol base must consider the mission and passive and active security measures. A patrol base must be located so it allows the unit to accomplish its mission.

- Observation posts and communication with observation posts
- Patrol or platoon fire plan
- Alert plan
- Withdrawal plan from the patrol base to include withdrawal routes and a rally point, rendezvous point, or alternate patrol base
- A security system to make sure that specific Soldiers are awake at all times
- Enforcement of camouflage, noise, and light discipline
- The conduct of required activities with minimum movement and noise
- Priorities of work

Security Measures

- Select terrain the enemy would probably consider of little tactical value
- Select terrain that is off main lines of drift
- Select difficult terrain that would impede foot movement, such as an area of dense vegetation, preferably bushes and trees that spread close to the ground
- Select terrain near a source of water
- Select terrain that can be defended for a short period and that offers good cover and concealment
- Avoid known or suspected enemy positions
- Avoid built-up areas
- Avoid ridges and hilltops, except as needed for maintaining communications
- Avoid small valleys
- Avoid roads and trails

Priorities of Work - Patrol Base

Once the PL is briefed by the R&S teams and determines the area is suitable for a patrol base, the leader establishes or modifies defensive work priorities in order to establish the defense for the patrol base. Priorities of work are not a laundry list of tasks to be completed; to be effective, priorities of work must consist of a task, a given time, and a measurable performance standard. For each priority of work, a clear standard must be issued to guide the element in the successful accomplishment of each task. It must also be designated whether the work will be controlled in a centralized or decentralized manner. Priorities of work are determined IAW METT-TC. Priorities of work may include, but are not limited to the following tasks:

1. Security is always the first priority. The patrol base is maintained at a level of security appropriate to the situation. As a rule of thumb, the patrol base does not fall below 33 percent security. That means one out of three troops are diligently watching their sectors of fire.

2. An alternate defensive position is designated. Typically, the PL informs the subordinate leaders that the ORP will serve as a fallback position in the event the patrol base is over-run. This information is disseminated to all of the patrol members.

3. An ambush team covers the trail into the patrol base. A small force backtracks approximately 100 meters from the 6 o'clock position and then steps off of the trail. This ambush team observes the trail for a half hour or so to be certain no enemy force has followed the patrol into the patrol base. This must be done immediately after the patrol base has been secured.

4. Communication is established between all key positions. Field phones or radios are positioned with the CP and each apex at the 2, 6, and 10 o'clock positions.

5. An R&S team conducts a recon of the immediate area. After communication is established, the PL dispatches a recon & security (R&S) team to skirt the area just outside the visible sectors of fire for the patrol base. Everyone must be informed. Otherwise, patrol members may fire upon the R&S team.

6. Mines and flares are implemented. After the R&S team confirms that the area immediately around the patrol base is secure, those positions designated to employ mines or flares carefully place them at the far end of their visible sectors of fire—no more than 35 meters out. These anti-personnel mines and early warning devices must be kept within viewable distance of the patrol base.

7. Hasty fighting positions are constructed. Barricades are the preferred method as digging and cutting can be too loud and may disclose the position. Fighting positions make use of available micro-terrain. If a hasty fighting position is necessary, care is taken to camouflage the exposed earth.

8. Plans are finalized or altered. The patrol's missions may be altered slightly or significantly in time. The PL makes these adjustments and every member of the patrol base is informed. If at all possible, shoulder-to-shoulder rehearsals are carried out in the center of the patrol base, prior to conducting missions.

9. Weapons are cleaned. This is particularly true if the patrol made contact during a mission or if the movement to the patrol base took involved moving through a particularly filthy environment—such as fording a river or being inserted onto a sandy beach. Still, no less than 33 percent of the patrol members maintain security.

10. Sleep and eating plans are initiated. If the situation dictates, the patrol base implements an eating and sleeping schedule, while maintaining security.

The Small Unit Tactics SMARTbook Index

T

U

V

W

The Essentials of Warfighting

Military SMARTbooks

SMARTbooks...making military reference and doctrine as easy as 1-2-3! Recognized as the doctrinal reference standard by military professionals around the world, SMARTbooks are designed with all levels of officers, warrants and noncommissioned officers in mind.

SMARTbooks can be used as quick reference guides during actual tactical combat operations, as lesson plans in support of training exercises and as study guides at military education and professional development courses. Serving a generation of warfighters, military reference SMARTbooks have become "mission-essential" around the world:

- Military education and professional development courses/schools: officer and noncommissioned officer basic and advanced courses, NCO Academy, West Point and ROTC, Command & General Staff College (CGSC), Joint Forces Staff College (JFSC) and the War College
- National Training Center (NTC), Joint Readiness Training Center (JRTC) and Battle Command Training Program (BCTP)
- Operational and training units across the full-spectrum of operations at the company, battalion, brigade, division and corps levels (active, reserve and national guard)
- Global War on Terrorism operations in Iraq, Afghanistan and the Asia-Pacific
- Combatant Command (COCOM) and JTF Headquarters around the world
- Allied, coalition and multinational partner support and training to include NATO, Iraq and the Afghanistan National Army